cannabinomics™

cannabinomics

The Marijuana Policy Tipping Point

CHRISTOPHER GLENN FICHTNER, M.D.

WELL MIND BOOKS

INTERNATIONAL STANDARD BOOK NUMBER: 978-0-9842588-0-2
U.S. LIBRARY OF CONGRESS CONTROL NUMBER: 2010921117

 well mind books

Northbrook, Illinois

Produced by Adams Press
Chicago, Illinois

MANUFACTURED IN THE UNITED STATES OF AMERICA

THIS BOOK IS DEDICATED TO

My mother and father,
Patricia Diane Thomas Fichtner and Palmer Jorn Fichtner
Who provided the crucible for the emergence of its spirit,

My partner for a quarter century,
Dr. Linda Sue Grossman,
Without whose enduring, loving support
I could not have completed this work,

And our pride and joy,
Aaron Glenn Grossman Fichtner and
Justin Ellis Grossman Fichtner,
Whose generation faces the imperative
Of correcting the mistakes of ours.

I love you all,
More than these words can possibly express.

TABLE OF CONTENTS

INTRODUCTION
CANNABIS IN CONTEXT 1

PART I
CANNABIS AND MEDICINE...................................... 31

FOREWORD

Eric E. Sterling

I.

LOTS OF PEOPLE don't give a damn about marijuana.

Many others are scared of it. Many are angry at marijuana. They remember it in connection with profoundly disturbing social change, and they are angry that it is still pervasive in the culture and in secondary schools, despite the best efforts of teachers and parents and the "war on drugs." More on that "war" in a moment.

At least 20 million Americans use it, most of them adults. More than two million Americans try marijuana for the first time every year, most of them young people, 18 years old, on average.

Hundreds of thousands of Americans make or supplement their income growing or selling marijuana. At the high end, Dr. Jon Gettman estimated that $35.8 billion worth of marijuana was cultivated in the United States in 2006. In addition, the Mexican drug trafficking organizations received about $8.6 billion in 2006 from marijuana shipments to the U.S. according to an estimate by the Office of National Drug Control Policy (ONDCP) in the Executive Office of the President. A much smaller calculation of the value of the marijuana market, based on what Americans spend, was made earlier in this decade by Abt Associates, Inc. for ONDCP. Their estimates ranged between $14.6 billion in 1992 and $10.5 in 2000 (both figures in 2000 dollars). The $10.5 billion then would be $13 billion in 2008 dollars if there were no change in consumption or price. For those in the illegal marijuana business, keeping it illegal keeps their profits high.

In 2005, Dr. Jeffrey Miron, then Visiting Professor of Economics at Harvard University, assuming that marijuana were legal and subject to extra taxes such as alcohol or tobacco, estimated the tax revenue that local and state governments and the federal government could obtain to be in the range of $6.2 billion annually. This revenue would be on top of an estimated saving in enforcement costs of $7.7 billion annually. These estimates are not a total economic analysis of marijuana. The analysis does not address the costs to society from marijuana use in automobile and other accidents or other consequences. Nor do these estimates include the income taxes that would be paid by employees of a legal marijuana industry nor the profits to investors and many other economic benefits.

Hundreds of thousands of other Americans make a good part of their living fighting marijuana: school prevention educators, D.A.R.E. officers, narcotics detectives, correctional officers, probation officers, court personnel, miscellaneous aircraft pilots and eradicators, and informants—tens of thousands of informants, often called snitches. For all of them, keeping marijuana illegal is tied to their livelihood.

If you use marijuana, you probably know people like yourself who use it as well—people at work, people in your profession, and people who share your interests in sports, athletics, music, art, recreation, or politics. Of course, to reduce your risk of arrest, you might use it by yourself secretly and know no one who uses it.

If you do not use marijuana, your idea about marijuana "users" is shaped by popular culture, the news media, and conversation.

What do *you* think about Cannabis?

If you never smoked pot and didn't know people who did (and so many of us never have and don't), you may easily wonder, "What's the big deal? Who the hell cares!" Its use is against the law, and that is the end of it. The fact that people—lots of people—break a law is no reason for repealing it. That's a perfectly reasonable approach to have.

Or perhaps you remember some of your own adolescence and post-adolescence. (And you do, in fact, remember—jokes about memory loss notwithstanding.) Maybe you remember schoolmates who seemed out of it, *wasted*, in class or at the park or the mall. Do you remember an acquaintance whose marijuana smoking seemed to have led to drug abuse or tragedy? Many of us remember such persons.

Or quite possibly, as one of the more than 100 million Americans who have used marijuana in their life, you remember not craziness or tragedy but good times, great times, camping trips, trips to the beach, hikes, boating, races, hunting, going to movies, concerts, parties, ball games, good times hanging out with siblings and friends, talking, laughing, relaxing, playing the guitar, making music or listening to tunes. Perhaps you remember the intensity of conversation, a movie, a play, a romance....

Every American generation has its particular frame of reference.

The parents of the baby boomers, now elderly, were shaped by the Depression and World War II. They may also remember the later shock of the 60s. They remember war protests, the "counter culture," the cultural and political confusion, the violence. As parents, most of them were shocked by changes they saw in schools and in the culture. Many others certainly were curious about "pot" and tried it, perhaps with their college-aged kids. But most did not. For most of the generation that fought in World War II and Korea, marijuana and drugs were part of what seemed like a breakdown in the stability, predictability, and values of the American culture. For many African Americans of this generation, pot was another drug that, like heroin, seemed to be destroying young adults when it was hard enough to get an education or a job.

The later "baby boomers" were too young for Woodstock and the like. The 60s washed over them in junior high school, and their associations with marijuana are with the many experiences of adolescence. Most American adults under the age of 50 were exposed to marijuana in high school, junior high school or middle school. About half of them tried marijuana by the 12th grade. Most of them never used it more than a few times. *For most Americans who try marijuana, they never use another illegal drug after they use marijuana. For most Americans who try marijuana, marijuana is the "terminus drug," the last illegal drug they ever used, not a gateway drug to more drug use.*

Now many of these "baby boomers" are parents or grandparents, and they are being warned that Cannabis today is high-potency and "Not the pot your father smoked."

But no matter what your own experience, chances are you have fears—that your kid might become a heavy pot smoker, might go on to use other drugs, might become an addict, might be killed in a drug or alcohol related accident, might stop caring about school, might become a failure! It is always possible.

Ever since there have been children, there have been youth who fought with their parents, who ran away to the sea, joined the army, ran away with a boyfriend, got pregnant, or got into other trouble. In part, because Cannabis is illegal, it has a great symbolic power for rejection of authority and is an opportunity for disobedience. It is a reasonable hypothesis that kids who might otherwise leave school and home in rebellion, use Cannabis instead—often on the sly—as a mild act of rebellion, staying at home and in school and, in a few years, assuming their role as productive adults. Most pot-using teenagers do— that is, if they escape getting caught, escape getting expelled under "zero tolerance" policies, and escape a crippling criminal record and the trauma of jail or prison.

It is the case that we are not talking about a large fraction of the population. According to the National Survey on Drug Use and Health, in 2007 persons who used marijuana at least once in the 30 days before they were surveyed amounted to 5.8 percent of the population older than the age of 12, which was a slight decline since 2002 but was higher than the decade 1990 to 2001.

The percentage of teenagers who used marijuana in the month before they were surveyed in 2007 was 6.7 percent, the lowest level since 1995, having steadily declined since 1997.

The fact of steadily declining teenage marijuana use over those ten years is very important because since 1996 medical use of marijuana has been increasing, and news accounts about medical marijuana use have become more and more numerous. In 1996 California's medical marijuana law got one million more votes than Bill Clinton received winning re-election. Since then voters and legislatures have enacted medical marijuana laws in Oregon, Washington, Alaska, Hawaii, Nevada, Colorado, Rhode Island, Vermont, Maine, and New Mexico. In 2004, as Montana was voting overwhelmingly to re-elect George W. Bush, it was passing a medical marijuana law. In 2008 Michigan voted 57 percent for Barack Obama and 63 percent for medical marijuana. All these campaigns generated extensive media discussion.

Three times in this period, cases involving marijuana went to the U.S. Supreme Court and were front page news, including the case involving Alaska high school senior Joseph Frederick who held a banner, "BONG HiTS 4 JESUS" during an Olympic Torch relay in 2002 (*Morse* v. *Frederick*, 06-278, 2007) and was suspended. It is clear that teenagers are not interpreting the use of marijuana for medical purposes (or as a tool for getting attention for a political protest) as a justification for using marijuana for social purposes.

Yet in December 2009, when the annual *Monitoring the Future* survey was released, the well-meaning anti-drug propaganda organization, the National Center on Addiction and Substance Abuse at Columbia University (CASA), asserted that a slowdown in the decline in teenage marijuana use was due to medical marijuana (http://www.jointogether.org/ news/features/2009/smoke-signals-marijuana-use.html?logevent=sp2f-view-item&nid=58960524).

But there was no evidence to conclude that youth social use of marijuana was changing in 2009 because of medical marijuana. None. In discussing the change in youth behavior and attitudes, CASA did not mention that the federally-funded, nationwide Safe and Drug Free Schools and Communities programs were found to be completely ineffective in an extensive White House Office of Management and Budget (OMB) review. This ineffectiveness was so clear, it resulted in the OMB's recommendation that the funding be eliminated, and Congress voted it eliminated! That had to be one worthless program. Could it be that certifiably ineffective prevention programs play NO role in teenage drug use trends and attitudes? It was simple propaganda to publish an analysis that implied that the primary influence on teenager's attitudes and patterns of marijuana use is the political debate regarding the medical use of marijuana. It is much more plausible that the counter-factual insistence of most drug prevention and drug enforcement professionals that marijuana has absolutely no medical value has undermined their credibility—at a time when credibility is desperately needed—and such loss of credibility contributed to any unwanted change in teenage views of marijuana.

II.

THE CONTROLLED SUBSTANCES Act of 1970 was developed and enacted during the Vietnam War. The Act placed marijuana in Schedule I with Congress declaring, with the encouragement of the Nixon Administration, that marijuana had "a high potential for abuse" and was so unsafe "there is a lack of accepted safety for use *under medical supervision*" (emphasis added). This is an absurd claim. But, of course, there were so many absurd claims made in those days.

The war, the widespread dissatisfaction with it among the troops, and the opposition to it in the civil society in many respects shaped the drug policy. Addressing "the drug problem" had an urgency that arose from a congressional discovery of the widespread use of drugs by American military personnel in Vietnam. Some Congressmen feared for the survival of the Army. Others feared for the entire society when "drug-addicted" former soldiers returned home. In the war on drugs, new agencies were created or merged and transformed into nascent anti-drug empires: the Bureau of Narcotics and Dangerous Drugs (BNDD), the Special Action Office on Drug Abuse Prevention at the White House (SAODAP), the Office of Drug Abuse Law Enforcement (ODALE), the National Institute on Drug Abuse (NIDA), and the Drug Enforcement Administration (DEA), to name the most prominent.

War and its logic and illogic have helped define and distort the thinking about compounds that affect mood, sensation, and thought processes for 100 years. The language of drug reformers (that is, the prohibitionists) in the early 20th century after the Spanish-American War, aligned with that of temperance advocates, was a narrative about insanity, degradation, depravity, and death. Throughout modern history, the actual physical and psychological effects of drugs have been misstated or exaggerated. Historically, there have been those who sought a genuine study of drug use and drug abuse—the Panama Canal Zone study of marihuana use, the New York Mayor's Commission to study marihuana, and as part of the 1970 drug Act, the creation of the National Commission on Marihuana and Drug Abuse (the Shafer Commission) for an in-depth, nonpartisan, objective review. Looking back from 2010, one particularly striking finding of that commission was its fear that the anti-drug bureaucracies would become self-perpetuating, ever-expanding empires.

The actual risks of harm to the users and to society have almost always been exaggerated. The nature and extent of the anti-social behavior of the users has been exaggerated. An accurate summation of this situation is reflected in a statement that sometimes is attributed to Timothy Leary (but is almost certainly apocryphal), "Marijuana is such a powerful and dangerous drug it commonly leads to delusions and paranoia—especially among persons who have never tried it!"

Almost every American who has used one of the drugs "controlled" under the Controlled Substances Act has done so despite the "war on drugs." Indeed, to call these materials "controlled substances" is an almost perfect oxymoron: there are no substances more out of control in the American economy or society than the so-called "controlled substances."

The primary cultural archetype of the 1960s is the image of stoned hippies: the "peace sign" waving, long-haired, bearded man wearing beads, accompanied by the barefoot woman of long, straight hair with a headband, both perhaps naked, and sharing a joint. These images remain powerful icons of a time in which illegal marijuana use was inseparable from war protest and social rebellion. In the illogic of the time, the pro-peace character of the early war protests was hijacked by frustrated activists and by undercover government agents into an excuse for property destruction and violence, even bombing, arson, and bank robbery. In late May 1970, I came upon the horrifying wreckage of much of the University of Wisconsin and the business district of Madison, Wisconsin, including a fire-bombed neighborhood supermarket, vandalized in the course of enraged protest of the U.S. bombing of Cambodia and the killing of student protesters at Kent State University in Ohio and Jackson State University in Mississippi.

If the Controlled Substances Act originated during the Vietnam War, the American crusade against drugs was enacted because of and during war. The first international anti-narcotics conferences were a response to the Boxer Rebellion and the violence of growing Chinese nationalism. After the United States took control of the Philippine Islands as a prize of the Spanish-American War, the U.S. confronted the fact that it had acquired Spain's monopoly on opium import and distribution. By December 1914 Congress had passed the Harrison Narcotics Act unleashing federal agents against drug users and their suppliers, quite aware that World War I had commenced in August, launching an epic bloodbath.

In World War I, there were perhaps 8 million combat deaths. During the especially bloody Battle of the Somme, in which about 1.5 million casualties were incurred between July and November 1916, German General Ludendorff commented that the British men ordered to charge from their trenches toward German machine gun fire and artillery barrages, "fight like lions." General Hoffmann, another German general replied, "Yes, but lions led by donkeys."

"Lions led by donkeys" perhaps aptly characterizes the personnel of the modern "war on drugs." The "donkey-like" leadership of the war on drugs is driven by its ambitions for power or fame, or by their fears. Police administrators and union officers fight to build their empires with larger budgets and more personnel, equipment, facilities, and weapons to fight the "drug menace" that they exaggerate. Indeed, by embracing the wrong strategy—prohibition—they make the problem worse and enrich truly dangerous and vicious criminals, as we are witnessing in Mexico. When they get the resources, they fail to deploy them appropriately or effectively. The anti-drug empires have grown steadily over the past three decades, yet the rate of those who die from drug overdoses has tripled, and the traffickers have become much more effective in delivering drugs—the average purity of heroin on the street has increased ten-fold, while the price has gone down steadily.

Some candidates for public office eagerly exploit the exaggerated fears of their constituents in their hunger for votes. In office, "donkey-like" legislators have used their populist anti-drug personas to conceal their careers dealing on behalf of powerful interests such as the financial industry. To legislative insiders they are "go-to-guys" for major banks and insurance companies, but in their press releases and television appearances, they are "leaders" in the war on drugs. How much leadership does it take to introduce a bill or offer an amendment to raise the penalty for a marijuana grower or seller? But standing in the legislative chamber, they beam as their colleagues praise their "courage" and "leadership" for offering a politically safe measure that is to be adopted by a near unanimous vote. Maintaining the façade of the anti-drug crusader is one tool that has sustained the political empires that deregulated the financial industry contributing to the savings and loan debacle of the 1980s and the crash of 2008.

Quite understandably some parents sometimes react to a tragic loss in their family by becoming crusaders against marijuana. They wear the special mantle of "victim," manipulating the respect for the loss they have endured and to which they are entitled into an unwarranted claim of expertise. Sometimes they appear to "selflessly" pledge to make the loss of their child into a campaign to save others. Sadly they frequently advocate ineffective or counterproductive measures, such as cruelly enforced "zero tolerance" mandatory punishments and expulsions from school, drug testing, and educational programs designed to frighten youth with exaggerations and falsehoods. Other parents, their fears inflamed by exaggeration or inaccurate media accounts and sympathetic to the loss, enlist in such crusades. An industry profits by supplying schools, churches, and youth organizations with "red ribbon week" and anti-drug paraphernalia—books, posters, DVDs, buttons, pencils, bags, stuffed animals, stickers, awards, certificates, etc.

The "donkey-like" anti-drug leadership rejects the strong evidence of the medical value of marijuana and would deny its therapies to the millions of persons who could benefit in order to "send a message" that marijuana use is dangerous and wrong. The youth who are the target of the message know they are being misled and thus justifiably mistrust what they are being taught, including the dangers of much more risky drugs. In their zeal, "donkey-like" policymakers reject measures designed to save the lives of young drug users. Their logic is akin to that of a parents group that would fight laws to require air bags or seat belts in cars claiming such life-saving measures "send the wrong message" that a car can be driven "safely" over the speed limit.

Most characteristically "donkey-like," the establishment anti-drug leadership ignores the law of supply and demand, and the economic reality that attempting to suppress a commodity widely desired like marijuana drives up the price, which inevitably attracts more entrepreneurs.

Around the world, armies of brave and dedicated law enforcement officers have been trained to combat criminal gangs, made rich with the profits driven up by prohibition, but they are deployed by "donkeys"—anti-drug politicians and bureaucrats—against users and addicts or, as in the case of California over the last decade, medical marijuana compassion clubs and collectives.

Each year a handful of "significant" drug raids are trumpeted by the U.S. Attorney General or the Administrator of the Drug Enforcement Administration or some other seeker of public acclaim. But every day in almost every courthouse in the nation, tens of thousands of low-level drug offenders are brought in shackles to the bar of justice. In 2008 in the United States, the FBI estimates there were 1,702,537 arrests for drug violations. Around the world users and addicts are rounded up, but in China, Singapore, Thailand, and Malaysia, they are beaten, tortured, and executed.

Annually during the last dozen years, the United States has arrested more than 200,000 juveniles for drug offenses, most of them for marijuana possession. Annually, for the past 20 years, the United States has arrested on the order of one million adults, overwhelmingly for marijuana possession. These arrests are not like traffic citations. In a drug arrest, police officers manhandle the accused, frequently pointing powerful firearms at their heads, and threaten the accused with death or grievous bodily injury if the accused make a wrong move. Occasionally, an accused reaches for a wallet or a cell phone, and the gesture is misinterpreted, resulting in the killing of the suspect.

Drug offense arrestees are taken to jails and detention centers. At the beginning of the 1970s, America's prisons and jails held about 250,000 persons. Now, a prison empire has been created, bursting with over 2.1 million adults and juveniles held in all manner of custody. Since jails are designed for the entire range of suspects including those accused of the most violent crimes, they are highly restrictive, and low-level offenders are often housed with serious, experienced offenders. This may result in assault, intimidation, or rape. Occasionally the accused—very afraid or very ashamed—commits suicide. These deaths are almost never counted by the authorities as "costs" of our drug policy. These tragedies are rationalized by the cruel adage, "If you can't do the time, don't do the crime." Of course this "time" is not a law of nature but an artifact of empire building and political gamesmanship.

In Mexico, over the past three years, at least 15,000 (and perhaps as many as 50,000) persons have been killed or "disappeared" in drug war violence. In Colombia in the 1980s and 1990s, thousands died in the battles over cocaine power and money. In both countries thousands of police officers, soldiers, prosecutors, mayors, police chiefs, Attorneys General, and candidates for president have been murdered in drug war-related violence. On a less dramatic scale, this violence is found throughout Central America and the Caribbean. Recently it has been carried to West Africa, as drug trafficking organizations exploit impoverished nations with little capacity to resist their power to more expeditiously ship cocaine to the European market.

The cause of this violence is control of the enormous untaxed profits that accrue in otherwise very poor societies. There are few barriers to entering the drug trade. One does not need a professional degree, a college degree, or even a high school diploma. One does not need much investment or infrastructure. The profits are so great that with a little money, a modicum of street smarts, and a lot of nerve, one can quickly make a better living than any peasant, menial laborer, or sweat shop worker.

Because of prohibition, drugs are enormously valuable. Unlike other stolen property, they do not lose their value when "hot." Stolen drugs are just as easily sold as any other drugs. Drug traffickers are not going call the police if they are the victims of robbery, theft, or embezzlement. Drug profits in cash and drugs are always at risk of being stolen. Traffickers build their own security establishments—well-armed, and ideally, notoriously ruthless in order to better deter such thefts. The violence of the drug traffickers—extreme and terrorist—has a tragic logic. But it is the system of prohibition, not the drugs themselves, that creates this logic. In Mexico (and formerly in Colombia) the intensity of this violence has effectively intimidated the rank and file police, the local governments, journalists, and common citizens. The intimidation makes the choice of cooperation— the complicity of corruption—a logical survival mechanism. If one wants to provide for one's family—indeed to protect them from retaliation—the choice of complicity is certainly rational. It may be immoral in societal terms and illegal but arguably moral on personal and familial terms.

The brave, "donkey" anti-drug leadership knows it must recapture state sovereignty and suppress the drug trafficking organizations. But it leaves its most powerful weapons—regulation, control, licensure, and taxation of business—out of its arsenal. Enforcing prohibition does not protect public safety or the lives of the troops.

The mounting deaths, in the tens of thousands, and the millions of prisoners cycling through the prisons, jails, and detention centers begin to approach the scale of casualties of the Battle of the Somme. By the end of 1916, the Kaiser thought Germany had won the war and sought assistance from the U.S. in mediating a peace. But unable to negotiate a peace, the war escalated. Unrestrained submarine warfare was instituted in an attempt to starve Britain. Germany attempted to instigate

Mexico to join it and to declare war on the U.S. Germany offered Mexico the opportunity to regain the territory it lost to the U.S. in the war of 1848. Such measures brought the U.S. into the war. New technologies and strategies were developed on both sides, and "donkey-like" generals were replaced.

World War I resulted in enormous political and social upheaval. Revolutions in Russia and Germany overthrew the empires, leading to the Weimar Republic and the Soviet Union. National independence movements, aided by the victorious powers, led to the dissolution of the Austro-Hungarian Empire and the Ottoman Empire. Will the war on drugs lead to political upheaval in Mexico? Will the violence and bloodshed diminish the legitimacy of the government and result in its replacement? In Afghanistan, in the war between the Karzai government and the Taliban, the Karzai family is reported to be corruptly earning money in the opium trade. The Taliban is reported to receive major funding from the opium trade. Formally, the Karzai government with U.S. and U.N. support is committed to eradicating poppy cultivation, which drives up the price for farmers. Would the creation of a legal market in opium build support for the legal government among farmers and deprive the Taliban of necessary funds?

In 2009, the Director of ONDCP in the Obama Administration, Gil Kerlikowske, said we should abandon the language and imagery of a "war on drugs." He says he wants to de-emphasize supply control measures and increase treatment and prevention. These nostrums were strongly advocated more than 20 years ago by former Administrators of the DEA, Francis Mullen and John Lawn, and are not strategic innovations. Kerlikoswke says "legalization" is not in his vocabulary, but he has no idea what the word means in policy terms. In August 2009 he said that legalization is simply the abandonment of laws controlling drugs. The Obama Administration does not appear to be fundamentally reviewing our drug control strategy, and the drug control empires remain unchallenged in official circles.

However, it is clear that the consensus supporting marijuana prohibition has broken. In December 2009, the National Association of Boards of Pharmacy spent a day studying the implications of legalized marijuana for medical use. California will vote on a marijuana legalization initiative in November 2010. In 2009, the Rhode Island State Senate voted to study marijuana legalization. Other states will consider similar measures.

Hopefully the end of the "war on drugs" will lead to the end of powerful empires: the "imprisonment empire" that in the United States now houses more than 2.1 million persons; the numerous "narco-cartel empires" (the drug trafficking organizations that threaten the sovereignty of the Mexican government and that operate on every continent but Antarctica); and the "police empires" that operate in scores of nations. These empires are characterized by internal cultures and operations that rely on the use of violence and coercion; disregard the human dignity of those under their control; are intent upon acquiring power, prestige, and money—either drug profits or a growing share of tax revenues; and have impunity for the crimes committed in their names.

One of the prominent popular historians of World War I (*The Guns of August*), Barbara W. Tuchman, wrote about the numerous instances of folly by officials who led their societies in war in *The March of Folly*. What struck her was that the blunders were not mistakes of honest judgment or fate, rather they were mistakes of inertia, of bureaucratic momentum; they were mistakes that were obvious and foreseeable at the time, not simply in hindsight. We have made the same mistake with our drug policy.

More than 35 years ago, the congressionally-created, presidentially-appointed National Commission on Marihuana and Drug Abuse recommended a departure from the "war on drugs." The Commission warned about the creation of permanent drug bureaucracies that would be invested in the maintenance of the problem, rather than developing appropriate solutions. It called for greater tolerance of the risks that drug use can create and recommended that marijuana be "decriminalized." People who use marijuana are not deviants and should not be punished. Sadly, neither the Congress nor the President took a moment to read the in-depth report, to reflect on its analysis and findings, or to weigh its conclusions and recommendations. It was ignominiously ignored in Washington. But almost a dozen state legislatures recognized the wisdom of its marijuana recommendations and enacted marijuana decriminalization laws in the years thereafter. Notably, the drug problem was no worse in any of those states than in their neighbors.

Will we be like the societies 95 years ago that persisted in trusting generals who sacrificed their men in futile charges across "no man's land" into machine gun fire? Will we maintain patently ineffective strategies until we fully entrench the fiends of the drug cartels in our politics and our economy? Will we continue to add millions of Americans to the tens of millions with criminal records who are forced to remain outside the productive workforce, leaving our economy weakened and uncompetitive?

Or will we move forward to regulating the Cannabis commerce, bringing it into the universe of legal and social control? Will we embrace the medical value of the unique compounds that the Cannabis plant creates? Will we provide the patients who suffer some of the most devastating and painful conditions access to relief and well-being? Will we enable parents to speak truthfully to their children about marijuana and to give them the information and skills necessary to make wiser and safer choices regarding substance use generally.

Cannabinomics is a prescription that, if followed, will help save many Americans and avoid and relieve a great deal of pain. I trust you will be enlightened, inspired, and empowered as you read it.

•   •   •

Cannabis in Context

"Interesting philosophy is rarely the examination of the pros and cons of a thesis. Usually it is, implicitly or explicitly, a contest between an entrenched vocabulary which has become a nuisance and a half-formed new vocabulary which vaguely promises great things....

"The method is to redescribe lots and lots of things in new ways, until you have created a pattern of linguistic behavior which will tempt the rising generation to adopt it, thereby causing them to look for appropriate new forms of nonlinguistic behavior, for example, the adoption of new scientific equipment or new social institutions."

RICHARD RORTY, 1989
CONTINGENCY, IRONY, AND SOLIDARITY

"[A]ll theory is metaphor...
Metaphor can create powerful insights that also become distortions,
as the way of seeing created through a metaphor becomes a way of not seeing."

GARETH MORGAN, 1997
IMAGES OF ORGANIZATION

3

IT HAS BEEN NEARLY FOUR DECADES since President Richard Nixon declared illegal drugs "public enemy number one in the United States" and launched the modern day drug war.[1] Drug policy reformers—an articulate minority within the legal and health professions, law enforcement, government, science, academics and the arts—have argued for years that the war on drugs does more harm than good.[2] More recently, explosive escalation of drug cartel violence in Mexico has generated wider recognition of the need for drug policy reform.[3] The issue has not been prominent in public conversation on healthcare or the economy or foreign policy even though it lingers at the horizons of all three.

Economic crisis, if not drug war bloodshed, brings the topic of drug policy closer to center stage in American awareness: in a Presidential town hall meeting in late March of 2009, the question of whether legalization of marijuana might provide a valuable stimulus for economic growth ranked highly—in fact, highest by some reports—in frequency among questions submitted online.[4] In California, the Governor has acknowledged that it is time to talk about taking a critical look at existing marijuana policies in light of experiences in other countries and especially in light of current economic realities.[5]

Consider some ironies of marijuana policy set in three contexts:

1. *War on Drugs.* Former presidents of Brazil, Mexico, and Colombia pronounce the war on drugs a failure and urge the United States to consider new policies including the decriminalization of marijuana, or cannabis, for personal use.[6] At the same time, a South Carolina sheriff contemplates pressing criminal charges against 23-year-old eight-time Olympic gold-medalist swimmer Michael Phelps for being seen photographed on the Internet holding and apparently inhaling from a marijuana pipe.[7]

2. *The Economy.* The State of California announces that its budget deficit will force it to pay some of its bills in the form of IOUs.[8] Meanwhile, marijuana prohibition is the only restriction preventing the simmering cannabis economy from boiling over in Mendocino County and other areas of northern California.[9] Looking beyond the West Coast, one recent estimate maintains that cannabis is the largest cash crop produced in the United States of America, exceeding the value of corn and wheat combined.[10] This reported leading cash crop apparently even beats grapes in California. Americans use a good deal of marijuana grown across the country. For some percentage of those users, the effects of cannabis are reported to be medicinal or therapeutic. In the political arena we balk at this reality and prefer to shell out unending taxpayer dollars on an ineffective drug war rather than reap the benefits of economic integration and legitimate regulation of a sizable industry.

3. *Healthcare.* Garry, a southern California medical marijuana consumer, begins a three-year felony probation

term almost three years to the day after local county law enforcement officials opposing the state's medical marijuana law paid him a visit at his desert dream home with the help of federal agents. Garry jumped out of bed early that morning in response to loud knocking. As he opened his front door, he was greeted by a battering ram and a physical takedown maneuver that left him with a dislocated left shoulder, right hand fractures, blunt head trauma, and a back injury that aggravated the arthritis for which he grew cannabis in his garage in the first place. Before the raid, Garry earned a six-figure income in his family-owned business installing custom window treatments. He now collects Social Security disability as a result of his injuries and worsening medical condition. The burden of medical and legal bills forced his family into mortgage foreclosure. Garry had to take more narcotic pain relievers because of his injuries and because his preferred medicine—which allowed him to use prescription opiates less often and more effectively—was confiscated. Garry's desert dream home is now featured in his wife's nightmares.

Political Paralysis and the Abilene Paradox

Yet another recent news item illustrates the paralysis of our politics. James C. McKinley, Jr., reporting in the *New York Times* on the killing of two Americans who crossed the border from El Paso to Juarez, noted that the El Paso City Council voted unanimously "to ask Washington to consider legalizing drugs as a way to end the violence." In response to the Council's bold and timely leadership, the mayor and local members of Congress respectively "vetoed the resolution and… warned that the Council's stance might imperil federal aid."[11]

In responding to the Mexican drug war crisis in late March of 2009, Secretary of State Hillary Clinton acknowledged the role of American drug money and then commented on the need to increase American efforts to reduce demand for substances of abuse through education and treatment. Watching her on the news, I wondered whether those oft-cited solutions that I too firmly believe in rang as hollow in her ears as they did in mine. I found myself thinking that the notion of a drug war is no longer a metaphor, to the extent it ever was; that the promise of demand reduction seems meager by comparison to the reality of escalating violence that has cost some 7,000 lives in Mexico in the last two years; that we have heard, followed, and embraced these ideas for a long time now, but they aren't working; and that we are avoiding an important public conversation.

Reflecting on American marijuana policy, I am reminded of a classic story told by Jerry Harvey, emeritus professor of management science at George Washington University. *The Abilene Paradox* begins at the west Texas home of the author's in-laws, in the early days of his marriage.[12] On a sweltering hot Texas desert day, he and his wife sat with her parents playing dominoes in their home, air-conditioned by a homemade fan-blown icebox, that was just keeping the temperature bearable. At the abrupt suggestion of Harvey's father-in-law, the group decided to drive more than 50 miles in a vehicle without air-conditioning to have dinner at *the* café in Abilene, during the hottest part of the 104-degree day. Drenched in sweat, coated with a fine layer of Texas dust, the group arrived at the restaurant and proceeded to have a regrettable meal. They returned home, under the same conditions, and were relieved to wipe the sweat off themselves and sit down in front of the icebox air-conditioner once again.

A while after returning home from the four-hour excursion, Harvey offered the comment, "It was a great trip, wasn't it?"

His mother-in-law, a bit irritated, admitted that she didn't enjoy the trip and never really wanted to go anyway. Harvey's father-in-law chimed in with a west Texas "shee-it," and the family went on to reflect on why it took that miserable trip together when they all would have rather stayed home. They all agreed that they never really wanted to go to Abilene. They'd been there many times before, knew the quality of the food, and were acutely aware of the heat and traveling conditions. So why did they go there? It seems the father-in-law was concerned that the guests might be bored, his daughter was politely receptive to the suggested outing, and no one wanted to disappoint the others. Harvey concluded that from the inception, as a group, they were unable to manage their agreement that the trip would be a bad idea.

Harvey coined the term *Abilene Paradox* to name "the tendency for groups to embark on excursions that no group member wants."[13] "Stated simply," writes Harvey, "when organizations blunder into the Abilene Paradox, they take actions in contradiction to what they really want to do and therefore defeat the very purposes they are trying to achieve."[14] Individual members recognize the need for change, but they keep their views to themselves or limit their open conversations to small groups where they may see eye to eye. But in an organization that has taken a trip to Abilene the members can't find their voice at the larger table, and the organization as a whole is unable to see or manage its collective agreement. The problem is perpetuated by the system's inability to talk openly about it. The majority of the group's members believe it is time to change course, but nothing new happens.[15]

I summarize Harvey's desert tale to invite reflection on the Abilene Paradox as a useful frame of reference for interpreting America's war on drugs. More specifically, I suggest that Harvey's trip to Abilene is an apt metaphor for the American war on marijuana and the unintended consequences of cannabis prohibition. To many readers the notion that American marijuana policy fits Harvey's concept of the Abilene Paradox—with American society pressing forward in a direction that no one really wants to go—will be immediately obvious.[16]

Perhaps a greater number of readers will be only vaguely aware:

- that many individuals have found therapeutic benefits in the use of cannabis and have therefore pushed against the constraints of our mainstream medical and legal systems in their efforts to gain legitimate access to it;
- that, while cannabis should not be seen as completely benign or harmless, the greatest harms related to marijuana are arguably a result of the laws against it rather than use of the substance itself;
- that some individuals have used cannabis to help find their way off harsher, more addictive drugs including alcohol;
- that there is no compelling evidence that laws against drug use have led to sustained decreases in substance abuse or addiction;
- that marijuana law enforcement yields no clear public health benefit or return on taxpayer investment; or
- that there are compelling reasons to believe that the war on drugs, of which marijuana prohibition is a subset, creates more problems than it solves.

Such readers are in the same position that I was in some seven or eight years ago. At that time, I was vaguely aware of the medical applications of cannabis and that the issue was politically controversial. I also knew that the cannabinoid compound considered the most active component of marijuana, delta-9-tetrahydrocannabinol (THC), had been made available synthetically in 1985 in the form of a capsule (brand name Marinol®, generic dronabinol) taken orally for the purpose of alleviating nausea or to stimulate appetite. Nevertheless, marijuana has been regarded as a substance of abuse since its prohibition, and that view of marijuana was strongly reinforced by the Comprehensive Drug Abuse Prevention and Control Act of 1970 (also referred to as the Controlled Substances Act of 1970). Physicians know that modern medicines have varied degrees of abuse potential, but even a medical education does not necessarily alert one to the possibility that a substance considered to be a drug of abuse and for that reason made illegal might actually in practicality be a primarily therapeutic substance with many applications and only secondarily—and perhaps less importantly—a substance of potential abuse.[17]

Just Say No

In 2006 a spokesperson for the director of the Office of National Drug Control Policy (ONDCP) referred to the debate over the medical use of cannabis as a "bizarre public discussion," as if input from primary consumers and their physicians were misguided, unnecessary, and irrelevant.[18] While disdain for public discourse seems to have been characteristic of the executive branch of American federal government during the first eight years of the 21st century, the suppression of thoughtful dialogue on drug policy is a legacy bequeathed to us from the Reagan years. The problem was characterized eloquently by Dan Baum more than a decade ago and recognized and quoted by Cermak:

> Just Say No finished the…job of closing the debate. In fact, it reduced the debate to a single word. Don't talk about why people use drugs, the slogan said. Don't ask why Halcion® and

malt liquor are legal drugs while marijuana and cocaine are not. Don't talk about the difference between drug use and drug abuse. Don't talk about the tendency of prohibition to promote violence and the use of stronger and more dangerous drugs. Don't talk about the lives, taxpayer dollars and civil liberties sacrificed for the Drug War. Don't talk about the culture and race wars waged under the Drug War battle flag. Don't talk about the medical potential of illegal drugs. Don't talk at all. Just say no.

The country's ability to discuss the problems of drug abuse and debate solutions had been withering for years…Just Say No, ostensibly aimed at children, finished the debate off. What replaced it was an unquestionable antidrug orthodoxy that skewed the work of every government agency, elevated drug users to national enemies, and limited even the language permissible in drug discussions…[T]he merest suggestion that the country pursue any path but total prohibition has been tantamount to forbidden speech.[19]

In the time since those words were written, problems with American marijuana policy have received increasing recognition through the activism of groups and organizations focused on specific subsets of the overall policy problem (for example, lack of medicinal access, excessive criminalization, economic waste). The number of Americans involved in this work has grown, and public conversation has become more audible especially where access to cannabis by those who need it medically is concerned.

Baum's incisive comments are consistent with the observation of Harvard psychiatrist Lester Grinspoon, M.D., in 1993 that "the political climate has now deteriorated to the point where it has become difficult to discuss marijuana openly and freely."[20] A decade later, author Jacob Sullum observed, "…It is difficult to distinguish between different kinds of drug use in a culture dominated by a simpleminded 'Just Say No' ethos."[21] At the level of public discourse, the concept of a beneficial "cannabis therapeutics" has been largely forgotten through a kind of disuse atrophy imposed by the engine of criminalization. In effect, Sullum summarized the "Just Say No" ethos as a policy conversation-stopper: With "Just Say No" there is nothing more to be said; there are no important nuances in conversations about cannabis use because "all use is abuse." Beyond the question of the desirability of abstinence in managing substance use problems, the embracing by drug warriors of "Just Say No" as an approach to drug policy was tantamount to dropping the subject as far as public conversation was concerned. But as Howard University Law School Dean and former Baltimore Mayor Kurt Schmoke has written even more recently, "Dropping the subject of the war on drugs means dropping any hope of solving some of America's most difficult social problems."[22]

In 2007 the editors of *Foreign Policy* wrote, "It has never been popular to say that a war on a social scourge like drug abuse is failing, but there is no other way to see it. Prohibitionist policies are ripping nations apart, and the social and economic costs are unacceptable."[23] The Mexican drug trade alone involves multiple prohibited substances, but it accounts for no more than half the marijuana in the United States and probably considerably less. Globally the drug trade is complex, and a one-size-fits-all approach seems unlikely to solve the problems of opium in Afghanistan, coca in Colombia, cannabis in Kentucky, or the trafficking of drugs across the Mexican border. But America's denial of its ownership interest in cannabis is a more focused and manageable subset of our larger drug policy failure. It is a problem amenable to multiple potential solutions of benefit to public health, the economy, and the healthcare consumer. And organizational learning derived from the process of implementing cannabis policy reform would likely be helpful in developing strategies for the management of broader global drug problems.

But without facing the challenge of managing a massive home-grown commodity for which there is very high demand, we will learn little to guide us through better policy solutions to more difficult global drug-related problems. Whether to facilitate medicinal access, minimize the damage of the drug war, or integrate valued resources and their associated revenues into the mainstream economy, our approach to accepting or tolerating the reality of American homegrown cannabis is a *management* problem that presents itself in the 21st century as ripe for a regulatory solution. Demand reduction is an inadequate response domestically, and military intervention is an inappropriate strategy for achieving supply reduction internationally. The war on drugs, as it has been waged, has not only failed to curtail drug use; it has become a major public health liability in its own right.

Public Interest in Marijuana Policy

In 2004 the ONDCP director, or so-called Drug Czar, attributed public interest in marijuana policy reform to a conspiracy on the part of major funding sources—the best known being George Soros—to legalize drugs, as if it were sufficient in the public arena to point the finger in *ad hominem* argument.[24] To most Americans that kind of analysis means little in comparison with real issues such as healthcare access and the preservation of sufficient individual freedom to allow consumers to make choices that have a tangible impact on their quality of life.

As a society, we are now becoming more aware of the broad agreement that exists at least implicitly regarding both our drug policy failures and our frank drug policy mistakes. At the very least it is becoming clearer to a growing number of Americans that the criminalization of marijuana creates more problems than it solves. Cannabis prohibition deprives individual consumers of medicinal benefits, unnecessarily creates crimes and criminals, fuels the black market and its associated violence, and deprives the mainstream economy of taxable revenue from a highly valued commodity. However, we haven't been able to manage our agreement that the policy has failed and a change of direction is in order. But how can we be so sure that there is an emerging if not yet apparent social consensus on this issue? How do we know that there is such broad, unmanaged agreement as to fit Harvey's illustration of the Abilene Paradox? Does the majority really hold these views, or is this just the author's political agenda?

I will address those questions in several ways: by sharing stories of medical cannabis consumers I have come to know whose cases have seemed to me compelling; by building a case for interpreting recent developments in marijuana policy in terms of three distinct policy trajectories reflecting broadly based popular concerns that are now converging; and by setting these observations in the broader context of social, cultural, economic, and policy considerations that expose the counterproductive nature of our society's approach to the management of cannabis. Such considerations include healthcare, consumer self-determination, individual patient centrality in the clinical practice of medicine, scientific knowledge, the nature of evidence, public safety, public health, economics, and potentially others. The three policy trajectories correspond to the three contexts with which we began, but we will consider them in a different order: 1. cannabis and medicine (consumer-driven healthcare), 2. cannabis and the drug war (public health), and 3. cannabis and the economy (regulated commercial integration).

What information might lead an observer to the conclusion that when it comes to our society's approach to managing marijuana, or cannabis, America has taken a trip to Abilene? Day-to-day conversation across the country seems to confirm opinion polls from a variety of sources: Nationwide, various polls reporting data from more than 10,000 respondents show that 62 to 85 percent supported making cannabis available on a medical basis.[25] Statewide polls reporting on more than 20,000 respondents from 28 states show similar rates of support—59 to 85 percent—for medical cannabis access with a physician's approval.[26] An October 2008 poll found 71 percent support for decriminalization of marijuana in Massachusetts,[27] and the following month voters passed such an initiative (Question 2) with 65 percent of the vote. A majority of voters in California now favor a tax-and-regulate approach to cannabis (56 percent by Field Poll).[28]

Recent years have seen bills introduced to Congress to stop federal interference with states trying to implement their own medical cannabis laws, and the current federal executive administration—through United States Attorney General Eric Holder—has expressed an intent to respect those concerns.[29] In 2009 Representative Barney Frank of Massachusetts introduced a more general decriminalization bill into the U.S. House of Representatives, as well as a bill to reschedule cannabis for medical use.[30]

Impending Change: Three Policy Trajectories

As Massachusetts enacted statewide decriminalization in 2008, Michigan became the 13th state to join the medical marijuana revolution that began in California in 1996.[31] In 2006 when South Dakota and Colorado voters weighed in on statewide medical and decriminalization initiatives with 48 and 41 percent of the vote respectively, a large minority of Nevada voters (44 percent) called for a tax-and-regulate approach to marijuana policy along lines similar to those that are now under serious consideration by lawmakers in California. These voter initiatives share the goal of establishing a rational approach to the management of cannabis in our society. Each of the three distinct approaches to cannabis policy reform has its own integrity. Independently, the rationale for each holds up to scrutiny from health, justice, and economic vantage points.

The 2006 popular initiatives in the states of Colorado, South Dakota, and Nevada spoke to a building momentum toward cannabis policy reform. Together they can be seen as a "weak signal" in the chaos theory sense—like the butterfly flapping its wings in a remote corner of the world.[32] Those initiatives failed to win a majority of the vote in all cases and by not becoming law remained below the radar screen of collective awareness at a national level. But the large minority votes that day were an indicator of impending policy change, collectively signaling a transformation even broader than that represented by those three states alone or combined.

Chaos theory teaches that small changes in complex self-organizing systems may become highly magnified through their interactions with other system elements or "attractors" and thereby have major impact on large systems.[33] Students of group dynamics learn that silent members of any group often hold thoughts and feelings that have the potential to shed tremendous light on the experiences of the whole group. Leaders, managers, and administrators—who have different but overlapping functions in organizations—may find that scrutiny of issues that are seemingly minor or hidden from plain view may open doors and create new leverage for system change.[34] Addressing unspoken observations may prove to be Archimedean—providing a fulcrum for organizational and social transformation. The three policy trajectories reflected in those state initiatives are converging for reasons that are both inherent and historical, and their impending intersection will be obvious by the end of my work here if I have been successful.

The *medical* or *consumer-driven healthcare* trajectory has found multistate traction and continues to build momentum. This is not surprising inasmuch as medicinal use of cannabis is historically well established. All state medical cannabis laws, under current regulatory constraints, represent a selective form of decriminalization for explicitly medical use.[35] Broader decriminalization—reflecting public health, harm-reduction, and basic constitutional civil rights concerns—began immediately after inception of the war on drugs and its criminalization of cannabis users. Oregon became the first state to adopt the recommendations of President Nixon's Commission on Marihuana and Drug Abuse by decriminalizing marijuana in 1973, and several states followed early on with laws decriminalizing possession of small amounts.[36] The 2005 Denver vote to remove all criminal penalties for possession of up to an ounce of cannabis by adults is of historic significance because of a campaign by the SAFER organization to expose and highlight the relative safety profiles of alcohol and cannabis.[37] That comparison, together with the realities of currently escalating drug war violence and the negative community health consequences of unnecessary or elective criminalization, establishes cannabis decriminalization as a *public health* policy trajectory in more ways than one.

Legalization proposals, reflected in Nevada's 2006 tax-and-regulate initiative, differ from decriminalization primarily in their projected economic impact. Inevitably, public conversation in this area is accelerated by the current economic crisis. However, use of the word *legalization* can be an inflammatory conversation-stopper for many through its lack of subtlety or specificity, not unlike the way "Just Say No" shut down intelligent thought on marijuana policy for decades. It is more constructive to refer to "tax-and-regulate" or "tax-and-tolerate" proposals as reflecting an *economic integration* trajectory. The latter accomplishes the intent of medicinal access and decriminalization and in addition offers the prospect of a new legitimate industry contributing tax revenue and improving quality control for consumers.

In the context of current events, the prospect of economic integration subsumes both medical and public health reform proposals, inasmuch as it offers solutions to both sets of concerns while responding to imperatives of innovation and economic growth. In theory, it would also solve the problem of commercial regulation for narrower medical use; however, such regulation, if it is to be fully implementable, can be achieved only by revisions in federal law. The reason for this is reflected in the 2005 U.S. Supreme Court decision in *Gonzales v. Raich*—namely, that it is the prerogative of the federal government to regulate commercial activity where cannabis or any other commodity is concerned.[38]

Listening to Consumers

The material that forms the starting point for the ideas discussed in this book comes from my conversations with individuals who have identified themselves as medical cannabis patients. Some of these consumers live in states with medical cannabis laws intended to protect them from arrest and prosecution at the state level, but others do not. Glimpses of the potential medicinal applications of cannabis are offered in my efforts to capture some of the stories of these persons: Seth, who turned to cannabis for control of his seizures (epilepsy) when prescribed medicines didn't work; Julie, who found that cannabis use alleviated a broader range of her multiple sclerosis (MS) symptoms than did standard treatments; Jason, who used cannabis to ease phantom limb pain that followed the amputation of his leg; Garry, introduced above, and others who found cannabis useful for pain relief in various forms of arthritis; Mary, whose post-stroke rehabilitation included cannabis for chronic pain as one component of a multimodal alternative treatment approach that helped her get off prescription medications with uncomfortable side effects; and Stuart, a man in his late 20s quadriplegic from cerebral palsy, who had recently completed his master's degree at the time that he thanked me for speaking publicly on this issue and told me that he relied upon cannabis to relieve his muscle spasticity and improve his mood.

There are many others, with whom I have had similar discussions, who will not be named, including AIDS, cancer, and hepatitis patients whose use of cannabis to relieve pain or chemotherapy-induced nausea or to stimulate appetite in wasting syndromes should no longer even have to be defended in books of this sort. Stories from consumers who report therapeutic benefits from cannabis are frankly disarming in their exposure of the absurdity of a social policy that prohibits them by law from gaining access to naturally occurring plant material they have found to be of value in relieving their debilitating symptoms. Anecdotally and historically, the medicinal applications of cannabis are numerous, and we touch on a number of them in the pages that follow. It is not the intent of this book, however, to provide a systematic review of the medical conditions from which cannabis use has been reported and documented to provide some degree of relief. Some of its uses are better established than others, and some are more controversial than others. There is really no debate, for example, over whether inhaled or orally ingested cannabis can reduce nausea and vomiting from cancer chemotherapy or stimulate appetite in AIDS wasting syndrome.[39]

Even in the United States, where federal government has resisted cannabis therapeutics research, controlled scientific studies are beginning to confirm medicinal applications of cannabis that were recognized long before our current methods of clinical scientific study were developed.[40] Outside the United States, there is so much emerging research that there is no more debate about whether cannabis has medicinal properties in general. In the abstract, the question is uninteresting because it has been more than adequately answered many times over for at least several indications. It is now time for studies to clarify which cannabis strains—which component compounds and which naturally occurring pharmacologically active chemical arrays—are most effective for which specific medicinal uses. Such studies also address safety considerations, which will be discussed in the course of this book.

Behavioral Health

Most of the individual cases discussed in this book are not patients under my care, and they include medical uses of cannabis that are relatively uncontroversial, such as relief of pain and muscle spasms. But I also discuss how the reframing of cannabis use has affected the clinical data that I do collect from my patients in the practice of psychiatry. This in turn affects my evolving views as a physician about the problems and prospects of cannabis use among patients treated for psychiatric disorders. *As a psychiatrist, I do not recommend cannabis as first-line treatment of choice for any psychiatric condition, as there are effective FDA-approved medications for most psychiatric disorders.*

But I do appreciate that there are patients who for various reasons find cannabis use helpful rather than harmful in their mental health recovery. Some of those reasons involve specifiable behavioral health benefits. Numerous patients have reported to me in the clinical examination setting that they have used cannabis to reduce anxiety, irritability, explosive violent outbursts, and self-injurious impulses. It is instructive to note that some have eliminated alcohol from their lives through consumption of modest amounts of cannabis, with life-saving results and improved mental health and behavior. These are stories, not studies of demonstrated effect across large samples, but they are illustrative in important ways. It is also noteworthy in this connection that the editors of *The Lancet* recently called for a global response to the problem of alcohol misuse.[41]

I will not attempt in this book to make the case that cannabis is superior to any of our evidence-based mental health treatment approaches. Nor, however, will I confine my comments to the potential of cannabis to exacerbate the symptoms of individuals suffering from certain forms of serious and persistent mental illness. Recent psychiatric research has emphasized the risk of precipitating or worsening serious illness through cannabis use by persons vulnerable to, or suffering from, schizophrenia. However, the potential relationship between cannabis use and schizophrenia is far more complex and much less clear than suggested by the conclusions of recent psychiatric articles on the topic and especially by their summaries in the popular media. In addition, such findings are really a small part of the overall cannabis story even in psychiatry, let alone in medicine as a whole.

Psychiatric research has focused on the potential adverse mental health effects of marijuana, but it has not established the substance as a cause of schizophrenia or other serious and persistent mental illness. There is evidence that cannabidiol (CBD), one of the many cannabinoid substances found naturally in *Cannabis sativa* and *Cannabis indica*, may *alleviate* some of the psychotic symptoms experienced by persons with schizophrenia and could explain in part the appeal of cannabis as self-medication.[42] Conversely, the primary psychoactive compound for which marijuana is typically bred—THC, ironically the only cannabinoid available by prescription—may aggravate such symptoms.[43] As a constituent of herbal cannabis, it does *not* in fact do so in all persons with schizophrenia, and in any case the psychiatric risks of THC are not in principle different from those of other medications. Physicians recognize that approved medications effective for some patients can worsen the symptoms of others, as antidepressants and stimulants may in schizophrenia or bipolar disorder.

The observation that THC may worsen some psychiatric symptoms for some patients may be the strongest medical reason—it is in fact also a public health reason—to favor not merely limited local access to cannabis on a medically decriminalized basis but a more universally and formally regulated commercial access to cannabis products. From the standpoint of a physician in clinical practice, it would be helpful to be able to caution vulnerable psychiatric patients against strains of cannabis or cannabis-containing products with higher THC concentrations. Even minimal regulation would be a meaningful public health intervention by providing that opportunity in much the same manner as package warnings for alcohol and tobacco. In fact, regulated access seems the best way to send the appropriate message to patients with schizophrenia or other serious mental illness. Herbal cannabis products could be labeled, and all users advised to discuss their cannabis use with their physician.

Medicine, Science, and Public Conversation

Beyond the simplistic dichotomy of high versus low THC content, the medicinal effects of THC, CBD, and probably other cannabis constituent compounds appear to vary in part based on their interactions with one another in human physiological systems. These interactions, and the therapeutic effects that correlate with them, could and should be better understood by medical science. But the desirability of more cannabis therapeutics research need not pre-empt regulation of cultivated herbal cannabis strains on a qualitative and categorical basis in order to minimize adverse effects and maximize therapeutic benefits for the consumer. The public health impact of regulated access to cannabis can be studied, but available data viewed critically do not support an expectation of a detrimental net effect.

Anecdotal data represented by cases such as those shared herein do not replace rigorously designed and executed medical scientific studies, and the observations in this book are not offered with that intent. On the other hand, quantitative data plotted on a graph and analyzed statistically do not necessarily capture the distinctiveness or quality of the individual healthcare experience. Both methods of investigation—scientific experimentation and individual case description—provide information that is critical to the practice of medicine, and can be informative or instructive for readers interested in comparing their own personal experience to the experiences of others who have struggled with similar problems. Physicians and other healthcare providers are trained to evaluate the health status of the individual patient, as well as to assess the implications of scientific medical research for the selection of effective treatment approaches. The medical evaluation or work-up is much more akin to a story than a scientific experiment. Science figures importantly into that story, but the results of controlled experiments do not replace the individual clinical case narrative that creates the context for medical practice.

The impasse that has blocked reasonable discussion about cannabis is not primarily a problem for science—neither the result of inadequate science nor amenable to a solution through better science alone. It is a problem of language—an inability to speak of the prohibited, to remember the collectively forgotten, and to hear the forcibly tuned out. So our task is to learn a new language or vocabulary, or to rediscover a forgotten one. This language places both science and law in the context of humanity and reminds medicine that it begins and ends with the patient's story. The medical cannabis consumer's healthcare story; the drug policy reformer's plea for justice and community health; and the economist's call for rational public policy and fiscal sanity—all have been barely audible against the din of a noisy anti-marijuana campaign. That noise has allowed these protests to remain unnoticed or unassimilated in our larger collective awareness, as the butterfly goes undetected against the blusters of the prevailing winds. But in this early part of the 21st century, the unfolding of history and the convergence of relevant policy trajectories resonate to clear the air of the noise that has masked emerging public conversation. The participants' voices, millions of them, can now be heard clearly, but only if we are listening.

Cannabinomics

This book's title represents an effort to frame the new public conversation with a shift in vocabulary, offered in part for the sake of improving our collective listening skills. The title is not intended primarily as a "portmanteau word," which is to say a combination of the words *cannabis* and *economics*. Rather, I use the word *cannabinomics* to denote the *management of cannabis* in a larger sense—beginning with the way we talk about it, conceptualize the issues, and draw distinctions between current policies and desirable ones. Etymologically its roots include the Greek suffix *-nomos* from *nemein* (to manage). The management of cannabis entails important economic dimensions but its meaning is not necessarily exhausted by those perspectives.

I offer the following as a more structured and complete definition:

cannabinomics (n.) | căn' • nə • bi • nom • ics; căn • nă' • bi • nom • iks | (1) Management of cannabis; (2) Rules, customs, or laws governing cannabis management; cannabis policy; (3) Natural laws pertaining to cannabis; cannabis science; (4) Implied: treatment of cannabis as a commodity or resource; (5) Connotatively and implicitly, the economics of cannabis; (6) More broadly, the language or vocabulary through which public conversation regarding rational and responsible management of cannabis becomes possible.

In general, my use of the term *cannabinomics* is always referable to the first definition but takes the liberty of a "linguistic turn" toward the usage reflected in the sixth definition.

Having said what the book's title is and is not, let me say more about the book's content in the same vein:

*This book is **not:***

1. a systematic presentation of the medicinal uses of cannabis;
2. a textbook or handbook on the medicinal uses of cannabis from either a historical or contemporary perspective, or a guide to the medical use of cannabis;
3. an in-depth discussion of the medicinal uses of cannabis for any specific medical condition, or medical advice regarding the use of cannabis;
4. a systematic or detailed review of the abuse potential of cannabis;
5. a comprehensive discussion of drug control policy or its history, the war on drugs or its casualties, specific drug laws or legislation, or the structure of the criminal justice system in responding to drug offenses (that is, the

nature of sentencing requirements, alternatives, or the relation between legislative and judicial roles and/or requirements);

6. a detailed analysis of the economics of marijuana prohibition or the war on drugs more generally, or an exercise in economically informed mathematical modeling of the expected consequences of policy transformation.

*This book **is:***

1. an effort to prompt a more open discussion of drug policy and, in particular, marijuana policy;
2. an active, purposeful attempt to change the vocabulary we use in conversing about cannabis, with a deliberate rejection of terms that keep the conversation locked into the realm of substance abuse;
3. a frank rejection of the term marijuana itself as too contaminated by a history of racism and government propaganda to be useful in an attempt to see the issues clearly;
4. a criticism of drug laws and their enforcement during at least the past several decades and an explicit condemnation of the process of malignant criminalization that they reflect;
5. a call for a critical look at the American alcohol problem and a demand that the relative safety of cannabis by comparison be acknowledged in public policy;
6. a contention that regulation of cannabis makes it possible not only to have better information about quality of herbal cannabis and cannabis-containing products but also to make cannabis more readily available for consumption in forms that do not depend on smoking (for example, cannabis-enhanced beverages currently pro-

duced for medicinal use, with potential application as alcohol substitutes);

7. an invitation to contemplate the proposition that cannabis management is a medical, public health, foreign policy, and economic issue and that our current policies take us in the wrong direction in every one of these areas;

8. a collection of case illustrations setting cannabis in the context of medicine, the drug war, and the economy, and attempting to represent the perspectives of consumers and advocates. The cases presented represent specific individuals and are not composites; the names are changed to protect confidentiality except in those instances where the individual's identity is already public information;

9. an interpretive exercise, involving redescription of historical, medical, public policy, and human interest data available to all interested observers, that finds Americans by and large ready for marijuana policy change *now* but lacking the vocabulary to articulate it;

10. a hypothesis that the resulting vacuum, which *cannabinomics* seeks to fill as a model of public conversation, sustains the illusion of a policy impasse that hides the imminent convergence of our three trajectories in what Malcolm Gladwell called the "one dramatic moment... when everything can change all at once...the moment of critical mass, the threshold, the boiling point...where the unexpected becomes expected, where radical change is more than possibility."[44]

The very word *marijuana* has become an American myth, reinforced by irrational social policy that fuels rage and madness not generally in cannabis users but in those who cannot see beyond punitive prohibition in addressing their concerns about marijuana abuse. As marijuana is demythologized, rational public conversation about cannabis and the drug policy questions it raises becomes possible. At the marijuana policy *tipping point*, a worn-out myth is deconstructed and discarded in favor of a new vocabulary. *Cannabinomics*, the language within which that vocabulary develops, seeks to replace policy predicated on fear, superstition, and prejudice with ideas based on science, practicality, and respect in a democratic society.

Cannabis and Medicine

From Renaissance to Revolution:
Consumer-Driven Healthcare

"We have now identified more than thirty symptoms and syndromes for which patients have found cannabis useful, and others will undoubtedly be discovered. Many patients regard it as more effective than conventional medicines, with fewer or less disturbing side effects."[1]

LESTER GRINSPOON, M.D., 2002
PROFESSOR OF PSYCHIATRY EMERITUS
HARVARD MEDICAL SCHOOL

"Marijuana is a colloquial term used to refer to the dried flowers of the female Cannabis sativa *and* Cannabis indica *plants. Marijuana, or cannabis, as it is more appropriately called, has been part of humanity's medicine chest for almost as long as history has been recorded."[2]*

GREGORY T. CARTER, M.D., 2007
PROFESSOR OF REHABILITATION MEDICINE
UNIVERSITY OF WASHINGTON SCHOOL OF MEDICINE

WHEN HARVARD PSYCHIATRIST Lester Grinspoon published *Marihuana Reconsidered* in 1971, he predicted that marijuana would be legalized within a decade.[3] Research he had begun in the 1960s to elucidate the harmful effects of marijuana, or cannabis, had led him to an unexpected conclusion. On critical review of the medical, scientific, and historical literature, he found little evidence of the substance's harmfulness but could not ignore its rich history of use as medicine in many cultures around the world including the United States of America. The information he collected was not only historical but also contemporary. Cannabis had been introduced to the U.S. as medicine in the mid-19th century, and actually remained a government-approved medicine until nearly the mid-20th century.[4] What seems to have astounded and fascinated Grinspoon was his finding that the use of cannabis for medicinal purposes was alive and well throughout the country. To be sure, there was no shortage of individuals—especially young people, artists, and musicians—using cannabis without specific medical intent, but Grinspoon found that there were also many who used the herb to relieve symptoms of well-recognized medical conditions.

Forbidden Medicine

More than two decades later, Grinspoon would look back on his prediction as naïve.[5] The Comprehensive Drug Abuse Prevention and Control Act (Controlled Substances Act) of 1970 categorized marijuana, or cannabis, as a Schedule I controlled substance, placing it in a class of drugs with no accepted medical use and a high potential for abuse. Grinspoon had envisioned that once the evidence was available to policymakers, the need for change would be clear. President Richard Nixon's Commission on Marihuana and Drug Abuse recommended decriminalization and acknowledged the history of marijuana's medicinal applications.[6] But Nixon had other ideas: "I am against legalizing marihuana," he stated. "Even if the commission does recommend that it be legalized, I will not follow that recommendation."[7] Nixon rejected his commission's recommendation and explained to the nation, "The line against the use of dangerous drugs is now drawn on this side of marijuana. If we move the line to the other side and accept the use of this drug, how can we draw the line against other illegal drugs?"[8]

Cannabis prohibition did not begin with Nixon, even though his 1971 declaration set in motion the contemporary policy misadventure known as the war on drugs.[9] Prohibition of cannabis had begun long before the Nixon presidency—in the early part of the 20th century, in a time frame overlapping with that of alcohol prohibition—and took nearly half a century to become federal law. In 1937 the Marihuana Tax Act essentially restricted access to cannabis by imposing a prohibitive tax on all but medical use, and with cumbersome paperwork for medical use doctors prescribed it less and less. After 1942 cannabis was removed from the *United States Pharmacopoeia* or national formulary—the list of pharmaceuticals approved for use as medicine.

From before the mid-19th century to well into the 20th, cannabis was used medically to treat a variety of ailments.[10] Cannabis was used for relief of pain of various kinds, including specifically dysmenorrhea (painful menstruation), neuralgia (neurogenic, neuropathic, or neurological pain) including tic douloureux (a severe facial pain syndrome), migraine headaches, and arthritis. It was used as an anticonvulsant, a muscle relaxant, and in tincture form as a topical analgesic. Its limitations as a pain reliever in comparison with morphine were recognized—morphine having superior strength and consistency—but it was also considered a prudent choice of medication when there might be concern about addiction. In particular, it was seen as a reasonable longer-term alternative to opiates because of problems with opiate tolerance and side effects and was also found to be useful in managing cases of frank morphine addiction. Cannabis was used to stimulate appetite and was thought to have potential application in the treatment of depression.

Various authors suggest a range of influences that may have been operative in the early 20th century prohibition of cannabis.[11] It seems reasonable to conclude that racial tensions, not limited to but catalyzed by the Mexican Revolution, were influential. In fact, marijuana prohibition began at the state rather than federal level. It was Harry Anslinger, Director of the Bureau of Narcotics, who shepherded the prohibition agenda from its state-level origins to the federal Marihuana Tax Act of 1937. It has been suggested that the lumber, cotton, and synthetic polymer industries profited from the demise of cannabis and that there was significant exercise of political influence consistent with the preservation of those interests.[12] For example, William Randolph Hearst—an Anslinger supporter, newspaper seller, and forest owner who turned large numbers of trees into newsprint—was among the influential figures who lobbied for the eradication of cannabis (also suitable for paper-making) from North America. Hemp, synonymous with cannabis but generally a term reserved for forms of *cannabis sativa* with very low THC concentrations, has many industrial uses. These include not only the manufacture of paper but also clothing, rope, and other applications.

By the time Grinspoon published the first edition of *Marihuana, The Forbidden Medicine* in 1993, a renaissance of interest in herbal cannabis as medicine had been precipitated by the AIDS epidemic. Individuals suffering from HIV disease discovered, as had many patients before them, that cannabis alleviated nausea from chemotherapy, stimulated appetite, and relieved neurological pain. By the time the book's second edition was published in 1997,[13] a medical marijuana revolution was in progress. In 1996 the people of California passed Proposition 215, which was the first of a new generation of medical cannabis laws intended to remove criminal penalties for possession of marijuana by patients who used it for medical reasons with the approval of their physicians.

NORML and Judge Francis Young

In the interim between Nixon's declaration of war on drugs and the passage of California's Proposition 215, while the number of marijuana arrests and incarcerations rose steadily, advocates worked hard to keep the issue of cannabis as medicine alive. In 1972 the National Organization for the Reform of Marijuana Laws (NORML) appealed the marijuana scheduling decision of the Controlled Substances Act (CSA), beginning a process of federal administrative review that would culminate in 1988 with an administrative law judge's recommendation that marijuana be transferred from Schedule I to Schedule II so that it would be available for medicinal purposes.

Administrative Law Judge Francis A. Young, of the Department of Justice's Drug Enforcement Administration (DEA), found after reviewing all of the available evidence and testimony that "the evidence in this record clearly shows that marijuana has been accepted as capable of relieving the distress of great numbers of very ill people, and doing so with safety under medical supervision. Marijuana, in its natural form, is one of the safest therapeutically active substances known to man...It would be unreasonable, arbitrary and capricious...for the DEA to continue to stand between those sufferers and the benefits in light of the evidence."[14] Young ruled that "the marijuana plant considered as a whole has a currently accepted medical use in treatment in the United States, that there is no lack of accepted safety for use of it under medical supervision, and that it may lawfully be transferred from Schedule I to Schedule II." The latter policy change would have opened the door to consumers attempting to gain access to cannabis as legitimate medicine across the country.

More than a year after Judge Young's ruling, however, the senior President Bush administration's DEA Director John Lawn rejected that recommendation and dismissed the outcome of the adjudication process as a "dangerous and cruel hoax."[15] Such has been the federal response to the consumer plea for medicinal cannabis access, not just in that instance but following numerous commissioned reviews and expert opinions throughout the 20th century.[16] Nonetheless, consumer advocacy proceeded along multiple avenues simultaneously.

Patient Zero

In 1976 Robert Randall, a glaucoma patient suffering impaired vision and at risk of going blind, began to receive cannabis from the federal government for medicinal use. Randall had been arrested for cultivating his own marijuana supply, and in court he was successful in applying a medical necessity defense. Cannabis had been known for some time to be capable of reducing intraocular pressure, which is the therapeutic effect required to treat glaucoma effectively. The court ruled that Randall could not be faulted for choosing to save his sight rather than comply with marijuana law. With news of his success other patients expressed interest in receiving similar help, and the federal government responded by cutting off Randall's legal marijuana supply. He responded with a lawsuit and then settled out of court, restoring his legal marijuana access by 1978 under a compassionate use Investigational New Drug (IND) approval.[17]

Following the outcome of Randall's case, the compassionate use IND program provided access to federally grown marijuana for a small number of patients. From the late 1970s to the early 1990s, some 35 states passed new laws permitting access to cannabis for medicinal purposes, in anticipation of working *with* the federal government in the IND Compassionate Use program. I generally refer to these earlier statutes as *first-generation* medical marijuana laws, in distinguishing them from California's Proposition 215 and the newer *second-generation* laws that followed. The older, first-generation medical marijuana laws were designed to allow access to federally produced marijuana under federally approved compassionate use provisions.

The federal government maintained—and still maintains—a monopoly on the legal production of cannabis for research use. Production of cannabis is regulated by the National Institute on Drug Abuse (NIDA) and intended for distribution to researchers engaged in substance abuse research. This has made access to cannabis for more general medical research—in particular, cannabis therapeutics research—unnecessarily awkward and difficult. About half the states with such laws did get approval for use of herbal cannabis for treatment of glaucoma and chemotherapy-related nausea in cancer patients between 1978 and 1984. However, approval for individual medicinal use of cannabis still required the IND process, and neither President Ronald Reagan nor President George H. W. Bush was comfortable with the idea of marijuana as medicine in the era of "Just Say No." Rather, they maintained that the very idea of marijuana as medicine would "send the wrong message" to American youth. So by 1992 in the interest of staying on message, the senior President Bush closed the doors of the federal compassionate use program.

In so doing, the senior Bush administration shut down access for 28 approved medicinal cannabis patients who had not yet begun treatment and denied a review for hundreds—perhaps thousands—of AIDS patients who were turning to the program for relief. With that action, federal cannabis policy had progressed from refusal to reschedule cannabis to provide for medicinal use, through the blocking of limited medical access on a compassionate use basis for seriously ill patients who could benefit from it, to refusal even to acknowledge the existence of known therapeutic applications for herbal cannabis. Of course, the final progression—to a stance of not acknowledging medical value in cannabis—was out of sync not only with available science but also with the policy recommendations of President Nixon's expert panel. Moreover, shutdown of the compassionate use program to new applicants put the federal government in the untenable position of denying the integrity of its own program; a handful of patients continue to receive federally grown marijuana as medicine to this day,[18] even though according to federal authorities cannabis has no accepted medical value.

Alternatives: Seth and the IOM Report

There were numerous commissioned reviews and reports on marijuana, or cannabis, over the course of the 20th century.[19] Consistently, they found less harm and/or more medical usefulness (depending on their focus) than American policy would acknowledge. Where they have addressed legal, as well as medical issues, they have all recommended some form of decriminalization. The National Academy of Sciences Institute of Medicine (IOM) report, *Marijuana and Medicine: Assessing the Science Base* (1999), was the last major American government-sponsored review to address the potential of cannabis as medicine.[20] It is often cited by advocates as supportive of the view that cannabis has medicinal properties, while at the same time the White House Office of National Drug Control Policy (ONDCP, formerly the so-called drug czar's office) has used it to support its position against medical marijuana. The IOM report is a useful reference point for contemporary discussion about cannabis and medicine.

The IOM report provided an analysis of the most likely successful applications of cannabis as medicine based on existing information about possible effectiveness in specific conditions and current availability of alternatives. The report acknowledged the apparent therapeutic benefits of cannabis for some patients and suggested that further studies of marijuana as medicine were warranted in at least some areas of medicine and for some potential indications. It concluded that smoked marijuana had no future as medicine because of the inherent and potential dangers of smoking. It advocated further research even with smoked marijuana for patients for whom there were no other alternatives but advocated more strongly for the development of safer delivery systems. Such systems were already beginning to be used by the time the IOM report was written, and they are now in widespread use. They include vaporization for non-smoking use of cannabis via the inhalation route and tinctures or liquid medicinal extracts for oral or sublingual (under-the-tongue) administration.[21]

The ensuing decade—the first decade of the new century—generated at least several noteworthy reports on cannabis and medicine. The American Medical Association (AMA) published a position statement on the issue in 2001, calling for more research while acknowledging existing clinical and anecdotal information on reported therapeutic benefits for some patients.[22] In 2002 the Canadian Senate's Special Committee on Illegal Drugs reviewed the matter and concluded that "there are clear...indications of the therapeutic benefits of marijuana in the following conditions: analgesic for chronic pain, antispasm for multiple sclerosis, anticonvulsive for epilepsy, antiemetic for chemotherapy, and appetite stimulant for cachexia."[23] The committee recommended revising Canadian federal regulations to allow therapeutic use of cannabis for these and other conditions, including AIDS wasting syndrome, migraines, and fibromyalgia. In 2008 the American College of Physicians (ACP) published a position paper, "Supporting Research into the Therapeutic Role of Marijuana." The ACP report called not only for more cannabis therapeutics research but also for putting an end to the criminalization of persons using cannabis medicinally with the approval of their physician under state laws passed for that purpose.[24] In late 2009 the American Medical Association (AMA) passed a similar resolution and called for a re-examination of cannabis DEA scheduling in order to facilitate medical research.

I met Seth through a local newspaper editor in the greater Chicago area who had interviewed me in the course of writing a story on the debate over the medicinal use of cannabis. The editor had included the personal stories of two individuals who used cannabis for its medicinal properties—in particular, its muscle-relaxing, pain-relieving, and mood-elevating properties in both cases. After reading the article, Seth e-mailed the editor to share the story of his struggle with epilepsy and his recent discovery of cannabis as a potential treatment for it and to learn more about the experiences of other patients.

Forty years old at the time I met him, Seth had suffered with epilepsy most of his life. His seizures went undetected until he began to have *grand mal* attacks, or frank convulsions, at the age of 20. In retrospect, Seth believes he probably experienced undetected seizures throughout his youth. The word *epilepsy* from the Greek *epilepsia*, meaning "a seizing upon" or seizure, literally "to take hold of as from above," conveys the force of an experience of loss of control and an acute state of psychobiological chaos. The concept reflects the perspective of the observer as well as of the observed; the patient experiencing a true convulsion, or *grand mal* seizure, loses consciousness and most memory of the event.

Seizures of all kinds share the physiological character of a sudden, excessive, disorderly discharge of cerebral neurons or brain cells. In the case of *petit mal*, or *absence*, seizures, the neurophysiologic disturbance is associated with a transient lapse in awareness in which the person may appear to others to be "spaced out" or daydreaming. In the case of focal motor seizures, limited motor activity, or movement, visible to others—for example, as in twitching of an arm—may occur with or without a partial disturbance of consciousness. But in the case of *grand mal* seizures, or generalized convulsions, the person loses consciousness and has generalized muscular contractions throughout the body—called tonic-clonic movements—that reflect the spread of the chaotic electrical discharge from the limited focus or site of its origins to other areas of the brain.

Seth and I first talked by phone and arranged to meet at an Evanston café near Northwestern University. Married and the father of a two-year-old son, Seth had been struggling to stabilize a seizure disorder that had been steadily worsening throughout his adult life. Born and raised on the East Coast, he graduated from New York University and later moved to the Chicago area where he now works as a licensed massage therapist and documentary filmmaker. Working with neurologists, Seth had tried numerous anticonvulsant (anti-epileptic) medications with limited success. At the time I met him, he had been on an anticonvulsant regimen for at least the previous two years, combining three medications: divalproex sodium (brand name Depakote®), lamotrigine (brand name Lamictal®), and levetiracetam (brand name Keppra®). During the summer of 2005, about a year before our meeting, Seth was experiencing two to three *grand mal* seizures a week, even though he was adhering to the prescribed regimen of three anticonvulsant medicines. Given Seth's persistent and frequent seizures, he and his wife had growing concerns about his ability to care for their young two-year-old son. At the suggestion of family members who had heard about other seizure patients using cannabis therapeutically, Seth agreed to obtain cannabis for a personal trial. Seth had never before tried marijuana, not even during his youth.

At our first meeting in Evanston, Illinois, Seth recalled how, in initiating a trial of cannabis for his seizures, he had been cautious and concerned about the effects it might have on his mental state and whether it would interfere with his ability to function as a husband and father. From his wife's perspective, the seizures were already interfering with Seth's functioning in those roles. As he described his approach to experimenting with cannabis, my own internal reaction—the thought that he was excessively prudent—served to underscore just how cautious he had been, not only to avoid harm but to learn as much as possible about the effects of anything he took into his body. He reported to me that he began with just "one inhale" per day in his vigilance regarding any possible impairment that might interfere with his child-care responsibilities. He continued his regular anticonvulsant medications as prescribed and began to monitor his seizure frequency after beginning the "one-inhale" per day cannabis treatment. In the months that followed, the frequency of Seth's *grand mal* seizures declined from several per week to one or two per month, and this was his new baseline seizure frequency at the time I met him.

That Seth was receiving therapeutic, anticonvulsant benefit from his use of cannabis seemed fairly clear. Having never used marijuana before, he had no interest in "getting high" by any definition of that phrase. And given the failure of his previous treatment regimens, the notion that the therapeutic anti-epileptic effects he experienced could be better explained by a placebo response (due primarily to his belief that it would help) is hardly plausible and certainly not compelling. Even more interesting than the effectiveness of cannabis as an addition to his medication regimen, however, was his experience of trying to introduce the topic with his physicians. While they were unwilling to discuss Seth's therapeutic use of cannabis, they were prepared to recommend surgical alternatives for treatment-resistant epilepsy.

One neurologist, quite reasonably from his perspective and by accepted professional standards, recommended the procedure of vagus nerve stimulation (VNS). In VNS an electronic device that resembles a pacemaker is surgically implanted beneath the skin on the chest wall with an electrical wire routed surgically into the neck in close proximity to the vagus nerve to deliver a precisely determined electrical stimulus at programmed regular intervals. VNS has been shown to be effective in controlling otherwise treatment-resistant seizures and is approved by the Food and Drug Administration (FDA) for that purpose. More recently, after studies showed that patients using VNS for seizure control experienced significant improvement in mood and depressive symptoms, VNS was studied specifically and then approved for use in treatment-resistant depression (defined as having failed trials with four antidepressant medications).

As an FDA-approved procedure, VNS is considered safe, although the possibility of complications from the surgical implantation of the device is generally acknowledged. Although VNS is generally well tolerated by patients choosing that form of treatment, there are reports from some patients of adverse effects including vocal cord paralysis, uncontrollable coughing, and difficulty swallowing. Despite the possibility of these outcomes, the recommendation of VNS for Seth was not unreasonable by contemporary professional standards. Both of the approved indications for VNS—epilepsy and treatment-resistant depression—are serious illnesses that can be life threatening.

In the spectrum of possible treatments for Seth, VNS would have to be considered relatively benign, if invasive. In contrast, another neurologist had recommended a different type of surgical solution. This second recommendation, again by a physician who refused to discuss the possible therapeutic use of cannabis, was that Seth undergo temporal lobe surgery to destroy a small amount of brain tissue at the anatomical site of the irritable seizure focus. The message Seth heard was clear: "Since your epilepsy is not responding to aggressive conventional treatment—three modern anticonvulsant medications in combination—we're prepared to move on to surgery, including brain surgery involving focused, selective destruction of a small piece of your brain tissue. But don't even think about discussing cannabis on a therapeutic basis." Indeed, we Americans live in a society in which it is acceptable practice for surgeons to destroy a piece of someone's brain in order to prevent seizures but where use of marijuana for the same purpose—even when it works for the individual in question—is a criminal offense. How could our vision have become so clouded? How could our national policy become so out of sync with core American values? It is inconceivable that there are clearheaded policymakers who would step forward to defend such a policy as consistent with our intentions.

Despite the recommendations of his neurologists, Seth opted to postpone surgery at least until he could find out for himself whether there was any truth to the claim that herbal cannabis had value in the management of seizures. At the time I met him, Seth reported that he was adhering faithfully to his prescribed medication regimen of three anticonvulsants, and in addition he continued his "one-inhale" per day use of cannabis. His seizure frequency was down to about one to two per month, and he was beginning to experiment with a twice-a-day "one-inhale" cannabis regimen. Again, he was very cautious, determined that his functioning not be compromised by cannabis use. When asked about the side effects of cannabis, and in particular its effects on his mental state, he was quite clear: in his experience, the effects of cannabis on his mental state— his thinking and alertness—were not nearly as disabling as the adverse effects he associated with his prescription medications. If anything, he felt better able to think clearly and carry out his day-to-day responsibilities. Given that realization, Seth was willing to experiment with an increase in his cannabis dosing from once daily to twice daily. From the perspective of an observer, Seth's wife confirms his report unequivocally. It is worth reiterating that the possibility of using cannabis medicinally was presented to Seth by family members—living in California, it so happens—who had learned about it through the stories of others.

With his epilepsy poorly controlled, Seth like many patients probably experienced significant mental clouding during periods between seizures (called "interictal" periods). Most likely, Seth's experience of greater mental clarity and improved behavioral functioning during therapeutic cannabis use has to do with reduction in the frequency of his seizures. Eventually, Seth began a gradual taper of his prescription anticonvulsant medications, and as of my last conversation with him he had experienced no increase in seizure frequency. Based on this experiment of Seth's own device, he believes that the mental side effects of cannabis are preferable to the mental clouding he experiences under the influence of his prescription medications.

Seth's epilepsy has stabilized with a seizure frequency much lower than that attained with approved medications under the care of two different neurologists. He has titrated, or adjusted, his cannabis use to optimize its effects (he now uses "two inhales per day," one in the morning and one in the evening) and has begun to reduce his other medications slowly on his own recognizance. With dose reduction of some of his other medications—and reduction thereby of his overall medication burden—he finds that he thinks more clearly and is more alert.

Interestingly, Seth's story is similar to that of Valerie Corral, a medical cannabis patient in northern California and co-founder of the Wo/Men's Alliance for Medical Marijuana (WAMM). Valerie Corral appears in director Jed Riffe's award-winning documentary film, *Waiting to Inhale*.[25] In the film, Corral gives her account of tapering and ultimately discontinuing her anticonvulsants or antiseizure medications. As of the making of the film in 2005, she was managing her seizure disorder with cannabis alone, with the supervisory and care giving assistance of her husband, and feeling that this approach had been her most successful treatment to date. More recently, both Valerie Corral's personal story and the history of WAMM have been the subjects of an excellent scholarly work of sociopolitical analysis by Wendy Chapkis and Richard J. Webb.[26]

There are at least two differences between Corral's case and Seth's that are noteworthy here, one strictly medical and the other more illustrative for our purposes. The notable medical difference is that Corral's seizures developed during adulthood as a result of traumatic brain injury in a car accident. Seth was observed to have seizures, probably resulting from fever, not long after birth; however, subtler seizures subsequently went undetected until Seth began having his *grand mal* episodes near the age of 20. Another important difference between Corral's situation and Seth's, illustrative for our purposes, is that Corral as a resident of California (where medicinal cannabis is available) has the opportunity to experiment systematically with a variety of cannabis strains and to select those that are most helpful in targeting seizure activity while minimizing unwanted side effects. In Illinois, where a first-generation medical cannabis law was passed in 1978 but never implemented, Seth has much more difficulty with quality control and no systematic approach to solving that problem. Since Seth has no past history of marijuana use, he has no established network of cannabis suppliers. Nonetheless, he is functioning better at this time— consuming cannabis medicinally as regularly as he can—than he has in many years.

The IOM report, in reviewing evidence for medicinal effects of cannabis in a wide range of conditions, did distinguish medical uses relatively well supported by preliminary research and clinical findings from uses less well supported. One of the potential medicinal uses of cannabis addressed by the IOM report was that of an anticonvulsive agent, or treatment for seizures or epilepsy. However, medical management and prevention of seizures did *not* emerge as one of the stronger potential indications for medicinal use of cannabis, because of a lack of conclusive clinical research findings as well as the availability of other anti-epileptic drugs. There are indeed reported positive findings, but coupled with negative, inconclusive, or mixed results from other studies, the net evidence for use of cannabis to treat seizure disorders was not viewed as compelling by the IOM report. Now, a decade later, developments in basic and clinical science appear to offer stronger support for the prospect of cannabinoids and/or herbal cannabis for use as anti-epileptic medications.

But the conclusion of the IOM review, that development of herbal cannabis as an anticonvulsant has little future for reasons that are mulifactorial, does not alter the fact that some patients with seizures experience relief reflected in decreased seizure frequency in response to medicinal use of herbal cannabis. The IOM analysis reflects a judgment that the current array of available anti-epileptic or anticonvulsant medicines is sufficiently broad to cover the treatment needs of the vast majority of patients and that, therefore, the market for cannabinoid therapies is too small—and perhaps the development costs too great depending on the Drug Enforcement Administration (DEA) scheduling of cannabis—to attract the interest of the pharmaceutical industry. That is all well and good as policy analysis goes, but if cannabis happens to help you or a loved one with seizures, you don't want to have to debate the likelihood of its having positive effects in other patients. Let other patients take what works for them. If your spouse had been having *grand mal* seizures several times a week while on a multi-drug regimen of modern FDA-approved anticonvulsants but had been almost seizure-free since starting to use cannabis medicinally, you might want access to cannabis for that purpose even if the vast majority of patients with epilepsy were better treated with other medicines.

The IOM report provided a reasonably thorough scientific review of the available evidence bearing on the use of cannabis in the treatment of medical conditions and of its prospects for development as a prescription medicine. But the report is not without a political context. In fact, it rather deftly weaves treatment effectiveness and safety data together with judgments about the likelihood of further focused research and development by the pharmaceutical industry. In the final analysis, the IOM report's judgment about the future of cannabis as a potential anticonvulsant rests primarily on its assignment of a heavy weighting to the question of whether cannabis could appeal to the pharmaceutical industry for prospective drug development. Several considerations in fact weigh against that, including obstacles associated with current scheduling restrictions and problems involved in developing patented products derived from a naturally occurring plant—especially where there is an interest in preserving the natural array of chemical compounds because the complementary actions of those substances play a role in determining the desired therapeutic response.

The IOM report concluded overall—not just with regard to the potential of cannabis as an anticonvulsant—that the future of marijuana as medicine lies not in herbal cannabis per se, but in the development of specific cannabinoid compounds as pharmaceuticals. This conclusion is driven not by science but by a political agenda that gives greater weight to the interests of the pharmaceutical industry than it does to the healthcare consumer. In the final analysis, the IOM report was useful as an orientation to the scientific literature on cannabis therapeutics, but it was not responsive to the need for healthcare to be consumer-driven.

Seth's story has other fascinating aspects. In roughly half of *grand mal* seizure cases, there is an "aura"—a motor or, as in Seth's case, sensory phenomenon that varies from patient to patient but is remembered by the individual as similar from one attack to the next. It seems to herald the onset of the seizure, but neurophysiologically it actually corresponds to the onset of the seizure itself; and the nature of the "aura" may provide a clue to the neuroanatomical location of the seizure's origin. In Seth's case, the "aura" begins as a tingling sensation in his lower abdomen, which then rises into his chest and upward toward the head and neck. Typically for Seth, by the time the aura approaches his head and neck, he loses consciousness in a *grand mal* seizure. One of the fascinating features of Seth's case is that he recalls episodes in which he managed to get his "one-inhale" cannabis dose just as the aura was arising in the midline of his lower abdomen and progressing upward, only to find that the aura literally descended back down and subsided immediately after cannabis inhalation. The evolving seizure, in those instances, had stopped. It is difficult to argue with such a story.

Physician Advocacy: The Conant Case

Other physicians have been compelled to respond differently to situations like Seth's. A 1997 action by a group of physicians in the San Francisco Bay Area provides a case in point. Led by Dr. Marcus Conant—a professor at the University of California Medical Center in San Francisco and Medical Director of the largest private AIDS practice in the United States, the Conant Medical Group—these Bay Area doctors sued the federal government for interfering with their practice of medicine, which included supporting some patients in their decision to use marijuana medically for symptom relief. Dr. Conant, his group, and other California physicians shared common concerns about therapeutic access to cannabis, largely driven by the high number of AIDS patients they treated. Cannabis has been found clinically by many patients and their physicians to have therapeutic value in HIV disease, primarily in stimulating appetite, in counteracting the AIDS wasting syndrome, and in relieving neurological pain associated with the disease. For some patients, the FDA-approved medication dronabinol (delta-9-tetrahydrocannabinol, or THC; brand name Marinol®), which represents the best understood of the cannabinoid compounds in marijuana and is often emphasized as the primary active chemical constituent, works just fine for this purpose. In fact, Dr. Conant had prescribed it for many of his patients.

Yet, some patients find herbal cannabis to be more helpful or better tolerated. For such patients, natural herbal cannabis may be a better treatment option, and for some patients it may be the only treatment option. Whole plant cannabis contains many other cannabinoid compounds, some of which may have therapeutic effects independent of THC or may interact synergistically with THC to produce beneficial effects beyond those produced by either compound alone.[27] Further research is necessary to understand the nature and extent of these apparent effects, as well as their biological mechanisms. In addition to experiencing stimulation of appetite and weight gain counteracting the wasting syndrome, many persons with AIDS find whole plant cannabis useful in relieving nausea associated with chemotherapy (similar to cancer patients) and in relieving pain associated with progression of the disease and its complications. Not surprisingly, cannabis is also a powerful mood elevator for some patients and may provide relief from depression associated with the disease.

The value of cannabis for some persons with AIDS has been sufficiently clear to those patients and their physicians to become a driving force in the medical marijuana revolution. California was the first state to pass—voting into law by popular initiative—a medical cannabis act that heralded a new generation of such laws. But the response of the Office of National Drug Control Policy (ONDCP), even during the Clinton administration, was to threaten physicians with loss of license or criminal prosecution for even discussing with their patients the notion of a medical use of marijuana. General Barry McCaffrey, the ONDCP director or so-called drug czar at the time, referred to the whole phenomenon of medical marijuana advocacy as a "Cheech and Chong show."[28] In making threats against physician licensure, he chose to fuel a conflict over states' rights in the practice of medicine.[29]

The Conant plaintiffs prevailed on September 7, 2000, when Federal District Court Judge William Alsup found in their favor and issued a permanent injunction against the government's effort to prosecute physicians or revoke their licenses for discussing medical marijuana with patients. The Ninth Circuit Court of Appeals upheld the decision in favor of the plaintiffs, and on October 29, 2002, the court ruled in *Conant v. Walters* that the federal government may not revoke the licenses of physicians merely for discussing the possible medical uses of cannabis with their patients. The court found that "physicians must be able to speak frankly and openly to their patients." Chief Judge Mary Schroeder quoted Supreme Court Justice John Paul Stevens in noting that federal courts should defer to states in "situations in which the citizens of the state have chosen to serve as a laboratory in the trial of novel social and economic experiments."[30] The United States Supreme Court declined the Bush administration's petition to review the case, so that the Ninth Circuit's decision remained in effect.

The San Francisco Bay Area physicians who rallied in that case were exemplary advocates for their patients in the face of an intrusive government presence. The case mobilized other notable members of the medical community: Dr. Jerome Kassirer, editor-in-chief of the *New England Journal of Medicine*, published an editorial criticizing the government's prosecution threats as "misguided, heavy-handed,…inhumane (and) hypocritical."[31] Not long after that, during the time period of the progression of the Conant case, the American Medical Association (AMA) issued its position statement on medical cannabis, integrating positive findings from the 1999 IOM report and calling for more cannabis therapeutics research.[32]

At Christmas time, 2006, Seth and his family went to visit relatives on the East Coast. Not wanting to travel with cannabis for obvious reasons, Seth inquired as to whether his family might obtain some of the herb for his medicinal use while he was their guest. They agreed to make arrangements to obtain cannabis for Seth, but when he arrived they had not yet acquired it. During the period of delay, while Seth had no access to cannabis, he had repeated *grand mal* seizures—as many as seven, according to Seth's wife, within a 24-hour period. When the family finally did obtain the cannabis and Seth was able to use it, his seizures subsided, and he enjoyed the remainder of his five-day holiday visit seizure-free. Seth reported to me, and his wife corroborated, that at that time he was continuing to take his prescribed medications. Apparently, in contrast to cannabis, they were ineffective in controlling his seizures.

As of our last communication, more than three years after our first meeting, Seth was still following a multi-drug regimen of three prescription anticonvulsants under the care of his neurologist. The dosage of one of his medications (divalproex sodium) had been decreased, and one medication (levetiracetam) had been discontinued and replaced by a new one, lacosamide (brand name Vimpat®). Seth's seizure frequency remained about the same as it had been in the months after he began experimenting with herbal cannabis—about one or two per month. He had experienced no increase in seizure frequency since the onset of his cannabis use; nor, however, had he seen any further decrease in seizure frequency since the initial improvement he experienced with cannabis. He reported, and his wife corroborated, that his seizures were better controlled than they had ever been to their recollection. I asked Seth whether he felt that herbal cannabis was still helpful for control of his seizures. He answered in terms of his experience with the seizure aura, or onset of the seizure: "It doesn't matter how close I am to becoming unconscious," he replied. "As long as I have the coordination to get to my pipe and take a single inhale, herbal cannabis is 100 percent effective in aborting the seizure."

In my early conversations with Seth, I suggested repeatedly that he would benefit from the active involvement of his neurologist in at least tracking his cannabis use and the course of his seizure disorder over time—to collaborate in at least considering whether cannabis might have a legitimate role in Seth's therapeutic regimen. To my mind, Seth's reported response to cannabis raised the question whether further dosage increase—perhaps with a shift to herbal cannabis edibles or tinctures—might lead to a further reduction in seizure frequency. But that is a decision that Seth and his neurologist should be able to make together. In my conversations with Seth I have always encouraged him to speak openly with his physicians about his concerns.

The practice of medicine includes listening not only to identify the patient's complaints and concerns but also to learn about anything in the patient's experience that may have been helpful in managing symptoms of his or her disease. If law prohibits obtaining natural herbal products that have demonstrated their value to the individual medical consumer—as cannabis has for Seth—then the physician will naturally work with the patient to explore therapeutic alternatives. A patient may insist, after reasonable trials of standard, approved alternatives, that cannabis contributes beneficially to the treatment. No one wins by ignoring that kind of information. In a case like Seth's, the learning for everyone involved—doctor, patient, and family—

may be profound. Seth's experience with cannabis was dramatic and could not be ignored by his family. Nor would they want to ignore it; family members suggested he try cannabis in the first place when prescribed medications weren't working.

Seth's is not a story of a lifelong "pothead" trying to find an excuse for smoking marijuana. The case is striking and drives home the point that there are forms of learning relevant to the practice of medicine that do not arise from the identification of a statistical cut-off value in a large study sample. This does not mean that findings such as those in Seth's case cannot be researched in larger samples. It does mean that cases such as Seth's provide important information for the stimulation of research and the conceptualization of new study designs and questions. There may be identifiable factors—genetic or otherwise—that may explain why cannabis works in some cases of a specific disease state but not others. Similarly, there may be factors that explain why some individuals tolerate cannabis well, while others do not. This is not different from what physicians see with approved medications. It is likely that future research with herbal cannabis will find patterns in the array of cannabinoid compounds that predict anticonvulsant activity or other therapeutic effects but are not explained by a single chemical compound acting in isolation from others. Such information will be valuable, but for Seth it will be no more valuable than the relief he experiences from cannabis use now.

The same can be said for cannabis use in other conditions, although the cannabinoid arrays that predict therapeutic effects will likely vary based upon the medical condition in question. But the voices of consumers seeking access to herbal cannabis for its therapeutic effects, especially when other medications have not been adequate, deserve to be heard. This is true whether the cannabis use is for the pain of AIDS neuropathy; the spasticity, pain, and bladder dysfunction of multiple sclerosis (MS); the pain and stiffness of rheumatoid arthritis; or adjunctive relief of mood and anxiety symptoms that may co-occur with any of those serious medical problems. I stress "adjunctive" because anyone with such symptoms deserves a trial of standard psychiatric treatments; they are powerful medicines that can really make a difference, and they are better studied, better controlled, and more reliable than cannabis hampered by lack of regulation in the current environment. But that does not mean those medications will be more effective for all patients; although the data are anecdotal, some individuals report that their mood and anxiety symptoms are more effectively managed with cannabis than with standard treatments they have tried.[33]

Language Games: Julie

Early in my tenure as state mental health director for Illinois from 2003 to 2005, I began a more deliberate effort to educate myself about cannabis therapeutics. In the years immediately prior to that appointment, I had served as chief psychiatrist for the state hospital system. At state mental health leadership meetings, mental health director Leigh Steiner and medical director Daniel Luchins, M.D. regularly set aside time for an "environmental scan" to review and reflect upon emerging opportunities and threats with potential impact on mental health programs and policies. The regular environmental scan helped maintain and reinforce the leadership group's strategic readiness in a changing system. From the vantage point of the state mental health directorship it seemed to me that an environmental scan for opportunities to invest public resources more wisely yielded no signal stronger than that of the war on drugs. Kurt Schmoke, Dean of Howard University Law School, reached a similar conclusion a few years back during his tenure as Mayor of Baltimore. Referring to the impact of national policy on quality of life in the city, he wrote, "Clearly there was no policy that had more impact than the way in which the national government was conducting the war on drugs."[34]

A high percentage of individuals with psychiatric disorders have substance use issues, and a high percentage of individuals with substance-related problems have psychiatric disorders. Individuals in jails and prisons have high rates of both mental health and substance-related problems, and problems in either area can bring about their initiation into the criminal justice system and/or perpetuate a criminal career. Health professionals generally see medical treatment as preferable to criminal prosecution in responding to an individual with behavioral health problems including substance abuse. There is also evidence that treatment is less costly than criminal prosecution and incarceration. Drug policy reform advocates generally believe in treatment, but they also recognize that a sizable fraction of identified drug problems are nothing more than an artifact of unnecessary and problematic drug laws. Eliminating that first tier of drug problems—merely by redefining them out of existence—is the first step toward a more cost effective approach that targets real problems including substance abuse disorders. The issue is relevant to mental health programs—and healthcare systems generally—in part because resources saved can be directed toward treatment where it is needed.

A feature of the "Just Say No" platform, the notion that "all use is abuse" when it comes to marijuana, is neither medically sound nor practically useful. And although this point extends beyond strict medical usage for cannabis-responsive conditions, the consumer plea for legitimate medical access is the most obvious case in point. Americans have been prepared for years to acknowledge these realities, as evidenced by the widespread passage of a first generation of state medical cannabis laws in the 1970s and 1980s. In 1978 the State of Illinois modified its Cannabis Control Act in anticipation of working with the federal government to permit limited access to cannabis on a medical basis through the federal compassionate use program. That statutory revision is an example of what I have referred to as first-generation medical cannabis laws. But the Illinois law was never fully implemented, and the years since have seen mounting efforts on the part of medical consumers and advocates to pass a second-generation law. In early 2006 Senator John Cullerton introduced a proposed revision of the Illinois Cannabis Control Act aimed at allowing access to cannabis on a medicinal basis for certain patients with the approval of their physician. Advocates asked if I would testify in support of the bill, which was under review by the Health and Human Services Committee of the Illinois Senate.

At that time, I had the opportunity to meet and work with Julie, a remarkable Chicago woman in her early 40s who has suffered with multiple sclerosis (MS) for more than 20 years. Multiple sclerosis is a serious neurological disease characterized by an inflammatory process that leads to destruction of nerve tissue with resulting loss of function.[35] More specifically, it involves deterioration of the *myelin sheath* that provides insulation for electrochemical impulse conduction by *neurons* or nerve cells. As such, MS is called a *demyelinating* disease. I was taught to think of its clinical manifestation as "multiple lesions in space and time." It tends to affect the optic nerves (and therefore vision), the spinal cord (and therefore sensory and motor capability), and brain (often associated with mood disturbance). MS can be difficult to diagnose early in the course of the illness because the presentation is variable and may be limited in extent (multiple lesions in space). The diagnosis is typically made after a period of remission followed by relapse (multiple lesions in time). Modern neuroimaging methods, especially magnetic resonance imaging (MRI) technology applied to the brain to visualize images of anatomical structures, have made possible the identification of lesions referred to as "plaques" that appear with progression of the disease and deterioration of neurological functioning.

Though it follows a remitting and relapsing course, MS is generally a progressive disease without treatment. It may declare itself with a sudden attack or develop more gradually. About two thirds of MS patients are diagnosed between the ages of 20 and 40, and the disease tends to progress more rapidly in younger adults. Symptoms can include visual impairment, weakness in one or both legs and/or arms, tremor, gait impairment, difficulty with speech and bladder control, mood disturbance, and sensory impairment that includes deep sensation and pain. With progression of the disease, muscle weakness is followed by spasticity and is associated with pain. MS is a disabling disease that is exceedingly challenging to live with.

Julie's testimony before the Senate Health and Human Services Committee in 2006 conveyed her powerful presence. She told the senators about her 20-year struggle with MS and the success of her regimen of three cannabis brownies daily in alleviating her symptoms. Like many MS patients, she had been prescribed muscle relaxants for her spasms, opiate analgesics for pain relief, antidepressants for her mood disturbance, and other medications for bladder control and the inflammatory disease process. These medications, separately and together, were unsatisfactory for a number of reasons. She experienced the muscle relaxants as highly sedating, had constipation as a side effect of the opiate pain relievers, and did not tolerate the prescribed antidepressants well. With the above regimen of herbal cannabis ingested orally (she generally does not use the inhalation route of administration), her need for opiates became only occasional and she was able to discontinue prescribed muscle relaxants altogether. With cannabis, Julie's mood was much improved and she had no need for prescription antidepressants. She also experienced improvement in bladder control.

Julie is inspiring, with contagious positive energy, a great sense of humor, a keen intellect, and impressive determination. She represents herself and other medical patients as an informed consumer and active leader. She makes healthy choices. She is a fighter, a winner, and a team player. With her cannabis regimen, Julie avoids prescription muscle relaxants, which had kept her bedridden because of sedation. She has a positive attitude and bright outlook, and she feels cannabis has been more effective in improving her mood than the antidepressants she was previously prescribed. All else being equal, health professionals agree that reduction of overall medication burden is a favorable outcome. But for Julie all else is not equal: she is stronger; has more stamina on her feet; is in less chronic physical and emotional pain; and sleeps, eats, and feels better when she is using edible cannabis. She carries a letter from her neurologist supporting her medicinal use. The naturally fluctuating course of MS makes it difficult to draw conclusions about medicinal effects, but that is a general characteristic of clinical practice with individual patients and is only partially ameliorated by even our best data on evidence-based practice (EBP).

Working with Julie, I learned something about cannabis and language. First, I learned not to talk to Julie about marijuana. To paraphrase her view or to give my own version of it, government has taken perfectly good botanical natural resources, *Cannabis sativa* and *Cannabis indica*, and negatively marketed them as marijuana. The rise of the use of the word *marijuana* in the United States occurred in the context of difficult cultural adjustments in the American Southwest following the 1910 Mexican Revolution. Harry Anslinger, Director of the Bureau of Narcotics from 1930 to 1962, jumped on that word and rode it all the way to its namesake, *The Marihuana Tax Act of*

1937. Before Anslinger unleashed his rage against these plant species—blaming them and the ethnic minorities he was sure used them for myriad social problems—*cannabis* had been a useful component of early patent medicines produced by pharmaceutical companies such as Lily, Squibb, and Merck. Physician and medical cannabis consultant David Bearman, M.D., of Goleta, California, writes: "There were 28 patent medicines containing cannabis on the market in 1937 and no problems with cannabis were known to the AMA."[36] Many such formulations required tighter regulation of contents—especially where opiate-containing patent medicines were concerned—but there was no urgency or even desire on the part of the medical profession to eliminate access to cannabis as medicine altogether.

Whether Anslinger's racially-profiled suspects or Nixon-Reagan-Bush's hippy-criminals, Julie will not be assigned by anyone to their particular profiled and marginalized groups. For Julie, cannabis in edible form is the herb that relieves her muscle spasms and pain and improves her strength, steadiness, bladder control, and mood. Julie will not entertain accusations about using marijuana. In the first place, she doesn't even smoke it; and, more importantly, she will not accept the hostile projections loaded into that term. The word *cannabis*, devoid of the racist connotations built into the official Anslinger-Nixon-Reagan-Bush concept of marijuana, has the better name and greater potential for inclusion in a more balanced, informed, and respectful form of American public conversation.

Expressed in yet another, more rhetorical way, *marijuana* is what they grow on the federal farm in Mississippi to use for research that strives to demonstrate that the plant can be understood only in the context of substance abuse; *cannabis* is what they grow in California and other states with medical use provisions under state law, in order to take advantage of the plant's wide range of therapeutic applications. *Not to confuse—*

marijuana *and* cannabis *are two different words denoting the same thing, possession of which can get you arrested no matter what you call it.* But our language shapes our experience, and Julie will not have her experience defined by the bigotry of others, even when it lays claim to official government policy.[37]

More Listening

Working with Julie and other medical cannabis advocates in Illinois, I found myself on a path that would lead me to collect numerous vignettes or brief case illustrations regarding medical cannabis. Even more remarkable to me than the broad array of medical uses of cannabis illustrated by these cases was the fact that once I began to talk about the matter the stories seemed abundant.

A Cab Driver

In Springfield, Illinois, in 2006 Julie and I took a taxi together from our hotel to the state capitol. I helped the driver load her wheelchair into the trunk and then briskly got into the cab's back seat against the bite of a cold February morning. We were nonetheless pleased to find the weather a bit less extreme 200 miles south than it had been earlier that week in Chicago. The taxi driver heard us discussing our agenda for the morning and inquired about the work we were doing. When we informed him that we were in Springfield to testify in support of the Illinois Medical Cannabis Act, he enthusiastically recalled that a friend of his had found cannabis to be helpful for symptoms of multiple sclerosis. He also told us that he himself had used cannabis for relief of back pain. A captive audience, we were also attentive as the driver went on with his own version of a lecture on drug policy. "It doesn't make any sense. Why shouldn't people be able to use it, especially if they get pain relief or other medical benefits?" He continued. "And yet alcohol is legal. I used cannabis for back pain. Guess how I got the back pain? I was in a car accident, hit by a drunk driver. *A drunk driver!*"

A State Police Officer

Later that same day in Springfield, we chatted with a security officer at the state capitol who shared with us that he had known at least two individuals who had used cannabis therapeutically. One was a woman who had used it for chronic cancer pain, and another was a man with HIV disease who had used cannabis with multiple benefits including weight gain and pain relief. Julie and I began to muse about how uncanny it seemed that everywhere we looked, another medicinal cannabis anecdote presented itself. We both observed that opening the conversation, broaching the topic, would often lead to yet another example of someone's own experience or a report of the experience of a friend or loved one who had found therapeutic benefit from cannabis for some condition or other.

A University of Chicago Physician Colleague

Even after my work with Julie and other advocates in the state capital, I continued to find that stories about the use of cannabis as a medicinal substance, usually in modest amounts and without disturbing side effects, were abundant. I did not have to look far or hard to find such stories; I merely had to be open to listening in the language of cannabis therapeutics. A physician colleague at the University of Chicago, where I was a faculty member at the time, told me that same year that his sister had used cannabis to control nausea associated with cancer chemotherapy. I asked him to clarify what he was telling me about her response to approved treatments: "So she tried virtually all of the approved medications for that purpose?" He replied, "She tried *everything!*" The collection of such stories repeatedly reinforced my sense that I needed to write about this issue and generated very little interest on my part in arguing with those who shared their personal experiences.

A Californian Traveling in Ohio

Several months after my work with Julie and other advocates in Springfield in the winter of 2006, I had occasion to visit The Ohio State University in Columbus. The visit had nothing to do with medical marijuana or drug policy generally. As I boarded the hotel shuttle van for transportation to the university, one other person boarded at the same time. A woman in her late 50s, the other passenger was wearing "z-coils"— springs under the shoes that cushion the impact of walking. She was also using a cane. I offered to assist her getting into the van. She thanked me and told me that she suffered from severe arthritis, believed to be post-traumatic in origin following a skating accident as an adolescent. She also informed me that she had been diagnosed with fibromyalgia as well as Sjogren's syndrome.[38]

Fibromyalgia is an increasingly well-recognized syndrome, the cause of which is not understood. It has been associated with chronic fatigue and depression but as a discrete syndrome involves musculoskeletal pain exhibiting a characteristic pattern particularly in, but not limited to, areas around certain joints. Emerging research suggests that there may be abnormalities in pain centers of the brain in fibromyalgia, but further study will be necessary before any conclusions can be drawn. In reviewing the case for medicinal cannabis use in 2002, the Canadian Senate's Committee on Illegal Drugs identified fibromyalgia as one of the conditions for which there is clear evidence of therapeutic benefit from the use of cannabis. Sjogren's syndrome is a chronic connective tissue disease involving glandular inflammation primarily in the salivary and lacrimal (tear) glands. And it may be associated with rheumatoid arthritis and related conditions. Impaired glandular secretion, believed to be an autoimmune phenomenon, results in dryness of mucosal tissues, which in turn can lead to damage in multiple organ systems including respiratory, gastrointestinal, neuromuscular, and other systems.

At the time of my trip to Columbus, I had been reading about medical cannabis indications—from historical reference material, current clinical anecdotes, and a growing body of cannabis therapeutics research literature to which the U.S. was only beginning to make a contribution. I had been reading about reports of medicinal use of cannabis for both arthritis and fibromyalgia, among various conditions. I asked her whether she had ever tried cannabis to relieve pain related to any of those conditions. "Oh, yes," she said, "I am a medical marijuana patient."

Somewhat puzzled, I asked, "Are you from around here?"

"No," she quickly added, "I'm from California."

"So am I," I said and added, "I grew up there. Now I live in Illinois, the Chicago area where my wife grew up. But I've been watching the developments in California regarding medical marijuana. And Illinois is working on a medical cannabis law. I'm curious about what your experience has been in California."

My fellow passenger had much to say about her multiple medical problems and about the important but limited role that cannabis played in relieving her suffering from these conditions.

"It's not a cure for everything," she began. "I have several different types of pain. For me, marijuana is most helpful with my fibromyalgia. It helps me with my arthritis, too, but I need to add other forms of treatment to manage the pain I get with arthritis when it really flares up. They say that the particular type of inflammatory process that I have—in my case, the arthritis began after an injury—is severe. But cannabis has been a life-saver for me in some important ways. I can't take the prescribed medications in high doses all the time. The narcotics—opiate pain relievers—that the doctors prescribe help with pain, but they also cause constipation and make you feel foggy-headed. I've been on a number of different nonsteroidal anti-inflammatory medications. You have to be careful with those, and I've had stomach problems as a result of taking them in the past. With cannabis, side effects are not a problem, at least not for me; and I know other medical cannabis patients who will tell you the same thing."

She informed me that she had traveled to Columbus on business. She talked about her use of other pain relievers, including opiates, which gave her constipation and tended to become less effective with repeated use over time (tolerance). She had required higher and higher doses but had been able to stop the cycle of dosage escalation by using cannabis to decrease her need for the opiates and, therefore, the frequency of her opiate use. With the passage of California's medical cannabis law, she had obtained her physician's recommendation for medicinal cannabis use and carried a registration card identifying her as a medical marijuana patient.

At the University of Illinois Law School

After awhile, I started bracing myself for new stories about the medicinal use of marijuana. That same year I participated as a member of a three-person panel on medical marijuana at the University of Illinois Law School in Urbana-Champaign. One of the other two panelists was a law professor and expert on the United States Constitution. The other was from northern California and had been CEO of an early medicinal cannabis dispensary that was raided and closed by police and federal agents in the late 1990s. Obviously, we were in a self-selected audience that was interested in the potential medicinal applications of cannabis. There were roughly 75 attendees at the presentation and discussion. I opened my presentation by asking for a show of hands of those who knew someone personally who had used marijuana for some specific medical problem such as nausea, appetite stimulation, or pain. More than half the audience raised their hands, and these individuals represented undergraduates, graduate students, post-doctoral fellows, law students, and some faculty members.

At Southern Illinois University

More than a year later, at Southern Illinois University (SIU) in Carbondale, I participated as a panelist in a discussion following a screening of Jed Riffe's 2005 award- winning documentary film, *Waiting to Inhale: Marijuana, Medicine and the Law.*[39] Half a dozen people lingered after the discussion to talk with me further. Three of those persons told me that they had been diagnosed with bipolar disorder. All three were taking conventional mood-stabilizing medications, and all felt that adherence to their prescribed psychiatric treatment was important. They wanted to talk further about the possibility that cannabis could be recognized as having therapeutic properties, and each had a story to tell about how cannabis had been helpful in his or her recovery.

There was one woman among the three individuals with self-reported bipolar disorder who told me that marijuana had at times been acutely helpful for her by alleviating her self-destructive thoughts and urges to cut herself. I have heard this report—the usefulness of cannabis in alleviating anxiety associated with the urges to self-cut—from at least a handful of patients I have treated who have discussed their experiences with cannabis. Of the other two individuals who approached me that evening at SIU to tell me they had been diagnosed with bipolar disorder, one man felt that cannabis was more effective as a mood stabilizer than conventional medications he had taken, and the other told me that after he had developed alcohol problems—he had been a binge drinker, and his alcohol consumption had led to problems with impulse control—cannabis use had helped him achieve alcohol abstinence and seemed to eliminate his interest in alcohol altogether. Reports along the lines of the latter two I have heard from other patients I have treated; it is always my practice to take such reports seriously, but in none of these cases has herbal cannabis been the recommended treatment. It does seem to me, however, that the medicinal potential of herbal cannabis as a mood stabilizer ought to be studied.

Two other individuals spoke with me at some length after the film screening. Stuart, in his later 20s, was quadriplegic from cerebral palsy and operated his wheelchair by mouth. He had recently completed a master's degree at the university. He reported that he had always found cannabis to be most helpful for relieving his muscle spasms and that he very much appreciated its mood-elevating effects. He could find no reason for believing that cannabis had caused functional problems; in fact, he could find no reason from his experience to see cannabis as anything other than medicinal or therapeutic in its effects. This man was positive in his demeanor and appeared both well organized in his life and skilled in getting about in the face of serious physical challenges; he had clearly accomplished a great deal despite major obstacles. In his view, cannabis use was not one of those obstacles but rather a part of his personal recovery tool kit.

Brett, the other young man who spoke with me at some length after the film screening, was in his early 20s and also confined to a wheelchair at that time. He was struggling with gradual and uncertain recovery of functioning in his legs in the aftermath of a serious motor vehicle accident. He had undergone a number of operations and had been prescribed many different muscle relaxants and pain relievers. He preferred herbal cannabis because it provided both pain relief and muscle relaxation, and he too felt that its mood-elevating effects had been helpful for him. He was actively involved in a physical rehabilitation program, and he was interested in emerging research on the potential protective and therapeutic effects of cannabis or cannabinoid compounds on the nervous system.

Politics, Practice, Research

Failure to acknowledge therapeutic dimensions in public discussions of cannabis denies the reality of the widespread experiences of its therapeutic effects.[40] Such benefits include, but are not limited to, the mood elevation associated with the cannabis "high"—a term that is less than helpful in that it has a connotation of impairment that is often not relevant in the context of modest medicinal usage. Medicinal cannabis consumers I have met are not generally struggling with impaired thinking, perception, or coordination as a consequence of using cannabis. In fact, in talking with medicinal cannabis patients I have found more commonly that they are relieved to have spared themselves adverse and debilitating side effects of prescription medicines. But there is no need to apologize for the favorable impact that cannabis may have on mood for many of its consumers. Donald Abrams, M.D., Professor of Medicine at the University of California, San Francisco School of Medicine, and the leading American researcher on the medicinal use of cannabis, found himself responding to an expression of concern following a research presentation on his work with AIDS patients that he did not "think that a drug that creates euphoria in patients with terminal diseases is having an adverse effect."[41]

The experience of an elevated mood after consumption of a substance does not in itself constitute grounds for exclusion from the realm of the medicinal. In fact, all else being equal, it would have to count as a positive outcome. One might, for example, recognize a maxim that ideal medicines have a neutral impact on feeling states. Such a maxim is not particularly helpful when many psychiatric medications are explicitly designed to improve and/or stabilize mood; nor when many other psychoactive substances—medicinal and nonmedicinal, but legal—have greater addictive and abuse potential and represent considerably greater health risk on an individual and population basis. Nonetheless, under such a "neutral mood impact" principle, it would be preferable—in erring significantly from the ideal mark—to have a positive or pleasurable effect rather than a negative or adverse effect.

From the standpoint of contemporary neuroscience research, the effects of most drugs of abuse—as well as the effects of many therapeutic drugs—are associated with stimulation of a final common pathway that serves as the brain's reward center. Still, these drugs act by different mechanisms and vary greatly in their likelihood of inducing toxicity, dependence, and patterns of abuse. They also vary in their interactions with individual biology, including genetic differences that may explain not only vulnerability to the development of substance abuse problems but also responsiveness to therapeutic interventions. There is nothing new about the idea that a substance used by some individuals for its medicinal and therapeutic effects might be abused by others; however, the wholesale transformation of a substance from medicine to "public enemy number one"—as occurred in the government-sanctioned paradigm for American public language (and permissible speech) concerning marijuana in the 20th century—is quite frankly bizarre and patently out of sync with core American values pertaining to individual freedom and personal choice.

The plea for patient access to cannabis on a medical basis stands on solid ground. Those who have found the herb to be helpful for their symptoms do not need a series of double-blind placebo-controlled studies to convince them. To imagine that they do is bad medicine, bad science, and bad philosophy. For the rest of us, who might require convincing, the controlled scientific study is helpful. Such evidence is not only helpful but also critical in establishing a basis for estimating the likelihood of desired medicinal effects and distinguishing those effects from patient responses associated with placebo or inactive treatment. But patients who find that cannabis relieves their muscle spasms, migraines, or arthritic pain require neither a larger sample nor a statistical analysis to appreciate that the treatment has helped. Such a perspective is human experience, not a theory, a finding, or a generalized claim. Medicine is a healing profession that utilizes science as a valuable tool to inform decision-making but looks first to the individual patient for data.

Individual patient information—the patient's presenting history—is itself inherently anecdotal, so it is not clinically useful to imagine that anecdotal data are irrelevant to the practice of medicine. As to safety, it would be difficult to design a study that would be any more compelling with regard to the safety profile of cannabis than the enormous wealth of knowledge and experience that already informs our understanding of the herb. That knowledge has been accumulated over thousands of years of human experience with herbal cannabis and is more than sufficient to establish a safety profile that compares favorably with, and may even be superior to, those of some over-the-counter (OTC) medicines. Grinspoon has made this point repeatedly.[42]

In February of 2007 the medical journal *Neurology* published a landmark article and perhaps the first American controlled scientific study in herbal cannabis therapeutics to appear in a major medical journal in several decades.[43] The researchers, led by Donald I. Abrams, M.D., professor of medicine at the University of California at San Francisco, examined the effects of inhaled cannabis on neuropathic pain in AIDS patients. Dr. Abrams had tried over a four-year period to gain approval for a trial of smoked marijuana for the treatment of AIDS wasting—a syndrome involving loss of appetite and weight that, in Abrams's words, leaves patients looking "like concentration camp victims."[44] Anecdotal data pointed compellingly to the value of herbal cannabis, including smoked marijuana, in AIDS, with patients tolerating it well and finding it helpful for more than one debilitating manifestation of HIV disease.

Dr. Abrams applied for use of federally grown marijuana so that his research could be conducted with the kind of systematic attention to detail and design necessary to meet scientific standards and regulatory requirements for approval of a medicinal pharmaceutical by the FDA. In fact, the FDA approved Abrams's proposal. It was the National Institute on Drug Abuse (NIDA), responsible for determining which research studies are permitted to go forward with access to federally grown marijuana, that ultimately rejected Abrams's application and blocked him altogether from studying herbal cannabis in AIDS wasting. In a sense, that's not surprising, given that Abrams's research has nothing to do with substance abuse, and NIDA exists for the purpose of supporting research in substance abuse.

The existing federal bureaucracy has been engineered to facilitate plausible deniability of any knowledge of such a thing as cannabis therapeutics. Cannabis is a substance of abuse, and its dangers are studied in the substance abuse department—so the thinking goes. The documentary film, *In Pot We Trust*, aired on television on Showtime in 2007, illustrates this with hu-mor, as United States Congressman Mark Souder (R-Indiana) hustles away from Aaron Houston, lobbyist for the Marijuana Policy Project, repeating to himself, "medical marijuana doesn't exist." From the federal bureaucratic perspective, public dis-course on herbal cannabis takes place only on the playing field of substance abuse.

In the context of Dr. Abrams's proposals and related events, the mid-1990s saw a bitter airing of concerns from medical and academic communities in the *New England Journal of Medicine*, which included the aforementioned editorial from Editor Jerome Kassirer, M.D.[45] It was only with Abrams's later proposal to study AIDS neuropathy—a neurological pain syn-drome that can be caused by the disease itself or, ironically, as a side effect of some of the medications used to treat the primary disease—that federal authorities approved the use of smoked marijuana for the first therapeutic research since the late 1970s. After complying with the requirement of first conducting a safety study in the same population, which was published in 2003, Abrams was finally able to initiate, complete, and pub-lish in 2007 the positive scientific findings of the therapeutic efficacy of smoked marijuana in AIDS neuropathy.[46]

Rather synchronously, the day before Abrams's study was published saw the unfolding of overlapping history. DEA Administrative Law Judge Ellen Bittner ruled in favor of the plaintiffs in the University of Massachusetts's lawsuit against the federal agency for denying biology professor Dr. Lyle Crak-er permission to grow research-grade cannabis for the study of its potential medicinal applications. She wrote, "there is cur-rently an inadequate supply of marijuana available for research purposes" and "competition in the provision of marijuana for such purposes is inadequate."[47] Current federal cannabis policy relies on the existence of a federal monopoly on the legal production of herbal cannabis, which occurs only at the University of Mississippi, administered under the auspices of the National Institute on Drug Abuse (NIDA). Medical researchers have been fighting to lift the federal monopoly on legal marijuana production so that medicinal grade cannabis can be produced elsewhere and researched for therapeutic purposes. Under President George W. Bush, the DEA denied Professor Craker and the University of Massachusetts the licensure necessary to grow cannabis for therapeutic purposes.

On January 7, 2009, as the Bush presidency was coming to a close, DEA Deputy Administrator Michele M. Leonhart rejected Judge Bittner's recommendation and denied the application of Dr. Craker and the University of Massachusetts.[48] This was the final decision despite the fact that Craker's research had been approved by the FDA. But Judge Bittner's administrative ruling recognizes the need for assessment and planning to move forward on cannabis therapeutics research. The current American system is not designed to support research in cannabis therapeutics. That's because the "official belief" is that cannabis therapeutics doesn't exist. The "official belief" is that the federal marijuana supply is adequate for the only kind of cannabis research there is—that is, substance abuse research. Such an "official belief" is not supported by available data.

John Halpern, M.D., another psychiatrist on the faculty of Harvard Medical School, testified in late 2008 before the American Medical Association (AMA) that he cannot reasonably conduct cannabis therapeutics research without supply options other than NIDA-produced marijuana, because the quality of federally-produced herbal cannabis is so poor as to be "designed to make the research fail."[49] Ironically, despite use of apparently substandard marijuana reluctantly released by government for therapeutic studies, at least ten controlled scientific clinical trials conducted over the past eight years in the

U.S. alone have produced favorable results on medicinal applications of herbal cannabis.[50] On an international scale there are many more. To facilitate management of the growing American demand for medicinal cannabis, the federal monopoly will ultimately have to give way to a more competitive process that can catalyze the development of quality products. There is certainly more clinical cannabis therapeutics research to be done. However, the basic case for legitimate access to herbal cannabis for therapeutic use requires not more research but acknowledgement of existing data and, equally important, respect for the consumer perspective in healthcare.

Dr. Lester Grinspoon, the Harvard psychiatrist whose work we recognized at the beginning of this discussion, has devoted much of his career to identifying the various medical uses of cannabis, understanding its therapeutic effects as reported by consumers, and advocating for patients who found therapeutic benefit in its use. When he made his prediction in 1971, he was drawing upon the extensive clinical information he had collected from patients, his own scholarship in reviewing the relevant clinical and basic science research, and his perception of the social climate at the time. More than 35 years later, normalization of cannabis as a medicinal therapeutic option moves inexorably forward. Outspoken medical patients, physician advocates, and policy reformers work together in courageous coalitions. They have worked hard to take a popular, widely supported political agenda forward in a social climate that has paralyzed elected leadership. Meanwhile, armed government enforcement teams have descended relentlessly upon private family homes and peaceful cooperative establishments that create opportunities for good American people to help one another. You don't have to be a doctor, professor, lawyer, or judge to figure out that there is something terribly wrong with this picture.

Mary in Illinois, The Farmacy® in California

One of the patients interviewed for the local newspaper article that originally drew Seth's attention was Mary, from Northbrook, Illinois. Mary is a 54-year-old woman who suffers from post-stroke pain in the aftermath of near-fatal cerebral vasculitis (inflammation of blood vessels). She uses smoked cannabis to relieve chronic pain and muscle spasms from which she has suffered in the course of her rehabilitation from two strokes. Three years before she was interviewed for the article, Mary developed a severe headache, was hospitalized with a high fever, and diagnosed with cerebral vasculitis. She was hospitalized for six weeks and had two strokes during that time period. Her husband and family were afraid they might lose her. Mary participated in intensive physical rehabilitation for three months and follows an ongoing post-rehabilitation exercise program. She has made a remarkable recovery but struggles to maintain strength and steadiness of gait and to overcome significant loss of strength bilaterally with right side weaker than left. She finds that the combination of acupuncture, massage, and cannabis provides good pain relief and muscle relaxation without the sedative toxicity of standard prescription muscle relaxants or the constipation and tolerance that are common with opiates. She has tried several of the standard medications but now rarely takes prescription medicines.

If Mary were living in California, she could go to an established dispensary and choose from among at least several—if not more than a dozen—cannabis strains and get help determining which strain works best for her muscle spasms. She might also find that rotating several varieties extends the longevity of the herb's effectiveness. Other patients report that this is a feature of their use of, and response to, the herb as medicine. Mary would even be able to find health professionals interested in the coordination and integration of her various treatment modalities. One such professional is pharmacist Joanna La Force, who manages an herbal medicine outlet that includes a medicinal cannabis dispensary in West Hollywood. Operating under California's Proposition 215, The Farmacy® offers a variety of herbal cannabis products for medicinal use. As we have already seen, Seth, too, would likely be better served with the kinds of options available in the California environment.

A registered pharmacist with specialty certification in geriatric pharmacy, Joanna La Force has a wealth of experience assisting patients and their physicians with the identification and management of drug-drug interactions. Her work with patients across the life span has included care for seniors that demands careful attention to the potential for both medication side effects and medication interactions. The Farmacy® offers various traditional herbal remedies in addition to a variety of cannabis strains and edible products. The cannabis-enhanced edibles include baked goods, candies, ice cream, butter, and even gourmet entrees like vegetarian lasagna. La Force maintains that cannabis should be regulated as an herbal therapeutic, not as a pharmaceutical and not as a scheduled controlled substance.

The Farmacy® is both elegant and modest, a tightly run and secure storefront shop on Santa Monica Boulevard that serves patients approved by their physicians to use cannabis medicinally. Patients shopping at The Farmacy® must provide documentation of their physician's recommendation in addition to their personal identifying information and their California driver's license or identification card. These consumers include persons of all ages, representing a variety of medical conditions. Most common among La Force's clientele are patients whose physicians have recommended cannabis for the management of pain. Most, but not all, of these patients discovered the therapeutic properties of cannabis on their own and then sought their physician's consultation and approval.

La Force's work with seniors has prepared her well for responding to the substantial numbers of late middle-aged and senior patients coming to the dispensary for medicinal cannabis. Many find it useful for the management of arthritis. One of the concerns voiced by this group is that it may be difficult for them to find a physician who will write a recommendation. Such recommendations have become something of a specialty with a forensic dimension. The forensic dimension is mostly about the physician's protecting himself or herself from vulnerability to intrusion by federal authorities—best exemplified by the McCaffrey agenda that eventuated in the class action case of Marcus Conant, M.D. and his colleagues. Fortunately, the Conant case was ruled in favor of physicians, finding that doctors have the right to discuss with their patients the use of cannabis for medicinal purposes or any other health-related issue. As a result, physicians are beginning to get more involved in writing cannabis recommendations, but this has happened gradually as the ambiguous legal status of medicinal cannabis use in California has continued to sort itself out.

The Farmacy® was one of roughly a dozen cannabis-dispensing operations raided by the DEA in cooperation with local law enforcement in the Los Angeles area on January 17, 2007.[51] The federal government, not recognizing the existence of medicinal cannabis—at least officially, recalling the handful of remaining compassionate use patients who continue to receive a regular supply of marijuana cigarettes for medicinal use directly from the federal government—has seen medicinal cannabis dispensaries as unambiguously criminal operations. This is disturbing for many reasons but notably—for a student of psychopathology and group behavior—because of all the participants in the medicinal cannabis debate, none is more ambiguous than the federal bureaucracy.

With a defunct federal medicinal program maintaining five grandfathered patients; with a monopolized cannabis production facility administered under the federal drug abuse research agency; with a Drug Enforcement Administration that has ignored the thoughtful and articulate recommendations of its own judicial review; with a pharmaceutical-grade "medical marijuana" that is not only synthesized in the laboratory at much greater expense than the cost of extraction from the natural plant (and therefore essentially unaffordable) but also classified as Schedule III (less likely to be abused than Schedule II); with a Food and Drug Administration that readily approves medications far riskier to use than cannabis; and with criminalizing drug enforcement that causes far more damage to public well-being than cannabis ever will—federal marijuana policy, while clear about its intent to label users as criminals, is, overall, quite frankly incoherent.

Until recently, the federal government has been clear about its intent to criminalize, prosecute, and otherwise harass persons involved with cannabis. Federal officials state repeatedly that marijuana has no medicinal value, yet government continues to supply marijuana to patients in the federal compassionate use program. Sadly, DEA officials have been willing to draw assault rifles and hold families, storefront dispensary operators, and cannabis farmers at gunpoint in order not to send "the wrong message." There is something radically wrong with this picture, and everyone paying attention knows it. Federal government faces the challenge of remaining relevant—which is to say, of overcoming its recent history of almost reflexive obstructionism—as the implementation of medicinal access to cannabis, for patients who can benefit from it, goes forward systematically in state after state. That is what is now happening, and there seems little reason to believe that the process will not continue. Since the January 2007 raid, The Farmacy® is not only up and running once again but has expanded and opened two new operations in Westwood near UCLA and in Venice.

Herbal Remedies and Pharmaceuticals

German physician Franjo Grotenhermen, M.D., has noted some authors' objection to medical use of herbal cannabis on the basis of its variable and uncertain chemical composition. In his view, this is the same argument advanced in opposition to the medical use of herbs in general. According to Grotenhermen, "The modern paradigm of drug treatment, particularly in the United States, that demands a selective pharmacological effect through the use of defined single chemical agents, is in fact pervasive, but without a strong basis. Many herbal products in Europe are standardized and have been clinically proven in double-blind placebo-controlled trials." He points out that the individual reaction of a patient to synthetic THC "is just as uncertain, variable, and idiosyncratic as the pharmacological effects obtained with an herbal cannabis preparation standardized to the same THC content. Drug therapy is not mathematics, but has always pertained to interindividual and intraindividual variability of numerous parameters: age, gender, general health status, concomitant disease, interaction with other drugs, absorption, function of digestion, liver, kidneys, etc."[52]

The "strong basis" for adopting a medication paradigm requiring "a selective pharmacological effect through the use of defined single chemical agents" would appear to be the need to accommodate the pharmaceutical industry's patenting process. This is in keeping with the priorities of the 1999 IOM report that, as previously discussed, seems fairly clear in its prioritization of the interests of the pharmaceutical industry over those of the healthcare consumer. But whereas input from multiple stakeholders including consumers and industry representatives is necessary to establish a viable regulatory process, prioritization of consumer-driven access to healthcare services and products is ultimately critical to the economic viability of healthcare in the broader system-defining payer context: federal government is the largest healthcare payer, and ultimately this means taxpayers. In addition, government systems at all levels are currently guided by commitments to support recovery models of healthcare access and utilization in which consumers of publicly funded healthcare services are responsible and accountable for self-management of health and illness with necessary supports.

The work of Harvard Business School Professor Regina Herzlinger on consumer-driven healthcare points to consumer choice as a key element of a vital healthcare system characterized by competition and innovation.[53] Herzlinger's work underscores the importance of consumer choice as a driving force in technological development, and it reminds us that consumer choice, competition, and innovation are elements of a thriving American economy in every sector. One of the most compelling aspects of the popular movement demanding access to cannabis as medicine, considered in the context of existing marijuana policies, is that the issue provides a particularly poignant example of the high cost, morbid consequences, and retardation of progress that can result from failure to respect the healthcare consumer. Cannabis policy is healthcare policy, and marijuana prohibition is a prism through which every healthcare policy issue that typically surfaces elsewhere (for example, government regulation, industry performance, consumer choice, professional practice, cost-effectiveness, payer mix) is naturally refracted and exposed for examination and critique. That observation, perhaps more than any other, makes the medical marijuana movement for me an interest sufficiently compelling to write about.

Some patients who receive benefit from cannabinoid medicines will do well with dronabinol or pharmaceutical THC. Others will do better with herbal extracts that preserve the contributions of other chemical compounds to the therapeutic effects of whole plant cannabis. In some cases the preference for herbal cannabis will be a function of the fact that chemical compounds other than THC are the primary therapeutic agents; in other cases, important therapeutic effects may result from the combined effects of more than one cannabinoid substance. It is not necessary to answer the question for every illness or therapeutic application before taking steps to facilitate access on the basis of reported benefits. The need for a more precise appreciation of the mechanisms involved and of the chemistry and genetics that predict individual therapeutic responsiveness and tolerability can be addressed through research in the context of a culture supported by policies that facilitate rather than impede consumer access. The primary stakeholder interest served by doing otherwise is that of the pharmaceutical industry, because withholding herbal cannabis from the population takes away that industry's major competitor in the cannabinoid medicine market.

GW Pharmaceutical of Oxford, UK, innovatively dissects this market with its ability to mass produce standardized whole herbal cannabis-based medicinal extracts, and this offers a therapeutic advance—and a regulatory and public health advance—in those countries where patients now have access to that kind of medication. Eventually, when the necessary studies are completed in the U.S., American patients will have access to Sativex®, the first medicinal cannabis extract that GW Pharmaceutical has taken to market. Whereas dronabinol or pharmaceutical THC may be helpful for some patients and

GW's Sativex® may be effective for others, patients may turn to a variety of herbal cannabis preparations based on their individual needs and the tolerability and therapeutic effects of those products. There is no good medical reason for preventing patient access to any of these treatment options if the benefits outweigh the risks in a particular case. In most instances where cannabis has been found helpful for serious medical illness, the risk-benefit analysis is not difficult.

Given the current state of knowledge, cannabis prohibition isn't consumer-centered or patient-focused; nor is it sound philosophically, scientifically, or clinically. Such a policy stance does not serve public health but rather works against it in a society that encourages and/or legitimizes consumption of substances like alcohol and tobacco. And a policy criminalizing medicinal access lacks integrity when viewed in the context of the known adverse effects of many actively marketed prescription and over-the-counter pharmaceuticals. There are reasonable concerns regarding cannabis safety, and, as with many substances, cannabis can be abused. But official government policy blows these concerns out of proportion in light of the recognized benefits and widespread therapeutic applications of cannabis. As Grinspoon and others have pointed out, the federal marijuana research agenda has been so aggressive in its mission to characterize the potential detriments of the plant that it has in fact contributed to establishing a rather robust and favorable safety profile.

On April 20, 2006, the FDA issued a statement reiterating its longstanding position that marijuana has no medical value. To be fair, the statement did specify smoked marijuana but in doing so skirted the issue of how whole plant cannabis differs from the synthetic cannabinoids now available as medicines. There are important differences, and it is becoming increasingly clear from scientific research that these differences have therapeutic implications. Cannabis preparations may be inhaled, eaten, or taken as a suppository. In addition, cannabinoid compounds may be administered sublingually (under the tongue) as a tincture or solution that is sprayed and directly absorbed through the rich supply of blood vessels in the mouth. There are also traditional medicinal applications of cannabis that involve topical applications in the form of creams, ointments or salves. Even more recently, at least one manufacturer has developed a transdermal cannabinoid patch as an alternative route of systemic administration for absorption and distribution throughout the body.[54]

Route of administration of cannabis makes a difference in several respects. First, there are many individuals for whom the ability to titrate (or adjust) the dosage rapidly is important. Individuals experiencing nausea, pain, or muscle spasms often find immediate relief from herbal cannabis taken via the inhalation route. This does not necessarily mean that the cannabis must be smoked, because the availability of vaporizers provides an alternative. Vaporizers are devices that heat the plant material to a temperature that releases the active compounds as vapor without causing its combustion or burning. Recently, Dr. Donald Abrams and his colleagues at UCSF published a study confirming that vaporization releases active cannabinoid compounds resulting in levels of THC comparable to those achieved by smoking, with little or no exposure to carbon monoxide and other gaseous combustion toxins.[55] Orally administered tinctures absorbed sublingually also act considerably faster than orally ingested cannabinoids absorbed through the gastrointestinal tract.

Relief of nausea is a widely recognized medicinal use of cannabis. In fact, the FDA-approved medication dronabinol (brand name Marinol®), or synthetically manufactured delta-(9)-tetrahydocannabinol (THC), was approved by the FDA in 1985 for use in alleviating nausea and vomiting associated with cancer chemotherapy. It is generally only used when other medications have failed, and for most cases of nausea other medications are effective. Dronabinol is also used to stimulate appetite in patients with AIDS wasting. The THC molecule is considered the most important psychoactive chemical compound in herbal cannabis and the constituent most responsible for the cannabis "high" or euphoria.

One important reason for making the inhalation route available to medical patients is that nausea and vomiting may prevent them from keeping the medicine down long enough for it to be absorbed. In the case of dronabinol, the medicine has to remain in the upper gastrointestinal tract for at least an hour and often considerably longer to achieve the substantial absorption necessary for medicinal benefits. There are various ways that physicians can work with patients to address this issue, such as pretreatment and/or the use of other medications, but if THC and/or other cannabinoids are effective for the individual in question, the inhalation route may be the easiest solution to the problem of vomiting up the medicine as well as meeting the need for rapid symptom relief.

There are many traditional medicinal uses of cannabis that have not been studied in controlled clinical experiments. Some uses have been better studied scientifically than others, and some uses are better supported by historical, anecdotal, and case report data than others.[56] Arguably, the best clinical scientific studies of the therapeutic effects of herbal cannabis have been produced by GW Pharmaceutical of Oxford, UK, working with medicinal whole plant extracts from various cultivated cannabis strains. In particular, GW Pharmaceutical has demonstrated the clinical efficacy of its product Sativex® in multiple sclerosis (MS). Sativex® is an orally administered herbal cannabis extract cultivated and processed to achieve a one-to-one ratio of tetrahydrocannabinol (THC) to cannabidiol (CBD).

Clinical use of cannabinoids in MS, even in a single patient, can be quite informative because they are often perceived by the patient to alleviate several distinct manifestations of the disease. Specifically, MS patients may report benefit from cannabis for one or more of the following problems: pain; muscle spasms; bladder dyscontrol; weakness, poor coordination and poor mobility; numbness, tingling, and other sensory disturbances; tremor; and depression and other mood disturbances. Some patients report improvement in all of these symptoms with herbal cannabis, leading some clinicians and scientists informed by other basic science research to postulate that cannabis may target not only individual symptoms of MS but the underlying disease process as well. Such a curative effect has not been conclusively established, but it is talked about among physicians and scientists as an interesting possibility that warrants further research.

GW Pharmaceutical's Sativex® is now available for prescription usage in Canada, originally labeled for use in MS and now also approved for use in cancer pain. Clinical trials of Sativex® for chronic cancer pain are underway in the United States. To put the availability of Sativex® into perspective in the broader medicinal cannabis discussion, it is important to remember that Sativex® is an extract based on a specific standardized production process designed to deliver a consistent product with a one-to-one ratio of THC to CBD. Reportedly, GW has developed some number of such extracts based on their collaboration with the Dutch company HortaPharm to cultivate various cannabis strains that can be characterized, cross-bred, further studied, and mixed in order to achieve specific outcomes in terms of desired ratios of identified active cannabinoid compounds.

Information available from U.S. federal authorities has maintained that "medical marijuana is already available" in the form of dronabinol (brand name Marinol®), described above as FDA-approved for relief of nausea accompanying cancer chemotherapy. For practical purposes, this is true for some patients. Not long ago, I met an individual with HIV disease who had been taking dronabinol for nearly 20 years to stimulate appetite and maintain weight and was pleased with the results. However, dronabinol is not the same as whole herbal cannabis. THC is but one of the 60 or 70 cannabinoid compounds found in the natural plant.

Generally, THC has been understood to be the primary active compound contained in the natural plant, although there are at least a handful of naturally occurring cannabinoids that are thought to be biologically active in humans, possibly of medical value, and relevant for the appreciation of the medicinal effects of cannabis. For some patients, dronabinol may be the right medicine. For others, this may not be the case. One reason, as noted above, may be the route of administration; that is, some patients may benefit primarily from THC but be much better served by an inhalation route. For other patients, route of administration is less important than the presence of cannabinoids other than THC. For example, it has been suggested that CBD may be a more important muscle relaxant than THC and may be a better anticonvulsant.[57] More research will be necessary to clarify these issues, but it seems fairly clear that these are compounds with therapeutic value. Some patients who are strong advocates for access to whole herbal cannabis on a medicinal basis do not use the inhalation route at all—either through smoking or vaporization—but rather, take cannabis orally with food.

There are many medicinal uses of cannabis that have been much less well studied than MS or nausea in scientifically designed clinical experiments. Epilepsy, as in the case of Seth, would be one of the reported uses for which the scientific research is considered inconclusive. The studies have been few and the results mixed. The IOM concluded: "Given the current state of knowledge, clinical studies of cannabinoids in epileptics are not indicated."[58] The IOM perspective is a potentially useful one for a number of reasons that need not be reviewed here, but it doesn't change the fact that cannabis at one to two "inhales" per day helps Seth with his seizures. One way in which the IOM report's perspective is useful is that it helps identify areas where investment in cannabinoid drug development and cannabis therapeutics has the greatest potential to create new value by adding needed alternatives to existing treatments.

On the other hand, a judgment that drug development in a specific area is unlikely to be fruitful—as suggested by the IOM report with respect to herbal cannabis as an anticonvulsant—is not in any way incompatible with a policy that permits patients to use whole herbal cannabis therapeutically. A business decision for or against investment of resources in search of new pharmaceutical products takes place on a different level from a social policy decision to permit or prohibit consumer access to substances for which they claim significant therapeutic benefits. The former is a matter of financial risk to entrepreneurs and stockholders, whereas the latter relates to an individual's right to make choices that affect his or her personal well-being.

If responsible use of cannabis relieves symptoms that are debilitating and have not responded adequately to other medications, or if cannabis is preferred over those medications for any number of potentially legitimate reasons—including side effects, cost, and unknown long-term effects—then the preference of the patient in question needs to be respected. Why should Seth, for example, suffer another seizure while he deliberates on his doctors' recommended surgeries, when he has devised his own regimen of "one inhale twice a day," and it seems to work? Seth doesn't have time to put his life on hold while scientists conduct experiments to quantify things we already know. Is it reasonable, by any known criteria of scientific, philosophical, economic, or moral analysis, for Seth to be denied legitimate access to an herbal substance that provides relief from a serious medical problem in order to collect data that will make medical scientists, government bureaucrats, politicians, religious leaders, educators, or anyone else more confident that he is telling the truth? Few will want to respond in the affirmative, and none will be able to provide a cogent defense for that response. There are no compelling scientific, philosophical, economic, or moral reasons for Seth to be denied access to herbal cannabis, especially if he can pay for it.

In the interim since the 1999 publication of the IOM report—which cited mixed results on the potential of cannabis as an anticonvulsant—several studies have provided compelling evidence not only of the involvement of the endocannabinoid system in the regulation of neurophysiological activity associated with seizures but also of the potential value of cannabis as an anticonvulsant.[59] In particular, the apparent importance of both THC and cannabidiol (CBD) in the anticonvulsant effects of cannabis would appear to point to the value of herbal cannabis as opposed to THC or other individual component molecules only. Some investigators have proposed that THC-to-CBD ratios may be important in determining therapeutic efficacy for some conditions.[60] Seth would, of course, embrace real cannabis therapeutics research—for example, research that systematically sought to determine the nature of the apparent synergies between different cannabinoid compounds within the naturally occurring array, studied correlations between strain and therapeutic effects, and developed ways of measuring and reproducing strain and product parameters that permit standardization (as has been done by GW Pharmaceutical with its product Sativex®).

There are known medicinal uses of cannabis that have not been systematically studied at all or have been studied minimally with equivocal or negative results. A number of these uses are supported by extensive anecdotal reports from patients who have benefited directly from medicinal cannabis use.[61] While positive experimental findings make a good case for any medicine's effectiveness, the lack of such findings for a particular chemical compound or herbal substance does not mean that the compound or substance is ineffective for medicinal purposes. The lack of such evidence, if the chemical compound or herbal substance has been extensively studied in clinical trials, would be reason to lack confidence in the substance's value as a medicine. Even then, however, it is neither proven nor demonstrated that the substance could not be effective or helpful for any particular individual or even subgroup. In the absence of scientific controlled studies, we lack a statistically defensible basis for confidence in the expectation that the substance will have medicinal effects. But that does not mean we lack all basis whatsoever for expecting therapeutic benefits. In Seth's case, he came to expect that cannabis was helpful because he found it to be so repeatedly and on a sustained basis over an extended period of time. Collecting serial measurements in one individual only, especially when medication effects are measured on and off the medication over multiple time periods, can be the basis of research designs in which data from multiple "N of 1" trials are combined.[62]

In the modern practice of medicine, scientific studies using sound methods and appropriate controls set the standard for drawing conclusions about the therapeutic effects of pharmaceuticals or herbal substances. Properly designed clinical trials allow for the separation of clinical effects attributable to the specific chemical compound(s) under study from effects attributable to other factors associated with the treatment. Such factors may include the doctor-patient relationship; the social, psychological, and biological processes involved in taking the recommended treatment and the meanings assigned to those processes; the passage of time; and the presence of other factors that may confound assessment of treatment effects by direct comparison (for example, individual differences or the presence of other therapeutic influences including other medicines). Scientific methods help to disentangle such confounding factors and can provide the information necessary to make a compelling case for a treatment's effectiveness.

In the absence of controlled scientific studies, the case for or against the effectiveness of potential therapies, pharmaceutical and nonpharmaceutical, relies on narrative reports from individual consumers combined with relevant clinical observations. In fact, such observations may be critical in many instances to the generation of hypotheses that can be tested by research. The latter may include objective measurements (for example, intraocular pressure, muscle spasm, or weight gain) as well as the evaluation of subjective reports (for example, decreased pain, improved mood). In the absence of controlled clinical experiments—trials of the sort required for FDA approval as medicine—anecdotal reports of therapeutic benefits on an individual basis are reasons to inquire further about possible therapeutic value. They always have been reasons for further study—they predate FDA controlled clinical trial methodology—and likely will be for a long time to come. This applies both to subjective patient reports as in pain relief or objective observations as in decreased intraocular pressure, measurable reduction in muscle spasms, weight gain, or a reduction in seizure frequency.

Further, the existence of numerous anecdotal reports from many individuals attesting to the same experience is, even in the absence of controlled studies, a good reason to entertain the notion that the substance may be effective for these people. And if the numbers of people reporting therapeutic benefit are large, persons with medical conditions similar to those of individuals claiming benefit from the substance would have reasonable grounds for inquiring about the potential value of the treatment for their own condition—especially if they have tried other treatments that have failed. Whether or not a physician should recommend herbal cannabis or any other remedy for a patient on the basis of some critical mass of anecdotal data is another question, however.

Evidence-Based Practice

Increasingly, mainstream medicine has avoided recommending treatments that are not "evidence-based," which in itself is a valid enough stance except for the fact that "evidence-based medicine" and "evidence-based practice" are concepts that are used with variable meanings. Their general meanings seem clear enough, but their specific interpretations, connotative meanings, and practical uses vary considerably. In some contexts, "evidence-based treatment" is used narrowly to denote only those treatments that have withstood the test of controlled scientific studies. In other contexts, "evidence-based treatment" is used to indicate a clinically disciplined approach to the practice of medicine, in which treatments that are well established scientifically are the first-line or first-choice therapeutic interventions. In this usage, physicians understand that there is a hierarchy of levels or types of evidence, with controlled scientific clinical trials being at the top—the "gold standard," as it were.

However, even the notion of the standard randomized, controlled clinical trial—used in gaining regulatory (FDA) approval—as the "gold standard" for ascertaining pharmaceutical product performance has come under significant criticism. While these studies are valuable, they are also limited. Their limitations typically include short study duration, laboratory versus real-world context, exclusion of patients with other complicating medical conditions, and exclusion of other medications that may often be used concomitantly for patients in real-world treatment settings. Further limitations include lack of a big-picture view with regard to economic considerations such as:

- cost of medication
- whether patients are insured
- impact of taking the medication on overall healthcare utilization, and
- the likelihood that patients will remain on the medication (adherence or compliance) longer-term in consideration of both biological effects (tolerability) and healthcare access (whether the existing system makes it easy or difficult for a patient to continue the recommended treatment)

For these reasons, there has been more interest in the last decade in "medical effectiveness" studies, which differ from randomized clinical trials in attempting to address these other considerations systematically in the research design.[63]

A physician may or may not feel comfortable recommending a treatment that lacks controlled study data supporting its use for the specific medical condition in question, but it is not uncommon for a physician to recommend a medication known to be effective for one condition for use in another related or similar condition. The physician's rationale may be theoretical or empirical. This would be especially true for more general syndromes such as pain. Mood disturbance and anxiety, generic attributes of a spectrum of more specific disorders, might be comparable conditions in psychiatry. Theoretical reasons would be based on an understanding of clinical and basic science—pathophysiology, pharmacology, and phenomenology, for example—whereas empirical reasons would be based on preliminary findings and observations drawn from case reports in the literature or physician-to-physician consultation regarding clinically observed success on a limited scale. Such an approach applies to the off-label use of a medication—that is, to the use of an approved medication as treatment for a condition other than that for which it has received an approved indication from the FDA. Physicians licensed to practice medicine have flexibility in making such recommendations and may choose—with patient collaboration and informed consent—to exercise their discretion in this area to varying degrees.

As one example of a common off-label use, the medication clonidine is FDA-approved for the treatment of hypertension, or high blood pressure. Pharmacologically, clonidine is a centrally-acting partial alpha-(2)-adrenergic agonist, which explains at least partly its action upon neuronal receptors in the lower brainstem region to affect sympathetic nervous system activity and blood pressure. Clonidine was introduced in the clinical psychiatry literature as an off-label adjunctive treatment for symptoms of posttraumatic stress disorder (PTSD) based upon the known mechanism of action of the drug and some of the known aspects of the pathophysiology of the disorder.[64] Specifically, clonidine decreases the tone—or level of activation—of brain physiological systems associated with the "fight or flight" reaction that is hypersensitive and/or hyperreactive in PTSD. The use of clonidine has also been extended to hyperactive children with PTSD alone or in combination with attention deficit hyperactivity disorder (ADHD) and as a second-line or adjunctive treatment when ADHD is the primary target of pharmacotherapy or medication management.

Even if a physician does not feel comfortable recommending a treatment lacking compelling scientific data for one or more indications, any physician can and should be able to provide feedback when patients come to them with their own reports based on personal experience or on information they have gathered from friends, family, popular literature, advocacy and patient support groups, or the Internet. In any given instance, a physician may not feel qualified to have a specific discussion of that nature, but that is where consultation or referral can be helpful to both physician and patient. Even in states that have not passed laws to protect patient access to cannabis on a medicinal basis, the physician is prevented neither from listening to the patient's story nor from collaborating with the patient in taking a critical look at the available information. Given the real systemic impasse that may exist in some cases where use of cannabis has been found to be therapeutic, some individuals have geographically relocated to gain medicinal access. Historically, medical recommendations have often been made on the best available information, not only in the absence of controlled clinical trial results but before such experimental methods were even developed. A number of well-known medicines were put into effective use long before the development of the controlled clinical trial as a scientific methodology; examples include aspirin, morphine, and digitalis.

Some clinical uses of cannabis have more supporting evidence than others. Its use in the control of seizures and migraine headaches, for instance, is considered by some formal evaluative reports—in particular, the IOM report—to be sufficiently lacking in supportive evidence as to warrant no further inquiry into the matter. This is in contrast to other uses, for which the IOM report clearly states that the evidence is substantial enough to warrant further study. However, the individual epileptic patient whose seizure frequency is drastically reduced after beginning to use cannabis—despite failing a number of single approved anticonvulsant medications as well as combination pharmacotherapy with several anticonvulsants at once—does not need to be convinced further. And when a single inhalation of cannabis aborts the progression of a well-established seizure aura in such a patient, the success is even more dramatic. In such instances, the clinical manifestations of the disorder and its response to treatment are compelling and cannot go unappreciated by the observant physician.

Similarly, when a patient experiences the onset of a migraine headache and finds immediate relief from inhaled cannabis, the individual patient does not need further convincing regarding the treatment's effectiveness. Both physician and patient may find an additional fact useful in establishing a rationale for cannabis as appropriate treatment: cannabis was commonly used for treatment of migraine in the U.S. in the late 19th and early 20th centuries, and some physicians at that time, notably the legendary William Osler, believed cannabis to be the most effective treatment available for migraine.[65] Given an individual patient's positive response to medicinal cannabis, he or she may be less interested in the question of the scientific rigor of the studies demonstrating the substance's effectiveness. The studies will no doubt make the doctor feel better but may strike the patient as less important than symptom relief. This is not to say that scientific studies are unimportant. To the contrary, they are extremely important.

Demonstration of the effectiveness of cannabis or any other potentially therapeutic substance in well-designed clinical experiments establishes a basis for making broader generalizations about the likelihood of a therapeutic response for the particular clinical syndrome or symptom in question. The practice of medicine is generally based upon diagnosis, and research findings based on rigorous standardized patient assessments strengthen the case for a recommendation—in either direction, positive or negative—regarding the potential use of any medicine for either symptom relief or primary treatment targeting the underlying pathophysiology or disease process.

Establishing cannabis as an evidence-based treatment, in the narrower sense of a treatment for which there is rigorous scientific evidence of its effectiveness (that it is more effective than placebo), would provide a rationale for recommending it as a medical treatment. Failure to demonstrate its effectiveness in that manner would not necessarily mean that cannabis could not be helpful for some individuals suffering with the medical condition in question, just as, conversely, the clear demonstration of a therapeutic substance's effectiveness (evidence-based treatment) does not mean that every individual will respond favorably to the treatment. This is a well-established feature of medical practice that must always be considered regardless of whether the treatment decision involves prescription medicines, over-the-counter pharmaceuticals, herbal remedies, non-pharmacological therapies, or chicken soup.

Selecting one effective treatment over another may be facilitated by reviewing scientific studies. Fortunately, for many medical problems there are treatment options, so that if one treatment fails, an alternative can be recommended. In many cases, within a particular disease or clinical syndrome, evidence for selecting one known effective treatment over another may be lacking. There are exceptions, and in part those exceptions are demonstrated by research that takes place after the general effectiveness of both treatments has been established. So, for example, certain clinical features of an illness or other patient characteristics may be useful in predicting the likelihood of a positive response to one accepted form of treatment versus another. Genetic differences in metabolism or underlying disease processes may in some cases provide a basis for selecting one medication rather than another, even when both have been demonstrated to be generally helpful for the medical condition in question. For example, individual genetics could be a consideration in selecting an antihypertensive or an antidepressant medication because of known clinical response rates or metabolic variations. *Pharmacogenetics* is the basic science that attempts to understand the relationship between genetics and medication action at various levels, from molecular and biochemical to clinical assessment and disease management.[66]

Confidence in a medication's effectiveness based on the results of well-designed medical research helps the physician encourage patient adherence to the treatment. Obviously, at the most basic level, whether or not a given patient actually takes a medicine prescribed by his or her doctor is critical. This factor has been referred to as *compliance*, although a more contemporary term would be *adherence*. The latter avoids the connotation of conformity to unilaterally established expectations and is more compatible with a collaborative model of medical practice in which consumer expectations, preferences, and activities are recognized as central to the doctor-patient relationship and plan of care. It is no surprise that medication is more likely to work if the patient takes it. Still, patient adherence to recommended treatment does not guarantee that a prescribed medication will be effective in every (or any particular) individual case.

Any given medication may not produce a favorable response in a given individual patient, even if the treatment has been demonstrated to work for other patients and is generally accepted as effective. The medication may also produce uncomfortable or dangerous side effects even when it works for its targeted signs and symptoms. Of course, if treatment produces uncomfortable side effects, patients will be more likely to discontinue medications and fall out of adherence to their physician's recommendations; in the case of dangerous side effects (for example, toxic effects on vital organs such as the heart, liver, and kidneys), the doctor will most likely stop the treatment.

Frequency of dosing can be an important factor in medication adherence; medications that can be taken once daily are generally less likely to be forgotten than those that must be taken three or four times daily, unless the therapeutic effects are perceived by the patient as immediate. Patient preferences are important factors in treatment relationships and treatment decisions and must always be taken into account. This does not necessarily mean that patient preferences must always dominate medical decision making; there is clearly a role for physician persuasion, at least through reassurance and education as appropriate, in helping patients to accept a course of treatment that appears to be in their best interests but that they may be reluctant or unmotivated to follow. But such persuasion will be more effective if it can be built upon consumer capacity for making some choices over others and can provide opportunities for consumers to exercise that capacity.

Good clinical research establishing a medication's effectiveness can be a useful tool in the physician-to-patient persuasion process. Patients can be encouraged to commit themselves to a demonstrably effective treatment instead of self-medicating with a treatment of unknown effectiveness. This is why it would be difficult for most physicians to recommend cannabis as *first-line* therapy for anything. However, if a patient has found cannabis to be helpful for his or her primary symptoms or chief complaint, that is an entirely different matter; the patient may now be in a better position than the physician to decide whether or not the chosen treatment should be continued. In addition, patients who have tried approved treatments and found them unsatisfactory might benefit from a physician-initiated recommendation regarding cannabis use, but such a recommendation would be tentative or provisional, not first-line. Expressed in terms of current guidelines in the evidence-based practice of medicine, a cannabis recommendation—in the absence of positive findings from clinical experimental studies—would be a late selection in any established treatment algorithm, set of clinical guidelines, or medical decision-making rules. Were cannabis approved for therapeutic study, it might well move further up the hierarchy in some treatment algorithms, depending on the results of research. So again, the value of rigorous clinical research is clear.

Safety

Effectiveness is one important criterion for a legitimate medicinal or therapeutic chemical compound or substance. Safety is another, and FDA protocol requires demonstration of treatment safety before effectiveness is studied. The 2006 FDA statement on marijuana skirted the issue of the effectiveness of cannabis, in either inhaled or ingested form, by limiting its claims to the assertion that "smoked marijuana has no medical value." Such language is crafted by seasoned bureaucrats working under the constraints of a political agenda unrelated to science. The statement implicitly provides room for future backtracking: it would not prevent federal officials from acknowledging that smoked marijuana might alleviate symptoms but still be unsafe; or that orally ingested marijuana might be safe and effective but unnecessary because its primary active compound, THC, is already available in pharmaceutical form as dronabinol; or even that other cannabinoid compounds—naturally occurring in herbal cannabis or developed synthetically in the laboratory—have real medicinal potential but require further study. As such, the statement leaves room for the introduction of products like Sativex®, now available clinically in Canada and undergoing research trials in the United States.

The April 20, 2006, FDA statement is, in fact, mostly consistent with the Institute of Medicine (IOM) Report of 1999, which pointed to the potential value of exploration of alternative cannabis delivery systems that would obviate the need for smoking. The qualification "mostly" is necessary because the IOM report clearly acknowledged that the known therapeutic effects of cannabis are such that for some patients there may be no better alternative at this point in time than smoked marijuana. But the IOM report overemphasizes the lack of known safety for use of cannabis as medicine. Is its emphasis important? Yes, but the smoking issue has been a red herring since the advent of vaporizers—devices that heat the plant material to a temperature at which active cannabinoid compounds are released in gaseous form without actual combustion. The burning of the plant material, avoided by the use of vaporization, generates the terpene tars that are known to have carcinogenic potential from tobacco studies. Despite the official federal position on marijuana, the available medical and public health information cannot support the view that cannabis—smoked or otherwise—poses a cancer risk comparable to that of tobacco or alcohol.

As compared to the vast array of available prescription medications, cannabis would rank nowhere near the top of the list in terms of potential for organ-system toxicity and serious adverse events. In addition, as a quasi-scientific document conceived and crafted in an ultimately political context, the IOM report overprioritizes the need to accommodate the commercial pharmaceutical industry in its assertion that "the future of cannabinoid drugs lies not in smoked marijuana but in chemically defined drugs that act on the cannabinoid systems that are a natural component of human physiology."[67] The IOM report almost appears to adopt the stance that accommodating the pharmaceutical industry is equal in importance to such sciences as chemistry, genetics, or pharmacology in arriving at an understanding of what is scientifically or medically possible. There is certainly a role for a reasoned pragmatism in planning ahead—so that it may be important to acknowledge that the pharmaceutical industry has little incentive to develop nonpatentable, nonproprietary products that exist in the public domain (for example, plants such as cannabis)—but the IOM report seems to prioritize that role over the needs of patients. The IOM report's allowable exceptions are patients who are essentially dying and have tried every single medication available to treat their condition. For such individuals, the IOM report recommends "interim solutions" until the pharmaceutical industry develops alternatives.

Both the IOM report and AMA 2001 policy statement call for making even smoked cannabis available to at least some seriously ill patients who find that it is a more tolerable and/or more effective alternative to standard treatments they have tried. Both reports also call for further research, not only with the goal of developing single cannabinoid compounds for therapeutic use but also to characterize the benefits and risks of herbal cannabis itself. Any serious discussion of the medicinal use of cannabis goes quickly to the fact that the availability of vaporizers and the option of oral ingestion render any critique based solely on the hazards of smoking largely irrelevant. This statement stands even without invoking existing scientific data that directly address the question of a relationship between marijuana smoking and cancer. The IOM report concluded, "Numerous studies suggest that marijuana smoke is an important risk factor in the development of respiratory disease."[68]

It also acknowledged, "Although cellular, genetic, and human studies all suggest that marijuana smoke is an important risk factor for the development of respiratory cancer, proof that habitual marijuana smoking does or does not cause cancer awaits the results of well-designed studies."[69] While it is relatively well-documented and not surprising that heavy cannabis use by smoking is associated with irritation of the respiratory tract and chronic bronchitis, clear links between cannabis use and cancer have not been compellingly demonstrated.

The basis for the assertion that cannabis smoke is associated with increased risk of lung cancer is both theoretical and indirectly empirical. It would be based on scientific knowledge that cannabis smoke contains some of the same tars as tobacco smoke. It would also be based on scientific knowledge that bronchial biopsies of heavy cannabis smokers are more likely to reveal dysplastic cells—generally accepted as precursors of malignancy, inasmuch as cells with dysplastic characteristics (premalignant cells) are more common in the biopsy histories of individuals who develop lung cancer than in the histories of patients without lung cancer.[70] These scientific observations do warrant a cautionary statement to the effect that we cannot assume that cannabis smoke is harmless, and—depending on any number of other factors, including heaviness of use—it might put users at risk of lung cancer.

Yet, the best scientific studies to date—population-based and case control studies—do not find a relationship between cannabis use and lung or head and neck cancer, even though the data confirm known relationships between tobacco and cancer, as well as between alcohol and cancer. In fact, the largest case control study to date found no relationship between cannabis and lung or head and neck cancer but, intriguingly, had findings that led observers to raise the question whether cannabis might even have protective effects. Donald Tashkin,

M.D., Professor of Medicine at UCLA, primary author of the 2005 study and a leading authority on the pulmonary effects of cannabis, was quick to disavow any such claim, though he readily acknowledged that the possibility of anti-cancer protective effects was not an unreasonable hypothesis.[71] The issue has to do with explaining findings, in the analysis of the data, of a pattern of lower cancer risk (mostly statistically nonsignificant) among cannabis smokers than among nonsmokers.

In an even more recent population-based, case control study of marijuana use and the risk of head and neck cancer, Liang and colleagues found that when they controlled statistically for the potential confounding effects of tobacco and alcohol use (known to be risk factors for head and neck cancer), marijuana use was associated with *significantly decreased risk* of a type of head and neck cancer called squamous cell carcinoma.[72] Interestingly, the findings of Liang and colleagues are compatible with other studies suggesting that cannabinoid compounds may have anti-tumor effects.[73] It is also interesting to juxtapose these scientific findings with studies pointing to a role for nicotine in the promotion of tumor growth.[74]

The assertion that cannabis is at least as harmful to the human respiratory system as tobacco is simply not warranted by the data. This means neither that cannabis is harmless, nor that it could not contribute to development of cancer in specific cases; in fact, it would be prudent to assume that it can. But the fact is that the scientific data do not lead to the conclusion that cannabis causes cancer. The possibility that heavy use may be a risk factor cannot be definitively ruled out at this point in time. With regard to tobacco use, however, an association with cancer is clear. There is good reason to suspect that tobacco use—at least more than very light tobacco use—puts the user at risk of developing cancer. And tobacco smoking is sufficiently addictive to be difficult for most people to consume in quantities consistently below the threshold of known significant risk. This latter problem—the difficulty of limiting use in ways that minimize risks—simply does not rise to the same level with cannabis.[75]

The entirety of the above discussion is a distraction from the more critical issue of whether access to cannabis by consumers with an interest in its therapeutic properties should continue to be prohibited, in consideration of the fact that there are alternatives to smoking as a means of medicinal administration of herbal cannabis. There are at least three alternatives currently. First, vaporization devices allow for the inhalation of cannabis through a process that does not result in plant combustion—does not burn the plant—with the result that little if any tar is generated in the inhalation process. Second, cannabis can be taken orally in the form of edibles, of which there are many excellent examples in the medicinal cannabis dispensaries of California. Finally, cannabis can be ingested in the form of tinctures and sprays, which are absorbed through the highly vascularized oral tissues, especially sublingually (under the tongue); when tinctures and sprays are used, some of the medicinal preparation is inevitably taken into the digestive tract—and this can be varied depending upon exactly how the tincture or spray is ingested. Such tinctures are available in some medicinal cannabis dispensaries of states that have passed medical cannabis access laws.

Jason's Phantom Limb

Jason, a 45-year-old man, was the first one to raise his hand and to speak after I had finished a lecture at a local college and opened the floor for discussion. Jason shared his personal experience using cannabis on a medicinal basis. Jason lost his left leg in his early 20s, after being hit by a car while riding his bicycle. Following the amputation, Jason suffered with haunting "phantom limb" pain for some time.

The phantom limb phenomenon was described in the late 19th century by Weir Mitchell, a physician who treated and studied Civil War veterans who had suffered amputations.[76] Contemporary physician and author Oliver Sacks has recently included a discussion of phantom limb phenomena in the context of his writings on music and the brain.[77] Specifically, Sacks considers cases of musicians who have lost a hand or an arm but for whom remembering music, listening to music, or attempting to play music may activate physiologically the missing limb's persistent representation in the brain. He summarizes neurological studies that find conservation, enlargement, and hyperexcitability of the area of the cerebral cortex corresponding to the missing limb. Sacks points out that phantom limb sensations and intended movements can be essential to the success of biomedically engineered prosthetic devices, facilitating amputee learning as existing neural signals and residual muscular movements are technologically amplified and translated into prosthetic movements. He writes that "phantom memories and images occur to some extent in almost all amputees, and may last for decades."[78] He notes that phantom limb phenomena "may be intrusive or even painful."[79]

Gruesome as it sounds, phantom limb pain is a well-recognized syndrome in which the patient experiences the amputated limb as present and painful. Sometimes the pain can be severe. Jason reported to the group during our discussion that cannabis had been the most effective remedy he had found. Doctors had recommended anti-inflammatory medications and then prescribed opiate analgesics that provided substantial relief on an intermittent basis. Problems with opiates were several. Most bothersome was the fact that there was a tendency to need to use more over time, a phenomenon called tolerance. With tolerance, a given dose of the medication that has been effective previously becomes less so, and the pain that is being treated begins to break through. This can generally be avoided by using the opiates periodically rather than constantly, but used in that manner Jason was unable to get sustained pain relief. However, if he took enough codeine or other opiate pain reliever to provide sustained pain relief, he experienced the common side effect of constipation. In addition, the experience of taking opiates at pain-relieving doses over a sustained period of time was uncomfortable for Jason. He felt "doped up," sedated, and unable to function his best mentally.

Jason learned to use cannabis regularly and discovered that it reduced his need for opiates to the point where he took them only occasionally when the pain flared up. Most days he experienced substantial pain relief from cannabis, without either the constipation or mental impairment that he experienced on opiates. Cannabis, unlike opiates, actually brightened his mood and his outlook, and, according to Jason, his work productivity improved when he started to rely on cannabis as the mainstay of treatment in managing the symptoms of his phantom limb pain.

Wounded Warriors

A plaque on my office shelf reads, "Presented to Dr. Fichtner for all your patience and understanding from the men in your Friday group at Hines from 1992-1994." With gratitude and humility I recall my first job as a psychiatrist newly graduated from residency: caring for veterans with combat-related post-traumatic stress disorder (PTSD). The Vietnam veterans in that Friday group gave me glimpses of the damaging impact of war on their lives through the thoughts, feelings, and behaviors that become the targets of therapeutic intervention for physicians in my specialty. The psychological and physiological havoc wreaked upon the soldier by combat has been described throughout history and clinically since the 19th century as shell shock, war neurosis, combat neurosis, battle fatigue, and Vietnam syndrome. In this first decade of the 21st century America is once again witnessing an influx of wounded warriors in need of healing and care.

As PTSD section chief at the Edward Hines, Jr., VA Hospital in Hines, Illinois, I had the opportunity to provide psychiatric medical treatment to combat veterans from every era. From the World War II navigator who became a prisoner of war (POW) after his plane was shot down over Germany to the African American woman who suffered disabling burns over a quarter of her upper body from an explosion in Operation Desert Storm, our PTSD Clinical Team identified veterans who had been traumatized by war and made our best efforts to provide mental health services that would help them in their recovery. I believe that the work of our multidisciplinary health professional team made a difference in the lives of veterans who came to our clinic at the Hines VA Hospital. Yet I am sure that our best efforts were not enough. And the need continues; new cases of war-related trauma afflict the bodies and minds of returning veterans and present a challenge to the resources of our federal healthcare system.

Combat-related PTSD is not an easy disorder to treat. Early post-trauma intervention helps, but in many cases years of psychotherapy may meet with limited success. The symptoms of the disorder can be grouped into three clusters: (1) re-experiencing traumatic events in the form of nightmares, flashbacks, intrusive memories, and intense distress with heightened physiological reactivity to reminders of the traumatic event(s); (2) avoiding of situations, thoughts, or feelings associated with the event(s), including the shutting down of memories, numbing of feelings, and withdrawal of affections, as well as loss of interest, detachment, and hopelessness as seen in many cases of major depression; and (3) experiencing persistent hyperarousal that may be manifested as sleep difficulty, irritability with angry outbursts, difficulty concentrating, hypervigilance, and an exaggerated startle response.[80] Given the choice, if you can get an individual with PTSD to go to a restaurant, he or she will usually prefer to sit in the corner where there will be no one behind him or her.

Medication can be at least partially effective in alleviating PTSD symptoms. Antidepressants can be quite helpful, and some of the newer selective serotonin reuptake inhibitors (SSRIs) have received FDA approval for use in PTSD. But it is unusual to see the full range of PTSD symptoms, spanning all three clusters, remit fully with a single medication—what we in medicine call "monotherapy." As a result, many other medications are used to manage the symptoms of PTSD, and it is not unusual for such patients to be treated with combination or multidrug regimens. In such instances, most of the medications will be used off label; that is, FDA-approved medications will be used to target PTSD symptoms even though their primary indication is for treatment of another disorder or medical illness.

As we know, herbal cannabis is not currently approved as medicine in the United States—even though a handful of patients still receive marijuana from the federal government for use in a variety of unusual conditions in the compassionate use program. Nonetheless, combat veterans with PTSD currently constitute the largest systematically documented psychiatric diagnostic group to gain access to cannabis on a medicinal basis; and in medical cannabis states where PTSD specifically, or psychiatric disorders generally (for example, depression and bipolar disorder), have not been included as allowable indications for medical cannabis access, veterans are actively petitioning to gain such access.

The late Berkeley psychiatrist Tod Mikuriya, M.D., (1933-2007), arguably the most experienced cannabis therapeutics consultant in the country, wrote some 10,000 medical marijuana recommendations mostly for patients managing pain and inflammatory medical diseases. However, of the roughly 35 percent of his cases in which the recommendation was issued for a primary psychiatric or behavioral health diagnosis, patients with PTSD made up the largest group. Dr. Mikuriya wrote of those patients, "Many of them are Vietnam veterans whose chronic depression, insomnia, and accompanying irritability cannot be relieved by conventional psychotherapeutics and is worsened by alcohol. For many of these veterans, chronic pain from old physical injury compounds problems with narcotic dependence and side effects of opioids."[81]

In addition to PTSD, many veterans suffer head trauma, neurological damage, and loss of limbs with attendant complications of chronic and severe pain. The view that these sequelae of combat trauma include many potentially cannabis-responsive symptoms is supported by both popular anecdote and emerging basic science findings. Research scientists writing for the U.S. Department of Health and Human Services have identified cannabinoids as having antioxidant properties and potential neuroprotectant applications—with beneficial therapeutic effects such as "limiting neurological damage following ischemic insults, such as stroke and trauma, or in the treatment of neurodegenerative diseases, such as Alzheimer's disease, Parkinson's disease and HIV dementia."[82] One published patent on a particular class of cannabinoid compounds notes that the antioxidant properties of cannabinoids may make them useful in treatment and prophylaxis of a variety of oxidation-associated diseases, including age-related inflammatory and autoimmune diseases.[83]

Vietnam veterans in Western states other than California have been petitioning to gain access to cannabis for the treatment of PTSD symptoms not primarily because they are "substance abusers" but because they find that in their experience cannabis provides symptomatic relief and therapeutic behavioral effects. New Mexico now stands out among states other than California for having added PTSD to its list of conditions for which a physician may recommend herbal cannabis for medicinal use. In so doing, New Mexico may be the first state to have specifically identified a psychiatric disorder among those conditions for which a physician can recommend herbal cannabis. California's medicinal cannabis law does not discriminate against patients with psychiatric disorders but provides for the exercise of physician discretion in recommending cannabis for medicinal use. Importantly for PTSD patients, as well as patients with other anxiety disorders and/or mood disorders, many individuals report less interest in alcohol when they have access to cannabis.

Combat veteran Colby Buzzell wrote in *Esquire* after he came home from Iraq, "For a year straight after I came back, I hardly ever left my room, and the only walking that I did was to the liquor store and back to numb myself in my room. I found that I was no longer interested in going out."[84] Buzzell sought help at the local VA hospital for apparent symptoms of PTSD and also obtained a medical marijuana recommendation from a California physician. He subsequently purchased some cannabis edibles from a West Hollywood dispensary. "I liked the marijuana a lot because it helped me sleep," he reported, "and if I could sleep all night and all day I would, and I slept all that weekend, probably the best sleep I'd had since the war, and on Monday I felt like a new person."[85]

The most interesting scientific question about cannabis and PTSD has to do with whether it has value in lessening the intensity of traumatic memories. Medical science does not know the answer to this question, but the matter is being researched in Israel. Basic science research findings also suggest that the endocannabinoid system—what *Scientific American* called "the brain's own marijuana"—is involved in the extinction of fear-related memories involving aversive stimuli in animals.[86] The potential protective effects of cannabis on the nervous system might make it particularly helpful in combat veteran "poly-trauma" cases—in which PTSD is complicated by traumatic brain injury (TBI), often concussive from explosions. And as noted above, some amputees report that cannabis relieves their phantom limb pain.

Further study of herbal cannabis in a variety of medical conditions, some of them psychiatric, is clearly indicated. How far such research takes us in being able to recommend cannabis-based treatments remains to be seen. Apart from the drug development process of the pharmaceutical industry, cultivation of herbal cannabis has reached a high degree of sophistication and deserves the positive attention of policymakers. Valerie Corral and her associates in northern California reached a point in their work at the cannabis growers collective WAMM where they actually began to accumulate data on the differential therapeutic effects of distinct cannabis strains they were producing.[87] Unfortunately, federal agents shook them down and confiscated their materials. Outside the United States, GW Pharmaceutical in Oxford, UK, has been able to take the process much further.

GW Pharmaceutical has developed a reliable and consistent alternative delivery system by producing medicinal whole herbal cannabis extracts that can be sprayed under the tongue for rapid absorption. The company has worked with medicinal cannabis extracts of various compositions, based on their cultivation of known cannabis strains under highly controlled greenhouse conditions and the combining of these raw plant cultivars to achieve mixtures that are standardized according to the measured ratios of active cannabinoid compounds of therapeutic interest. The molecules in these herbal extracts are not isolated and then recombined; the extraction process seeks to preserve the naturally occurring chemical array but to shift the balance of known active chemical constituents.[88] GW has taken its first product, Sativex®, to market in Canada, where it is approved for treatment of MS and chronic cancer pain. Research on this product is underway in the U.S. for potential FDA approval. Meanwhile, GW is engaged in ongoing development of other cannabis extracts, with differing ratios of known active cannabinoid compounds, for potential medicinal applications.

Research with Sativex® should be accelerated and expanded and not necessarily limited to tertiary applications in esoteric disease states. Current awareness of the reported therapeutic benefits of herbal cannabis warrants a more expansive therapeutics research agenda with a wider view of potential medical indications. There is no reason why such research should not include the exploration of effectiveness in PTSD and combat polytrauma. Other standardized medicinal cannabis extracts under development by GW Pharmaceutical or other innovators also warrant clinical research trials. We will return to this issue later in the book, especially in connection with issues related to economic development and business opportunity.

At this point in the history of development of cannabinoid medicines, it seems appropriate to think of GW Pharmaceutical as pioneering a new gold standard in cannabis therapeutics through its development of highly standardized medicinal cannabis extracts. Sativex® is a product that will likely be reckoned with much more broadly than expected based on its current testing in research trials as an experimental treatment for cancer pain that is not responding to standard medications. But it is, after all, one company's effort—albeit a pioneering, field-defining effort—at producing a standardized herbal cannabis medicine. In the course of that effort, the company has created a new index of standardization, and as such the concept of a benchmark-creating gold standard seems appropriate. But that does not, in itself, rule out consideration of other approaches to standardization of either medicinal cannabis extracts or raw herbal cannabis strains on a more categorical or qualitative basis. The model developed by GW Pharmaceutical does not, in itself, invalidate other approaches to the use of herbal cannabis for its medicinal or therapeutic properties.

The economic trajectory depicted in this book (Part III) becomes most compelling when we raise the question why participation in this new competitive production and marketing process should be limited to corporations outside the U.S. Responsible Americans are poised to do something potentially and in theory similar. In an economically responsive, regulated environment that did not export American business opportunities overseas, what would be the California alternative to "Oxford Gold"? There may be a tentative answer to that question.

The Farmacy®, a producer of medicinal cannabis dispensary products discussed earlier, now offers a cannabis-enhanced coffee or herbal tea beverage labeled to reflect its standardization in terms of three of the naturally occurring cannabinoid compounds. Based on their use of accepted measurement technologies (gas chromatography and mass spectrometry), the Farmacy® is able to assure the consumer that each bottle of the product contains 25 mg of THC, 8 mg of CBD, and 12 mg of cannabinol (CBN). Each bottle of the product is intended, as labeled, to provide "three medical servings." The cost of the bottle is $15. The same amount of pure prescription THC, even as "generic" dronabinol rather than brand name Marinol®, costs in excess of $50. Of course dronabinol is FDA-approved only for the treatment of nausea and to stimulate appetite in wasting syndrome, and for those problems a pill seems likely to be better than a beverage. Still, as we have seen, individuals use cannabis for a wide range of medical conditions and therapeutic needs. Moreover, the cannabis-enhanced beverages of the Farmacy® include a naturally occurring array of cannabinoid compounds from herbal cannabis, with potential benefits not limited to those of THC alone. In the world of *cannabinomics*, the widespread consumer choice of herbal cannabis for anxiety, insomnia, and alcohol substitution offers reason enough for the medically informed to ask why cannabis-enhanced beverages should not be available as legitimately regulated alternatives to alcoholic ones.

PART II

Cannabis and the Drug War

From Prohibition to Public Health:
Slippery Slope or Moral High Ground?

"The scale of (the) campaign against marijuana makes pot prohibition the worst injustice perpetrated by our frayed criminal justice policy in the twenty-first century."[1]

JUDGE RUDOLPH J. GERBER, 2004
RETIRED, ARIZONA APPELLATE COURT

"The plain and simple truth is that alcohol fuels violent behavior and marijuana does not."[2]

NORM STAMPER, 2009
FORMER CHIEF, SEATTLE POLICE DEPARTMENT

IN LATE 2008 Guy Lawson wrote in *Rolling Stone*:

In the United States the War on Drugs is a political slogan for a policy disaster that has cost taxpayers at least $500 billion over the last 35 years. In Mexico, it is a brutal and bewildering conflict—a multisided civil war that has taken 3,000 lives this year alone and brought the federal government to a state of near-collapse.[3]

Lawson's informative journalism is also an incisive commentary on a time bomb bequeathed to the 21st century by Richard Nixon. The months preceding Lawson's article and the months immediately following it saw the media flooded with exasperated commentary, frightening statistics, and increasingly gruesome reports of a house of horrors fulminating in Mexico and working its way northward. *Los Angeles Times* articles in the "Mexico Under Siege" series put the death toll in Mexico at nearly 4,000 in the preceding year and more than 6,000 in less than two years; by the end of 2009, Philip Caputo writing in *The Atlantic* put the estimate at 14,000 over roughly the past three years.[4] What *Forbes* magazine called the "Mexican Meltdown" competes with the economic crisis, healthcare, and our foreign policy more broadly as the news item most likely to be updated on the front page of major American newspapers.[5]

Lawson observed in *Rolling Stone* that Mexico is of interest to the narcotics industry because it offers "proximity to the largest market on earth." There is a take home point here more about ownership than geography. The contemporary global war on drugs is an outgrowth of America's own demand for drugs. While it may appear that "the drug war has spread to the U.S.," it is more useful to think of it as having come home to roost. Mexican drug war violence holds a mirror to the American face, even though the collective view is obstructed by a wall of denial and projection that offers little recourse but the conversation of recycled drug war slogans.

Malignant Criminalization

American ownership of this drug war madness is easier to recognize in pettier stateside battles waged by law enforcement officials who seem to have lost their sense of proportion. Southern California medical cannabis consumer Garry, introduced at the beginning of the book, is a case in point. I offered his case earlier to make the point that a war on marijuana—especially when it involves raiding the home of a medical user in a state that passed a medical cannabis law a decade previously—doesn't produce good health outcomes but does incur excessive costs without evidence of a positive return on investment for the taxpayer dollar. In Garry's case it undermined a consumer-driven approach to healthcare, created new and unnecessary health and economic problems for his whole family, squandered hard-earned taxpayer dollars, and further depleted the tax base by taking a productive member of society out of commission. But Garry's case illustrates the malignant nature of the criminalization process—the drug war—as well as it illustrates bad health economic and public health practices.

I met Garry several months after the raid on his home, and he shook my hand from the wheelchair he had been using since that time. New injuries had complicated his arthritis; he was not completely wheel-chair bound, but he could walk only for limited distances without developing back pain. We met in Washington at our nation's capital, where we worked together as part of a team to educate members of Congress about medicinal use of cannabis. Our group, which consisted of two teams that each included a physician, a primary medicinal cannabis consumer, a researcher, and a policy advocate, urged members of Congress to vote for an appropriations amendment intended to eliminate federal participation in the kind of law enforcement activity that landed Garry in his wheelchair. The Hinchey-Rohrabacher Amendment was proposed to restrict the Drug Enforcement Administration (DEA) from spending taxpayer dollars to raid cannabis-growing operations that are functioning within rules established by state law. Our group was brought together in Washington by Steph Sherer and Caren Woodson of Americans for Safe Access, an advocacy organization dedicated to medicinal cannabis access.

Garry was in his early 50s and had been using cannabis medicinally under the California Compassionate Use Act of 1996 (Proposition 215). Garry suffers from rheumatoid arthritis with ankylosing spondylitis, a form of arthritis of the spinal column. The disease can become quite severe, with fusion or growing together of the vertebral bones (vertebrae) through fibrous and bony interconnections that result from the inflammatory processes characteristic of the disease. Mobility can be severely restricted and the disease disabling. As it progresses, patients may be wheelchair-bound and suffer from severe pain. Not surprisingly—given clinical observations and patient reports in cases of other painful inflammatory conditions—some patients with this problem have reported finding relief through the use of herbal cannabis.

Garry obtained his cannabis for medicinal use by growing it at home in his garage in a small cooperative relationship with five other patients. With cannabis use Garry's arthritis was sufficiently well-controlled to permit him to continue managing and laboring in his family-owned business, designing and installing custom window treatments—draperies, blinds, and similar products. His work can be found in medical and professional buildings, hotels, restaurants, and homes in the Palm Springs area. Garry is proud of his work, and his business flourished.

When Garry talks about opening his front door that unfortunate morning, he remembers an array of automatic weapons—numbered by his account at 27—pointed at his home. From his garage the officers did confiscate marijuana, including some plants growing in a "sea of green" and some harvested cannabis in mason jars preserved for medical use. Following the raid, Garry was treated at the local hospital emergency room for his injuries. His back bothered him much more, with greater restriction of his mobility and more severe pain. In the months following the raid on his home, Garry's condition made work difficult and at times impossible. A repeat MRI of his spinal column revealed measurable worsening of his condition. His wife Krista had to take on a much greater share of responsibility for the family business, while caring for Garry as he recovered.

Six months after the raid on Garry's home, the District Attorney's Office issued a policy white paper that asserted, "despite the attempts of several states to partially legalize marijuana, it continues to be wholly illegal since it is classified as a Schedule I drug. As such, there are no exceptions to its illegality."[6] The position statement invoked the 2005 U.S. Supreme Court ruling in *Gonzales v. Raich*, which upheld the federal government's authority to enforce marijuana prohibition—even if the cannabis is not grown for commercial purposes—based on the federal interest in regulating commerce. The white paper over-simplified and ignored important facts in asserting that there are no exceptions to the illegality of marijuana. There *are* in fact definite, inarguable exceptions that are the federal government's own; there is still a handful of patients served in the federal compassionate use program.[7] As discussed in Part I, those individuals receive federally grown marijuana every month for their own personal medicinal use based on medical findings supporting their individual need for it as patients.

The position articulated by the white paper seemed not to grasp the nuances of the California medical cannabis law as enacted in the Compassionate Use Act of 1996 (Proposition 215) and the Medical Marijuana Program Act (Senate Bill 420) passed by the state legislature in 2003 and put into effect in 2004. The white paper reads as if it was written to underscore the importance of enforcing federal law, whereas the whole point of the state law was the intent of Californians to resist be-ing co-opted into enforcing a federal law perceived as irrational and morally bankrupt. That view is not unique to Californians or other advocates; it is, essentially, the view articulated by DEA Administrative Law Judge Francis Young when in 1988 he rec-ommended rescheduling cannabis so that it could be made available for medical use. In passing their medical cannabis law, the people of California were in effect refusing to do the federal government's "dirty work." Correspondingly, the upshot of the *Gonzales v. Raich* ruling was to affirm that the federal govern-ment has a right to do its own. Strictly speaking, the California law doesn't legalize anything from a federal vantage point; it merely refuses to enact the malignant criminalization agenda represented by the federal prohibition of marijuana even for medical use.

In any case, the matter was subsequently clarified when, on December 6, 2006, California Superior Court Judge William R. Nevitt, Jr., ruled in favor of the state's medical cannabis program in a case in which several counties had challenged the medical cannabis law on the grounds that it was illegal under federal law. Judge Nevitt wrote that in relation to federal law, "Requiring the counties to issue identification cards for the purpose of identifying those whom California chooses not to arrest and prosecute for certain activities involving marijuana use does not create a 'positive conflict.'"[8] In May of 2009 the U.S. Supreme Court declined to hear the case, so that the state Superior Court ruling stands, as does the California medical cannabis law.

The California Superior Court's ruling took place about six months after I met Garry and nine months after the incident that shut down Garry's capacity to grow his own cannabis for personal medicinal use. At that time I had the opportunity to see Garry again when I visited him at his home. In the months since his medicinal supply of cannabis had been disrupted, Garry's use of opiate pain relievers had increased. Garry's severe sciatica, with a burning, itching feeling, responds better to cannabis than to any of the other medications. How do we know this? We know it because with access to cannabis, Garry is most comfortable and requires the least medication overall. With cannabis, he doesn't use morphine at all, and he avoids the nausea, and sometimes vomiting, that he experiences with it. He will use Dilaudid® (hydromorphone) but much less frequently. Garry says that, for him, the side effects of cannabis are much less of a problem than those of opiates. This kind of information is important, even critical, in evaluating the effectiveness of medical treatment. Side effects are important considerations, as is total medication burden (total number of medications, doses, frequency of use) to which the patient is exposed.[9]

Pain management is not my medical specialty, and neither Garry nor his wife Krista is my patient. But as a psychiatrist I am troubled by the observation that both have been struggling with symptoms of psychological trauma in the aftermath of the raid. Having treated hundreds of patients with posttraumatic stress disorder (PTSD), it is not difficult for me to recognize its symptoms. Both Garry and Krista have suffered from sleep disruption and nightmares related to the event, and their anxiety levels have increased with hyper-vigilance and easy startling. They both have intrusive recollections of the event, and Krista has had frank flashbacks with panic attacks. They continue to struggle with the emotional and material impact of the event, and I am repeatedly impressed with the positive attitude that Garry has managed to maintain throughout the ordeal. Krista's ongoing support has been instrumental in Garry's recovery, but the experience has taken a toll on her emotional well-being. I have suggested that she obtain an independent psychiatric evaluation, as her symptoms have been distressing but they can respond to treatment. Krista is not a cannabis consumer, for medicinal purposes or otherwise.

It was only about six weeks after the California Superior Court ruling upholding the requirements of the state's medicinal cannabis law that federal agents spent a day raiding a dozen Los Angeles area medicinal cannabis dispensaries. Manuel S. Klausner, attorney and founder of the Reason Foundation, commented in the *Los Angeles Times*:

> In the fictional world of the hit show "24," federal law enforcement agencies are pouring every last resource into the search for a nuclear terrorist in Los Angeles. In the real world, federal agents apparently have so much free time that they can dress up in bulletproof vests and masks in order to raid clinics that serve patients battling cancer, AIDS, and other diseases.[10]

American Psychosis

In the title essay of his book *Reefer Madness* (2003), Eric Schlosser observes that "a society that can punish a marijuana offender more severely than a murderer is caught in the grip of a deep psychosis."[11] He points out that on average, an American found guilty of murder can expect to serve 11 years and four months in prison; and he then tells the extreme stories of Americans sentenced to live out their years behind bars for being involved with marijuana even indirectly. He exposes law enforcement priorities and sentencing practices that seem beyond reason. He paints a compelling portrait of an American marijuana policy that has lost its grip. Andrew Weil, M.D., and Winifred Rosen comment similarly on drug policy more broadly: "Current drug laws are the product of society's fears and prejudices and would certainly strike an unbiased observer as irrational, if not insane...."[12]

Many tend to assume that cannabis-related offenses have relatively minor impact, compared with other drug offenses, on crime statistics in individuals and communities. In Illinois, however, cannabis arrests have outnumbered those for all other controlled substances combined, including cocaine, crack, heroin, crystal meth, psychedelics, and various prescription drugs.[13] The Illinois statistics are not atypical. On a national scale, nearly nine out of ten cannabis arrests are for simple possession.[14] While some states decriminalized possession of small amounts of cannabis long ago, mandatory minimum sentencing laws (for example, Anti-Drug Abuse Act of 1986)—including school zone laws—have led to penalties for marijuana offenders that seem beyond reason and manifestly counterproductive. Examples abound, in which the application of mandatory minimum sentences has led to harsher penalties for marijuana offenses than for violent crimes ranging from battery through sexual assault and even to murder.[15] In America we have fueled a harsh and punitive approach toward offenders on drug use issues—without discernible benefit.

An escalated war on drugs has been the major driver of the rising incarceration rate in America. With an aggressive rise in the use of jails and prisons since 1970, the number of persons incarcerated in the United States has increased six-fold.[16] The U.S. has the highest *per capita* incarceration rate in the world at 738, five to ten times higher than the rates of comparable industrialized nations.[17] The U.S. incarcerates more people for drug offenses than the entire European Union—with 100 million more citizens—for all offenses combined.[18] Incarceration rates have risen more rapidly for nonviolent drug convictions than for any other major crime category, accounting for more than half the new prison sentences between 1985 and 2000.[19] Although it may be argued or assumed that the war on drugs targets high-level suppliers rather than individual users, the data suggest otherwise. Between 1980 and 1992, the odds of going to prison following a drug crime arrest in the United States quadrupled.[20] Both the likelihood of prison time following arrest and the length of drug-crime sentences compared to those of violent crimes have skyrocketed.[21]

As a psychiatrist with a special interest in social systems, I would not reject Schlosser's diagnostic assessment—essentially, social or mass psychosis. He basically identifies a profound loss of a sense of proportion about marijuana in America collectively and labels it psychosis in an effort to describe an absurd situation. To the extent that the perpetuation of the drug war, especially as it relates to marijuana, reinforces our collective view that we are acting in America's best interests, that loss of proportion does have the quality of a collective paranoid delusion—that is, of a reality distortion accompanied (perhaps driven) by unfounded fears about others. Unfortunately, this paranoid condition and the criminalization malignancy with which it is associated, have an even greater and disproportionate impact on minority groups. Overall, African Americans constitute 12 percent of the nation's drug users, with whites accounting for 75 percent and Hispanics 9 percent.[22] Although African Americans account for only 12 percent of drug users, they represent 32 percent of arrests for drug possession.[23]

These patterns and trends have been studied by Kathleen Kane-Willis, Jennifer Janichek, and Daniel Clark of Roosevelt University in Chicago. Kane-Willis and her colleagues, of the Illinois Consortium on Drug Policy based at Roosevelt's Institute for Metropolitan Affairs, published the report of their findings in 2006.[24] The report, *Intersecting Voices: Impacts of Illinois' Drug Policies*, found that the overall rate of incarceration for drug-related offenses increased dramatically between 1983 and 2002 in Illinois as it did across the nation.[25] The report's data analysis ranked Illinois first among states in per capita incarceration rate of African Americans for drug possession offenses.[26] Overall, total number of drug offenders admitted to prison increased more than 27-fold during that period, with convictions for possession increasing more than 37-fold and convictions for sales and/or manufacture increasing by 20-fold. These figures are striking enough in themselves, especially with regard to the large number of prison sentences for possession— almost double the rate for sales and manufacture. However, in the case of African American offenders, prison sentences for possession have increased 58-fold during the same time period with sales and manufacture convictions increasing 50-fold.[27]

Caucasian drug offenders, by comparison, have been subject to 10-fold increases in possession convictions and a four-fold increase in convictions for sales and manufacture. Total number of offenders admitted to Illinois prisons for any drug conviction increased 53-fold for African Americans in the period from 1983 to 2002 and less than seven-fold for Caucasians during the same period. *In other words, during a period when the number of prison sentences for drug-related convictions increased dramatically for all drug offenders, it increased for African Americans at roughly eight times the rate of increase seen for Caucasians.*[28]

For several decades, government solutions to the incarceration problem have, for the most part, been similar across the country: build more prisons. This has begun to change in the past five years, with a shift toward programs that divert offenders into substance abuse treatment.[29] In 2004 the Illinois Department of Corrections proposed to close two prisons.[30] This was an entirely reasonable proposal given that 25 percent of the offenders in the Illinois prison system were serving sentences for nonviolent drug related convictions. In California the passage of Proposition 36 providing for treatment as an alternative to incarceration for first- and second-time drug offenders has led to estimated cost savings of at least $2 billion since the program's inception. Savings during the first five years were more than $1 billion, with approximately $500 million related to the decision to forgo the building of a new prison that had previously been planned.[31]

In the absence of initiatives like California's Proposition 36, which Walter Cronkite called "the single biggest piece of sentencing reform in the United States since the repeal of Prohibition,"[32] the pattern has been to lock up drug offenders at significant cost to taxpayers without making a significant impact on the actual availability of drugs in our society. Attempts to manage problems with drugs in our society by locking up the offenders—whether they are users, dealers, or both—are demonstrably ineffective. Substance use is a human activity, as evidenced by the legal markets for tobacco, alcohol, and coffee. Changing the patterns of substance use in society as a whole requires effective education about the relative harms and benefits of specific substances. The "Just Say No to Drugs" approach fails on two counts: first, it allows for no alternatives to abstinence from whatever substance happens to be of concern (unless of course the substance is legal, like alcohol or tobacco); and second, other than the legal/illegal distinction, it lumps drugs together as though there were no differences among them worth discussing. But, of course, there are differences.

SAFER

On November 5, 2005, the people of the City of Denver voted to enact Initiated Question 100 (I-100), removing all penalties for possession of up to one ounce of marijuana by adults. The passage of I-100 was of special importance not simply because it was a progressive decriminalization bill—it was indeed that, but other states had taken steps in that direction several decades earlier and some local jurisdictions more recently. The 2005 Denver law was nationally and historically significant because of the context created by its driving force, the SAFER campaign for alcohol-marijuana equalization. Although the ballot language of I-100 made no reference to alcohol, the momentum for its passage was developed and sustained by an organization named for the acronym derived from "Safer Alternative for Enjoyable Recreation."[33]

The initiative was explicitly promoted on the basis of what is known about the respective safety profiles of cannabis and alcohol. The SAFER campaign's strategy is public education, and it offers a model of a public health orientation in drug policy reform. The ballot option selected by a majority of voters made no mention of the SAFER rationale for eliminating criminal penalties, including fines, for possession of up to one ounce of marijuana. But the rationale of the campaign had been well-publicized in Denver and called for voters to acknowledge the medical and public health evidence that alcohol is a serious problem in American society and that, by comparison, comparable evidence for cannabis is minimal. In Jed Riffe's documentary film *Waiting to Inhale*, Lester Grinspoon recalls the findings of his studies reviewing the known harms of marijuana: "The greatest harm did not derive from any inherent psychopharmacological effect of the substance, but rather from the way we as a society were treating it."[34] The most significant public health problem clearly linked to cannabis is the criminalization of its users. Fixing this problem means changing the law.

Where is the rationality in penalizing American adults for making healthier choices about personal use of substances? A colleague of mine, a fellow psychiatrist, noted that some years ago he attended a medical school grand rounds presentation by a former federal drug policy official. The former federal official commented to my colleague in a one-on-one conversation after the presentation, "I won't be quoted on this, but in the 1930s they made the wrong drug illegal." When a person uses cannabis, the risk of arrest and criminal prosecution is real. From a strict medical perspective, however, there is no basis for asserting that marijuana is as harmful, let alone more harmful, than alcohol. The converse, however, is not the case. The medical literature and clinical experience with the damaging effects of alcohol are extensive. Even without direct head-to-head comparison of the two substances, it is not unreasonable on the basis of existing science and practical experience to make the generalization that alcohol is more harmful than cannabis. Domestic violence, motor vehicle accidents, multiple forms of cancer, and medically well recognized physiological toxicity and organ system damage are much more strongly linked to alcohol than they are to marijuana.

Examples of the latter include gastrointestinal pathology such as alcoholic gastritis, hepatitis, and cirrhosis; neurological toxicity including brain damage, dementia, and extensive peripheral sensory and motor impairment; nutritional and hematologic compromise; and at higher doses, cardiovascular toxicity, respiratory suppression, and death from poisoning. Alcohol-dependent patients—persons with serious alcoholism—can have seizures during alcohol withdrawal and may develop the fever, tremor, and psychosis of delirium tremens. These are serious and even potentially fatal medical complications. Alcohol use, not uncommonly, may precipitate seizures in patients with epilepsy and aggravate a seizure disorder that was previously medically stabilized.

Arguably, alcohol has a similarly destabilizing effect on persons with cycling mood disorders. As I have paid more attention to these issues in my clinical practice and modified my approach to taking clinical histories in the area of substance use, I have learned from patients that decreased interest in alcohol use is among the reported benefits of cannabis for some individuals. This has been no small matter for some of my bipolar mood disorder patients, who are at very high risk of alcoholism and experience alcohol use as a destabilizing factor in their illness. Alcohol can be associated acutely or chronically with psychotic symptoms (hallucinations and delusions), but much more often its primary psychiatric manifestation is delirium, or globally impaired sensory, perceptual, and motor functioning. The rage, violence, and carelessness so often associated with alcohol abuse reflect weakened brain executive functioning that is sufficiently global to result in the primitive behavior often seen with alcohol intoxication—and, in some individuals, with even mild alcohol intoxication.

The passage of I-100, amending Denver city law, has taken place during a time of widespread movement in states across the country to make marijuana available on a medical basis for patients who may benefit from its therapeutic effects for a wide range of conditions and have their doctor's recommendation. In fact, Colorado is one of more than a dozen states to pass such new generation medical cannabis laws. The Denver initiative was developed along an entirely different trajectory of policy advocacy: SAFER's Mason Tvert argues strenuously that the scientific, medical, and public health evidence points to the conclusion that marijuana is in general a safer substance than alcohol.

From my perspective as a physician and psychiatrist, there is little medical evidence that cannabis has anywhere near the number of specifically associated disease states, or the extent of toxic effects, that alcohol does. In fact, one is hard pressed to argue for any and can probably conclusively argue for very few—chronic bronchitis and short-term memory impairment persisting beyond periods of intoxication are the most likely ill effects associated with heavy long-term use and are much less likely with light to moderate use. And, in the case of even well-researched and documented persistent short-term memory impairment following many years of heavy marijuana smoking, it is far from clear that the degree of impairment is clinically important.[35] This list is much less frightening than the list of alcohol-related diseases, not to say the tobacco list. Arguably, the benefits of occasional cannabis use—for example, to facilitate creative work, to create a freshness of perspective, or simply to relax at the end of the day—could outweigh its risks for some people. The argument for cannabis access becomes compelling when therapeutic benefits in the treatment of definable medical conditions or specific cannabis-responsive symptoms are at stake.

So, why should adults be subject to criminalization for making what on thoughtful reflection in light of experience and available science seems like a healthier choice? Cannabis is not completely benign or harmless, and there is a consensus among substance abuse researchers that cannabis abstinence after sustained use can be associated with symptoms of withdrawal and a craving for the substance.[36] In addition, acute overuse of cannabis can certainly create impairment that prevents optimal performance on tasks requiring concentration or coordinated motor movements.[37] To suggest that cannabis is safer than alcohol is not to promote driving under its influence. However, neither the existence of an identifiable withdrawal syndrome nor the problem of overuse by some individuals is of sufficient proportion to place cannabis in the same league as alcohol or tobacco in terms of dangerousness or addictive potential.[38] Tobacco is highly addictive and linked to multiple serious health problems. The health consequences of binge drinking or alcohol dependence or withdrawal can be dire or even deadly. The subtler health risks of cannabis vary based on how it is used and may be outweighed by its benefits for informed consumers. Some temperance groups are reported to have advocated cannabis as an alternative to alcohol prior to Prohibition.[39]

This has been the case made by the SAFER campaign, and it is, I believe, its frankness and honesty that accounts for the campaign's success. Its executive director, Mason Tvert, is a bulldog-like, in-your-face guy with little tolerance for fictitious propaganda when it comes to sending the right messages about drugs. He is respectful about it but unapologetic and unrelenting in his criticism of contemporary American drug policy. Mason knows that the SAFER campaign is doing the right thing and will be successful in the long run. He has a terrific grasp of just how loudly the facts on this issue speak for themselves. That's why he got involved at the level of the college campus in the first place.

The SAFER approach arose in part as a response to concerns of students, parents, and educators about student deaths from alcohol poisoning, in some cases after participating in competitive drinking games. The SAFER movement to highlight the relative safety profiles of marijuana and alcohol has its origins in university communities in Colorado, particularly Boulder and Fort Collins. Similar concerns have arisen and are being addressed in other university communities including Austin, Texas, and Columbia, Missouri. The federal government, through the Department of Health and Human Services, cautions parents and students about the dangers of excessive college student drinking and "its aftermath—violence, sexual aggression, and even death…So while people who drink may temporarily feel elated and happy, the feeling does not last and alcohol's depressive effects take over…They may become restless and aggressive. They may be more inclined to get into fights, trash a house, or make unwise decisions about sex… Under the influence of alcohol, even normal activities such as swimming, running, or just crossing a busy street can become truly dangerous—and potentially life threatening."[40]

Canadian research has found cannabis use to be associated with a higher risk of automobile accidents compared to use of no detectable substances based on urine drug screening, but the same studies show the risk associated with alcohol use to be several times that of the increase associated with cannabis.[41] Research in France has found an even greater difference between the substantial elevated risk of automobile accidents associated with alcohol use and a much more modest elevation with cannabis.[42] These studies are also consistent with Australian studies that have found that alcohol use is consistently much more powerful as an explanatory variable with respect to automobile accidents and that the relationship for marijuana use is much weaker and less consistent.[43] Some studies have suggested that after using cannabis, drivers may be more cautious on the road; while changes in driving are detected after cannabis use, they include such changes as slowing down, increasing the distance behind the vehicle ahead, and increasing minor side-to-side movements suggestive of overcorrection in steering.[44] As with many other substances, including alcohol and many medications, impairment in motor coordination and reaction time after cannabis use tends to be dose-related.[45]

Current activity on the issue of the relative dangers of alcohol and cannabis, as reflected in the SAFER campaign, may not be dissimilar to concerns regarding the safety of alcohol as our society approached the repeal of Prohibition in the early 1930s. With alcohol unregulated, the risk of obtaining forms of alcohol even more toxic than those now legally available was real and posed significant medical risk. So again, local communities are starting to change their minds. Parents have serious health concerns about the way their college-age children are using substances—concerns that are sufficiently serious to lead to recommendations for policy change in the direction of viewing marijuana and alcohol comparably. Parents do not want to see college students penalized for making a healthier choice, and they certainly do not want to see them criminalized.

If parents communicate honest information about the relative dangerousness of alcohol and cannabis, does this mean that they encourage these youth and young adults to use the latter? No. It means they caution them honestly, informed by an awareness of relevant medical science, public health issues, and preventive education. They caution them that cannabis is a powerful substance with medicinal and therapeutic potential that should not be approached frivolously. It is appropriate to discourage young people from cannabis use, unless there is a specific medical reason for using it. The fact that growth of the human brain is not complete until the mid-20s is a good reason to avoid substance abuse in young adulthood. In addition, young people, because of their level of development, are often less effective than adults at regulating their consumption of substances that are potentially intoxicating. These are reasons enough to caution young people against all drug use. The reported association between adolescent marijuana use and later adult psychosis is another reason to discourage early cannabis use. *But since people do use various substances before and after the ages of 18 and 21, it is important to provide them with accurate information on the relative harms of various substances they may be offered.*

Because young people are generally less sensitive than adults to the sedative effects of alcohol, they may drink longer before becoming drowsy. The binge drinking "challenges" that have led to alcohol poisoning deaths on college campuses are tragic examples. While use of cannabis is not free of risk, the risk is not comparable to that associated with excessive alcohol use. In fact, cannabis cannot be humanly consumed in quantities sufficient to induce anything approaching the massive internal organ damage that can be attributed to excessive alcohol intake nor the coma and death by respiratory suppression that can occur with alcohol poisoning. While the work of the National Institute on Alcohol Abuse and Alcoholism (NIAAA) to educate parents is much appreciated, current American marijuana policies are not in alignment with what is known about the relative standings of alcohol, tobacco, and cannabis from medical and public health perspectives.

It is important for parents to caution their children that experimentation with any drug—even a drug that is relatively safe in small quantities—could lead to overuse, dependence, and health problems. With cannabis, there is always the risk that they may want to use it with a frequency or regularity that is not healthy for them. For that reason, it is generally better to defer such experimentation until adulthood, when self-management skills are better developed and the central nervous system is more mature. The important message is one of respect for the fact that cannabis is a powerful naturally-occurring substance with properties that many people have found therapeutic, that it is unwise to consume cannabis carelessly or excessively, and that even the safest of substances can be dangerous when used that way. If there is a family history of schizophrenia or psychosis, parental caution should be even stronger given the evidence from some studies that young cannabis users are at higher risk for subsequent development of mental illness in early adulthood. Timmen L. Cermak, M.D., has written an excellent book for parents on how to approach discussion of marijuana use openly and honestly with teens.[46]

Under the assumption that cannabis use in the teen years may contribute to the later development of schizophrenia or other psychotic illness in young adulthood—a causal explanation for the association is but one of several possible explanations and not necessarily the most compelling—the surest way to avoid contributing to the risk of mental illness through cannabis use is to avoid experimenting with cannabis altogether. *But it would be a mistake, from a personal health or policy standpoint, to suggest that to avoid cannabis in favor of alcohol—even over the age of 21—is to make a healthier choice that will help prevent development of behavioral problems or exposure of psychiatric vulnerabilities.*

Young people are entitled to be informed that some adults use cannabis because they find its effects therapeutic, and they prefer it to alcohol because they find it to be less impairing when used carefully, judiciously, and responsibly. The reported therapeutic effects are not limited to symptoms of the major physical health problems that have been its primary indications in those communities in which medicinal use has been advocated. There are perhaps small but substantial and important subgroups of patients that use cannabis for its anti-anxiety and mood-elevating effects. Even among patients with mental illnesses that include symptoms of anxiety and mood disturbance, some report that cannabis use has been more helpful than harmful in their recovery. Often that is because cannabis use has helped them abstain from alcohol. Overused, cannabis may lead to problems, and use by young people should generally be discouraged. However, *young people should not be led to believe that there are no important differences between use of cannabis and overuse (or abuse) of cannabis, because that simply is not true.* In the context of medicinal use, there are even examples of beneficial effects of orally administered herbal cannabis in some pediatric cases of uncontrolled aggressive behavior and severe mood disturbance.[47]

Available scientific and medical data cannot support the view that cannabis poses health risks that approach those incurred with overuse of alcohol. This is true, notwithstanding the existing data relating adolescent cannabis use to a higher incidence of psychosis in early adulthood. In addition, there is no compelling evidence that use of cannabis is associated with health risks that approach the magnitude of those posed by tobacco use.

The official federal government perspective has run counter to these statements for years, with emphasis placed by the ONDCP on the role of marijuana use during adolescence as a potential contributing factor to the later development of mental illness in early adulthood. Caution regarding this possibility is appropriate, as is caution about use of mind-altering substances generally and in particular by young people. But historically, federal policy rhetoric in this area has taken liberty with existing data by making claims that the observed relationships are stronger and/or more conclusive than supported by science. In addition, even at the level of public policy it is not necessary to take an "all or nothing" approach on this issue.

It is not necessary to reject the notion that cannabis use may in some cases worsen symptoms of depression and/or psychosis and may even increase vulnerability to later mental health problems when used by youth, in order to acknowledge that there are also reports that cannabis may be helpful to persons recovering from these conditions. Psychiatrists and other physicians routinely make judgments related to the use of approved medicines that may be helpful for some patients but could potentially worsen the medical symptoms of others.

The statistical association of adolescent cannabis use with later development of psychosis in early adulthood is consistent with hypotheses other than those appealing to a causal role for cannabis. There are other possible explanations: adolescents who inherit the genetic predisposition (diathesis, or vulnerability) to develop schizophrenia may use cannabis as a form of self-medication for anxiety present in the early subsyndromal, subclinical, or prodromal (early) phases of the illness before all of the symptoms of the illness have become apparent. Alternatively, some of the factors predisposing to the development of schizophrenia or other psychoses may also predispose to the use of cannabis directly. While caution regarding the use of any substances is appropriate for individuals with a family history of schizophrenia or other mental illness, it would be a mistake to think that there is any greater risk of poor mental health outcome for users of cannabis than for users of alcohol.

Dangerous Drugs and "Health Facts"

The March 18, 2007, Chicago Sunday *Sun-Times* Health Page included a table—"The Health Fact"—presenting data on college student drug use drawn from the National Center on Addiction and Substance Abuse at Columbia University. The data presentation illustrated well the broad distortion that characterizes officially accepted representations of drug problems in our society. The table was preceded by the bullet Health Fact, "The percentage of college students saying they took potentially dangerous drugs during the previous year is up." The data presented in the table were drawn from the population of college students who had used "any illicit drug" during the previous year. According to the table, this percentage increased from 30.6 percent in 1993 to 36.6 percent in 2005. The drugs listed included marijuana (up from 27.9 to 33.3 percent), hallucinogens (down from 6 to 5 percent), inhalants (down from 3.8 to 1.8 percent), cocaine (up from 2.7 to 5.7 percent), and heroin (up from 0.1 to 0.3 percent). But the "Health Fact" table made no mention of alcohol. This is no minor omission; from a "big picture" standpoint, alcohol use is both so frequent and so toxic that it is by far the most relevant substance in making any generalization about trends in dangerous drug use among college students. Trends in alcohol use are the most relevant statistics in determining whether *dangerous drug use* has risen or declined among college students.

Why no mention of alcohol? Is it because alcohol is not an illicit drug? For college students under the age of 21, alcohol is prohibited. But we do not immediately think of it that way. Neither do college students. The implicit message is that, although as a society we don't condone underage drinking, the problem doesn't rise to the level of dangerousness associated with use of "any illicit drug." Yet alcohol accounts for many more deaths, addictions, and serious medical problems than any of the drugs listed on that table—in fact, more than all of them combined. Ironically, the "Health Fact" note was printed at a time when current events in Chicago appeared to be speaking directly to the potential harms of alcohol—the evening news featuring video clips that captured the beating of a female bartender by an off-duty male police officer apparently because she was hesitant to pour him additional drinks. Failure to mention alcohol in a table that summarizes 12-year trends in "dangerous" and "illicit" drug use among college students involves at least several communication distortions: failure to identify alcohol as an illicit drug for college students; failure to identify alcohol as a dangerous drug; failure to reflect the magnitude of the alcohol problem in proportion to problems with other drugs; and the profiling of marijuana as the most prominent "dangerous drug" problem on college campuses.

To be clear, *all drugs are dangerous*. In fact, all *illicit drugs are dangerous even if they are not used*, because having them in one's possession can lead to criminal penalties. This observation raises the interesting and important question whether, for any particular substance of potential abuse, the greater dangerousness lies in its biological effects or in its criminalization. As we have seen, even government and law enforcement officials have expressed earnest concern that the criminalization of drugs in American society may cause more harm than drug abuse itself. Nowhere is this more obvious than in the case of cannabis and the laws pertaining to it—as pointed out three decades ago by President Jimmy Carter: "Penalties against a drug should not be more damaging to an individual than the use of the drug itself. Nowhere is this more clear than in the laws against possession of marijuana for personal use. The National Commission on Marijuana ... concluded years ago that marijuana use should be decriminalized, and I believe it is time to implement those basic recommendations."[48]

Illinois

Illinois has built momentum on the issue of medicinal cannabis access over the last several years. On May 27, 2009, the Illinois Senate passed Senate Bill 1381, the Compassionate Use of Medical Cannabis Pilot Program Act.[49] As of this writing, Senate Bill 1381 has been passed by the House Human Services Committee and is slated for debate on the House floor.[50] With negative publicity surrounding implementation conflicts in California—fueled by federally supported raids, media sensationalism, and the scapegoating of consumers for problems that reflect law enforcement bias—advocates in Illinois have been inclined to distance themselves from the California experience for strategic reasons. As a result, the Illinois proposal has been modeled largely after the Colorado law.

While I appreciate both the strategy of minimizing unnecessary negative rhetoric (along the lines of "Look what's happening in California…") and the need for Illinois legislators and other stakeholders to take carefully measured steps on what they perceive to be a controversial issue, I have argued to advocates and interested parties in Illinois that California's medical cannabis law is actually the better model. Why make this point? California's law is the best available model because its language supports broad discretion on the part of physicians. The California law in effect designates physicians as custodians of the policy question regarding the public health impact of cannabis usage.

One of the features of the Illinois medical cannabis legislation proposed in 2009 is that it sets a list of allowable medical uses for cannabis. The proposed law establishes a Commission to oversee implementation, and the Commission is charged with regular review of the list of approved medical uses in light of petitions that may be submitted for the addition of other medical conditions to that list. All of the listed indications are supported by abundant anecdotal data, and for some (for example, multiple sclerosis, AIDS neuropathy, nausea, appetite stimulant) there are rigorous clinical scientific findings supporting medicinal use. The bill provides a mechanism whereby the list can be expanded on a petition-and-review basis. The Commission is responsible for consideration of proposed modifications to the list of approved medicinal cannabis uses and for developing rules to guide the review process. This proposed legislation and similar efforts in other states reflect good work on the part of states trying to piece together compensatory regulatory mechanisms to stand in for a defunct federal process. The Illinois proposal allows for three possible general means of access to cannabis for approved patients: they can grow it themselves; they can obtain it from an appointed caregiver; or they can obtain it from a larger not-for-profit dispensary that serves a number of medicinal consumers.

Interestingly, while passage of the proposed new law will set Illinois definitively on a course toward implementation of medicinal access, it may also be unnecessarily restrictive and in some ways even counterproductive. First, the proposal for an amended Illinois Cannabis Control Act would establish a list of indications for recommendation of cannabis on a medical basis. Physician recommendations for medicinal cannabis use could be written, under the new law if passed, for the limited number of medical conditions on the list of indications. The list would be established, reviewed, and modified by the Commission created under the new law.

Illinois was one of the earliest states to pass one of the "first generation" medical cannabis laws, introduced on a bipartisan basis and passed with nearly unanimous support in 1978. The Illinois law passed at that time specified two medical conditions—glaucoma and nausea from chemotherapy—for which cannabis could be recommended. But the law also provided that cannabis could be recommended for other medical conditions if determined to be medically necessary by a physician (literally, "or such other procedure certified to be medically necessary"). This latter provision allows greater latitude for physicians to exercise their medical judgment in determining which patients may benefit from medicinal cannabis use and for what conditions. Arguably, this more substantial role for physician discretion in recommending access to cannabis on a medical basis is in the best interests of patients. It also actively enlists physicians in the process of redefining a concept that has been silenced for many years in American healthcare and in American public conversation generally—that is, the concept of cannabis as a therapeutic substance.

The language of the 1978 revision of the 1971 Illinois Cannabis Control Act acknowledges that in the final analysis the breadth of medicinal applications of cannabis depends upon physician practice—which will be linked to patient demand in a consumer driven healthcare system. The 1978 Illinois law is like the California law in that it uses inclusive language that allows for broader exercise of physician discretion in making a medicinal cannabis recommendation to a given patient. In California, a physician can recommend cannabis to a combat veteran because it helps the individual relax, sleep better, and stay away from alcohol. Strictly speaking, under the 1978 Illinois law, were it implemented as written, similar applications could be made because physicians would have broad discretion in the recommendation of cannabis for medicinal use.

The 2009 Illinois medical cannabis proposal was written to replace the 1978 revision with much more detailed and specific language that includes general rules of implementation. Its provisions for implementation represent clear progress toward medicinal cannabis access for patients in need. The 2009 proposal includes a more extensive, but also more restrictive, list of conditions. Under the 2009 proposed Illinois law, a veteran with posttraumatic stress disorder (PTSD) seeking access to cannabis for medicinal use would also have to have a definable pain syndrome to qualify for a physician's recommendation.

The Illinois proposal is not substantially different from proposals implemented in other states. Until recently, California has been the only state that has not discriminated against psychiatric patients seeking access to cannabis for its anti-anxiety and mood-stabilizing effects. As discussed in Part I, New Mexico has added PTSD to its list of indications for which a physician may recommend herbal cannabis for medicinal use. Proposed medicinal cannabis access legislation under consideration in Wisconsin in 2009 follows the New Mexico example with regard to PTSD.

It will not be surprising if, by and large, veterans with PTSD are polytrauma cases with co-existing physical symptoms. Nor is it unusual for PTSD patients to experience physical pain as an aspect of heightened physiological arousal and emotional re-experiencing of the traumatic event(s). Patients with panic disorder may experience similar physiological storms in the absence of clear precipitating events. But PTSD as a clinical syndrome is defined in the realm of behavior and emotional pain.

The second respect in which the new Illinois proposal creates tighter controls is in its reintroduction of more severe criminal penalties for patients and caregivers who abuse the system—for example, by exceeding allowable quantities or by permitting diversion for nonmedical use. It is interesting to note that the trade-off of increased criminal penalties, in exchange for a medical cannabis law that can be implemented, is proposed at a time when the Illinois Drug Policy Coalition has been formed by advocates committed to moving broader drug policy in Illinois toward a public health model of control and intervention rather than a criminal justice model.

The Illinois Drug Policy Coalition is one of nine regional projects of the National African American Drug Policy Coalition formed by a group of distinguished African American government and community leaders. Based at Howard University in Washington, D.C., Coalition leaders include the Honorable Kurt L. Schmoke, Dean of the Howard University Law School and former Mayor of Baltimore; Clyde E. Bailey, Sr., Esq., a Past President of the National Bar Association; and the Honorable Arthur L. Burnett, Sr., a senior judge of the Superior Court of Washington, D.C. who took leave from that position to become the Coalition's Executive Director. The Illinois Drug Policy Coalition announced its formation and mission to move Illinois toward a public health rather than criminal justice drug policy strategy the day after Martin Luther King Day, 2007.

At a time when African American community leadership has been working to promote drug enforcement alternatives to imprisonment in Illinois, legislation that re-felonizes marijuana offenses inevitably falls out of sync with emerging trends and overall policy goals. The 2009 proposed Illinois medical cannabis legislation would be more in line with contemporary public views and community needs if the proposed criminal penalty enhancements were converted from felonies to fines. Put differently, a viable state-level medical cannabis law in Illinois would be in the better interest of public health if coupled to a broader decriminalization law. Consistent with this approach was the July 2009 vote of the Cook County Board to decriminalize possession of up to ten grams of cannabis in unincorporated Cook County.

Physicians, Public Health, and Harm Reduction

Broader physician discretion on the acceptable range of medicinal cannabis applications, which happens to be written into the existing 1978 Illinois Medical Cannabis Act but is best modeled by the California law, taps medical expertise in a way that extends readily into the public health domain. Data available from clinical practices in medical cannabis states are instructive in this regard. The late Berkeley psychiatrist Tod Mikuriya, M.D., consulted on medicinal cannabis use in a wide range of cases, the largest proportion of which represented pain syndromes and inflammatory diseases. Gieringer reviewed the diagnostic distribution of Mikuriya's clinical caseload and found that 27 percent were receiving medicinal cannabis recommendations for a primary psychiatric diagnosis, the largest psychiatric subgroup being posttraumatic stress disorder (PTSD).[51] If substance use disorders and insomnia are included in behavioral health indications in Mikuriya's practice, the number increases to 35 percent.

More than 5 percent of the patients reported by Gieringer were using cannabis as a form of medicinal substitution, managing substance use problems within a harm reduction model; the majority of those patients were recovering from alcohol dependence with a much smaller but significant group managing their recovery from opiate dependence. Before the Marihuana Tax Act of 1937, some physicians viewed opiate dependence as one potential indication for the medicinal use of cannabis. Dr. Mikuriya's consulting practice ultimately grew to nearly 10,000 cases. Extrapolating from Gieringer's publication of the diagnostic distribution of his cannabis consultation practice, Mikuriya would have recommended cannabis to some 500 patients for the purpose of supporting their efforts to become alcohol-free. *Physicians could play an important role in managing the transition from a culture of government-defined marijuana abuse to a culture of consumer-driven and person-centered medical management of both cannabis therapeutics and cannabis-related problems.*

Marijuana has been so highly profiled as the country's greatest drug problem that the exercise of physician discretion more broadly beyond a defined list may make physicians and others squeamish. On that basis, a defined list may be viewed as more desirable. To be clear, it is my view that broad physician authority on this issue is a desirable feature—and I believe that this feature has allowed California's law to be successful in ways that have not extended to other states with tighter controls. A simple, practical solution to the problem of determining appropriate latitude for physicians in making medicinal cannabis recommendations would be to accept the concept of a defined list of acceptable indications but permit medicinal applications beyond the established list when two conditions are both met: (1) a second, concurring physician opinion is obtained, and (2) a petition is filed to add the medical condition in question to the list of accepted indications. This represents an alternative strategy broadening patient access in the absence of a broader inclusion clause such as that found in the Illinois Cannabis Control Act as revised in 1978.

What is the value of permitting broader patient access and physician discretion in recommending cannabis? With the opportunity to exercise broader discretionary judgment regarding conditions for which cannabis may be made available to patients, depending upon the clinical need, a physician can legitimately support patients who choose to use cannabis, and do so responsibly, because they find it to be helpful in ways that other medications are not or in ways that complement the therapeutic effects of other medications. Especially important for behavioral health is the fact that some patients report that when cannabis is available to them they are less likely to use alcohol and that it is a healthier choice in their lives. Patient reports to the effect that they are less likely to use alcohol when they have access to cannabis and that alcohol is much more predictable in its tendency to exacerbate their mood and/or anxiety disorder by comparison with cannabis are to be taken seriously, because they are not, in my clinical experience, uncommon and because they are consistent with what is known about the effects of alcohol in these psychiatric conditions.

In the above types of cases, the harm reduction is medical in nature: patients with a mood disorder complicated by alcoholism or alcohol problems may find that cannabis enables them to abstain from alcohol use—and for some, it even takes away their interest in alcohol. This is not by any means the case for all or even most individuals with alcohol problems. But it most certainly is the case for some, and for that reason this issue deserves earnest medical, public health, and public policy attention. In the case of the SAFER approach, the harm reduction intervention of recommending cannabis for a patient with alcohol problems is in effect broadened as an option more generally for adults who may experience alcohol as toxic even in small quantities and less agreeable than cannabis. *The Colorado-based SAFER approach can be seen as the public health extension of the medical practice of alcohol harm reduction by cannabis substitution.*

In November, 2006, Mason Tvert and his colleagues took the Denver SAFER campaign statewide in Colorado, and 41 percent of the voters supported the decriminalization initiative (I-44). In Illinois, state government will ultimately reaffirm the intent of the 1978 revision of its Cannabis Control Act, which articulated conditions under which patients in need might receive cannabis for medicinal use with the approval of their physician. But Illinois now has an opportunity to implement medical cannabis access at a time when the need and public cry for broader drug law reform have become clear. For this reason, the strong recommendation can be made that the revised Act manage any cannabis infractions in a manner consistent with a decriminalizing policy trajectory. Harsher penalties for those abusing the medical system may be appropriate; but, if so, the state could consider shifting penalties from felonies to fines—large fines, if indicated, but not re-expansion of prison use for cannabis offenses.

A broad inclusion clause or other mechanism allowing physician discretion would encourage recognition of patients who may benefit from therapeutic cannabis use for medical conditions other than those most commonly cited. A revised Illinois Medical Cannabis Act could also be linked with decriminalizing statutes at the state or county level that would better conserve law enforcement and court system resources and perhaps generate revenue in the form of fines. The SAFER campaign has the advantage of sending an appropriate message about the relative harmfulness of cannabis and alcohol—a message that is consistent with broader medical access to cannabis, particularly as it relates to the reduction of alcohol-related harms. As a psychiatrist practicing in real-world settings, I support this type of access as a matter of policy because consumers of healthcare services are entitled to make these choices.

At the same time, however, any discussion that I would have in response to questions from an individual patient about whether herbal cannabis could be helpful in his or her recovery from alcohol problems would necessarily include a review of available prescription medications that have been shown to be effective for that purpose. For example, most recently acamprosate (brand name Campral®) has proven to be very effective in helping patients maintain abstinence from alcohol. Such evidence-based treatments would virtually always rank higher than cannabis as potential therapeutic options. But to repeat yet again a point made previously in this book, when an individual patient puts personal cannabis use on the table as a strategy that has been helpful for his or her recovery, a physician who is receptive to consumer-driven strategies in recovery management will generally serve the patient more effectively.

Working Group Conversations

Julie, whose struggle with MS and medicinal use of cannabis were discussed in Part I, worked with George Pappas of IDEAL Reform (Illinois Drug Education and Legislative Reform) to establish a discussion forum where individuals interested in learning more about medicinal applications of cannabis could come to exchange information. Such exchange included website information, literature in the field, early reports of practice experience in other states, the status of existing law and proposed legislation regarding consumer access to cannabis as medicine in Illinois, and personal accounts of therapeutic benefits experienced with the use of cannabis—both within and outside of Illinois. I attended a number of these meetings, and the forum was referred to as the Medicinal Cannabis Working Group.

In one of the earliest meetings of the Medicinal Cannabis Working Group, several men shared, with very different stories, that they had used cannabis as an alternative to alcohol. Two of them considered themselves recovering alcoholics and found that by using cannabis they had been able to remain completely alcohol-free for years. In one case, a 62-year-old man shared his personal history of alcohol problems and identified substitution for alcohol as his primary reason for cannabis use. For this individual, cannabis use prevented alcohol from taking a further toll on his health than it already had. With access to cannabis, he avoided both the severe acute impairment of alcohol intoxication (he had a history of blackouts) and the longer-term consequences of further damage to multiple organs including his liver (he had a history of alcohol-induced hepatitis), stomach (he had a history of gastrointestinal bleeding), and brain (he had also been depressed and had even had thoughts of suicide).

In the second case, a 45-year-old man had used cannabis to relieve the pain of arthritis but had identified alcohol as problematic and had gradually given it up in favor of cannabis as an alternative to help him relax in the evening. In fact, using cannabis for arthritic pain, he found that he lost interest in alcohol and generally felt better without it.

A third middle-aged male shared that he had used cannabis generally in the evenings as a substitute for alcohol. He told the group that he had not been a regular user during most of his adult life and had generally been a light social drinker. Over time, he had found that even small amounts of alcohol produced undesirable sedative and depressant effects. He found that light cannabis use could lift his mood in the evening and at times even improve his attention to work-related tasks. In contrast with alcohol, cannabis use did not leave him feeling fatigued the next day. All three of these individuals were in effect practicing a form of harm reduction by substituting cannabis for alcohol.

Finding such stories compelling, I have modified my approach to taking a clinical history in my practice of psychiatry. Interviewing patients, I now follow up more consistently on acknowledged marijuana use, not just with questions about the ways in which it may have been a problem but also to inquire as to whether the patient has found cannabis to be beneficial. I have learned much more from patients as a result of this approach. More than a handful of young adult patients, mostly but not exclusively female, have told me that they recalled times when cannabis use had quelled their urges to cut themselves; they felt that cannabis had powerfully reduced the intense anxiety that they were experiencing. Certainly, there are numerous ways—pharmacological and nonpharmacological—to manage anxiety, and in psychiatry we have a large pharmacopoeia for that purpose. However, self-cutting and other self-mutilating behaviors can be some of the most difficult behaviors to manage effectively and consistently over time. That cannabis may at times be useful for such patients is no small matter; in the field of psychiatry self-injurious behavior is of such major importance that anecdotal reports of success in stopping it warrant further exploration. In fact, we psychiatrists often prescribe medications for that purpose that have potential side effects or toxicities that are medically more worrisome than cannabis.

With a provision for the exercise of physician discretion in making determinations regarding appropriate medicinal applications, legislation establishing medicinal cannabis access has the potential to be even more effective. As we have seen, one example of such an extension is the use of cannabis on a medicinal basis to help achieve abstinence from, or reduction in use of, alcohol. In addition, a broader provision for physician discretion is more likely to open up use of medicinal cannabis for more controversial—though not unrecognized—applications, including some behavioral health conditions. Although recent psychiatric research has been interpreted as implicating cannabis use as a factor in the exacerbation of psychosis and in hastening the onset of schizophrenia in vulnerable individuals, the research findings are also compatible with other explanations including a self-medication hypothesis. That is, patients predisposed to some mental illnesses—including schizophrenia—may use cannabis because it reduces anxiety or stabilizes mood.

The notion that medications beneficial for individuals with some conditions may worsen the conditions of other patients is not new to the field of psychiatry; psychiatrists are accustomed to using caution in prescribing certain medications for certain patients—for example, stimulating antidepressants for patients with schizophrenia or bipolar disorder. Psychiatrists may avoid using such medications or prescribe them in lower doses with gradual dosage adjustment and frequent follow-up to monitor closely for both the desired therapeutic benefits and potential adverse effects including worsening of the patient's primary symptoms. For psychiatric disorders other than schizophrenia, clinical anecdotes—some of which have been compiled in case reports and case series and some of which have been reported directly by patients in writing and/or verbally—attest to therapeutic and harm-reducing effects of cannabis in a number of conditions including PTSD, bipolar disorder, depression, ADHD, explosive behavior generally, and alcoholism and some other addictions.[52]

In the practice of psychiatric medicine, I would not recommend cannabis as first-line treatment for any of these conditions. But equally importantly, I am appreciative of the fact that some patients have found cannabis helpful in their overall recovery. For some individuals, cannabis may have provided relief from psychiatric symptoms or insomnia and may have been more agreeable or better tolerated than prescribed medications. More often in my experience as a practicing clinician, patients with mood, anxiety, or other psychiatric disorders recognize their need for prescribed treatment and accept it; they may then choose to use cannabis to lessen their interest in alcohol and because they find it much more compatible with goals such as reducing irritability and sleeping well.

Even in patients with schizophrenia, cannabis use does not consistently worsen psychotic symptoms; some patients with schizophrenia have reported to me that cannabis not only decreases their anxiety but also reduces or eliminates their auditory hallucinations. This is an important area for further medical research, and the observations almost certainly point to an interaction between individual genetics and the specific chemical composition of the cannabis strain in question. Still, at this time, patients with psychotic disorders should be cautioned by their psychiatrists—as is standard practice—that existing medical research does identify cannabis use as a potential risk factor for mental illness, and some controlled clinical experiments demonstrate that direct administration of prescription THC can in some cases, under certain conditions induce similar symptoms in otherwise normal individuals.[53] But prescription THC is not herbal cannabis, and as Weil and Rosen have pointed out it may not even be as safe.[54]

Mental Health

A number of studies have reported an increase in the risk of developing schizophrenia or related psychotic symptoms, and possibly depression, in early adulthood for adolescents who have used cannabis.[55] There is debate about whether the data actually point to a causal relationship between cannabis use and subsequent psychosis (or depression), or the higher rate of use reflects self-medication. The case can be argued in either direction; the causal hypothesis is neither entirely implausible nor unequivocally established. The claims of some patients with schizophrenia that cannabis has been beneficial for them extend well beyond my clinical practice and have been documented, for example, in the work of Mikuriya and Gieringer.[56]

Several recent reviews have analyzed studies reporting on the associations between cannabis use and adverse mental health outcomes including psychosis and mood disturbances.[57] A recent meta-analysis arrived at a figure of 40 percent as the increase in risk of developing psychosis among adolescents who use cannabis, with evidence of a dose-response relationship such that chronic heavy users incurred risk of psychosis up to double that of nonusers.[58] A meta-analysis is a study that makes a systematic attempt to integrate the findings of a large number of published primary research studies that vary to a greater or lesser degree in their methods and statistics. The meta-analysis creates a uniform database from those studies and then analyzes the data statistically.

A meta-analysis introduces theoretical, methodological, and statistical assumptions, but my purpose here is not to engage in criticism at that level. For our purposes here, we can grant the validity of meta-analysis generally and of the study being summarized more specifically. The authors of the study acknowledged that their methodology—as well as the methodologies of the primary studies they used—does not permit a conclusive causal interpretation, and such a cautionary note is appropriate. Use of cannabis and future development of psychosis may be linked by a third factor that explains both—such as, for example, higher levels of anxiety, depressive moods, and/or social withdrawal in adolescents who have inherited a diathesis or genetic vulnerability for the development of schizophrenia. Such a scenario would be compatible with a self-medication explanation and perhaps other theories.

The meta-analysis also found that the statistical association between cannabis use and later schizophrenia was weaker than that for cannabis use and psychotic symptoms more generally. This is important, because psychosis is a broad concept that refers to sensations and ideas that are distorted and unrealistic in their divergence from the consensual reality that most of us routinely inhabit. Hearing voices, for example, when no one else is around is a psychotic symptom. But even with regard to the general psychiatric concept of psychosis, problems must arise for the individual as a result of such thoughts or perceptions in order for a diagnosis of a psychiatric disorder to be made. The thoughts, perceptions, and associated behaviors may be disturbing to the individual or to others in the environment, but in one way or another they have to be identified as a problem. The phenomenon of voice-hearing, for example, has been studied in nonpsychiatric contexts, and it is not altogether unheard of that people may have such experiences and not be bothered by them.[59] In such cases, without the identification of problems in living—in clinical language, without a "chief complaint"—no psychiatric diagnosis is appropriate.

I elaborate on this matter because when it comes to schizophrenia, as opposed to psychosis in general, functional deterioration is always an issue. This does not mean that persons with schizophrenia inevitably deteriorate to low levels of functioning or that recovery and a rewarding life are not possible. But problems with work and/or social functioning are invariably identified when a diagnosis of schizophrenia is made, and most commonly the functional impairment is severe and, without treatment, progressive. I have known a few ministers who told me that they *literally* heard a voice—which they took to be the voice of God—calling them to the ministry. These people were not suffering from psychosis in any clinical sense, and they certainly did not have schizophrenia.

The studies that examine the relationship of adolescent marijuana use to the later development of psychosis in adulthood are casting a methodological net that is broad enough to capture perceptual phenomena that could be labeled "psychotic symptoms" without any functional consequences. In addition, "psychotic disorders" that are functionally relevant but short-lived, unsustained, or minor in their impact may be included in patients identified as having developed psychotic symptoms by the time of follow-up in adulthood. Individuals identified as having a history of such symptoms at follow-up assessment will include persons that have had experiences that are relatively inconsequential by comparison to the psychotic symptoms associated with the serious functional problems that lead to a diagnosis of schizophrenia.

The meta-analysis examining the relationship between marijuana use and the subsequent development of schizophrenia or other psychotic disorders found a weaker relationship statistically between cannabis use and schizophrenia per se than between cannabis use and psychosis more generally. When psychiatric symptoms are explicitly linked to functional problems—which, in practice, is the way psychiatry functions as a medical specialty and social control mechanism—the connection between cannabis use and mental health problems becomes statistically weaker. Certainly cannabis use can be mind-altering, but that does not in itself make it problematic or a target of psychiatric intervention. In addition, there is less evidence pointing to a link between cannabis use and subsequent depression than there is to a link with either schizophrenia or psychosis.

Clinical experience suggests that some patients with mood disorders, including bipolar disorder and major depression, find therapeutic benefit in cannabis use.[60] Similar anecdotal reports have been made for anxiety disorders, especially PTSD, amounting to substantial numbers of cases.[61] One large study based on an Internet sample found that cannabis users experienced less depressive symptomatology than nonusers.[62] In a controversial study—methodologically sound but controversial because of its findings—Berkeley researchers found that adolescents who had experimented with drugs, but were not heavily involved with drugs and did not have substance abuse disorders, were less anxious and better adjusted than those who had no experience with such experimentation.[63]

If it is assumed that the 40 percent increased risk found in the meta-analysis reflects a causal relationship between the use of cannabis as an adolescent and the later development of schizophrenia as an adult—and this is clearly an assumption based on an observed association, not a demonstrated or proven fact—then the incidence of later schizophrenia among adolescents who use cannabis would increase from about 1 percent or 1 out of every 100 people, to 1.4 percent or 1.4 out of every 100 people. Put differently, in the general population of adolescents, roughly 10 out of 1000 will go on to develop schizophrenia; but if the population is limited to cannabis-using adolescents, 14 out of 1000 will develop schizophrenia. Such an increased risk—amounting to four additional cases of schizophrenia per 1000 cannabis-using adolescents—would be sufficient to require a product warning, as with tobacco and cancer or alcohol during pregnancy, which could only be instituted under conditions in which cannabis was regulated. The need to communicate this information to the general public would be an argument for commercial regulation (legalization), with age-restricted access.

Interestingly, in their discussions of the potential policy implications of their findings, the authors of the meta-analytic study that derived these numbers state that it is important for people to be informed about these results. From an American perspective the authors' warning seems strangely anachronistic, inasmuch as Americans have been subjected to at least two decades of politically driven messages of alarm about the detrimental effects of marijuana based on questionable research, a distorted research agenda, inappropriate extrapolation from limited research findings, unwarranted causal inferences based on existing research, and the suppression of research itself in deference to all of the above.

If a causal relationship is assumed for the sake of further policy discussion, with cannabis use contributing to the risk of later development of psychosis in proportion to the extent of cannabis exposure, the risk could be compared statistically to the heightened risk of developing schizophrenia for individuals hospitalized during childhood for viral central nervous system (CNS) infections. A recent study calculated a risk ratio of 1.5 to 1.6 for such individuals; that is, there is a 50 to 60 percent increased chance of developing psychosis, including schizophrenia, in early adulthood.[64] The authors referred to this finding as a "slightly increased risk" for developing psychotic illness and "a weak association between viral CNS infections in early childhood and the later development of nonaffective psychotic illnesses."[65] In the case of specific viruses for which the risk is known to be much higher, notably cytomegalovirus and mumps virus, the risk ratios were calculated to be 16.6 and 2.7 respectively. An individual exposed to cytomegalovirus during early childhood is more than 16 times more likely to develop schizophrenia or other nonaffective psychosis than an individual not exposed to the virus. This is more than a 1,600 percent increase, compared with the 50 to 60 percent increase associated with viral infections generally (more specifically, viral infections that attack the central nervous system) and the 40 percent increase associated with adolescent cannabis use. Individuals exposed to mumps for whom the risk ratio was 2.7 were 270 percent more likely to develop psychotic illness in early adulthood.

The observed association between cannabis use in adolescence and subsequent development of schizophrenia or other psychosis in adulthood is not the only consideration in evaluating the potential public health impact of legitimately regulated access to cannabis on behavioral health outcomes. In considering cannabis use in the population as a factor in public mental health, consideration would be given to the incidence of alcoholism, depressive disorders, and anxiety disorders; and the question would be posed how best to understand the relationship of cannabis use to these conditions and the individuals who suffer from them. In practices that have reported experience with medicinal cannabis recommendations that have included subgroups of patients with psychiatric disorders, the largest diagnostic groups have been PTSD and major depression. In these real-world clinical settings, cannabis has also been recommended as a substitute for alcohol for patients with alcohol-related problems including alcohol dependence.

Whether the statistical association of cannabis and subsequent psychosis reflects a causal relationship or not, and whether cannabis is therapeutically useful for any one of several other classes of psychiatric disorders or not, psychiatrists already work with types of medications that are appropriate and life-saving for some patients but potentially risky or even contraindicated for other patients. Psychiatrists recognize, and regularly work around, the fact that some medications that are highly effective in persons with some disorders may precipitate or exacerbate psychosis or mood instability in others. For example, physicians understand that antidepressants must be used with caution in persons with psychosis and in persons with a history of mania (bipolar disorder). This does *not* mean that antidepressants cannot be used in these populations. Psychiatrists understand that if these medicines become necessary in the course of treating such conditions, the treatment must proceed cautiously with frequent follow-up and close re-evaluation.

Current knowledge of cannabis is such that if legitimate public conversation regarding the herb's medicinal in addition to problematic qualities were occurring, we would be asking how systematic cannabis breeding could be used to minimize the adverse effects of cannabis on persons with schizophrenia—or a family history of same—who choose to use cannabis. Could we actually recommend one strain over another based on a lower likelihood of exacerbation of psychosis or precipitation of mania? My reading of the evidence suggests that we are not very far from being able to do so. Such an approach would amount to a form of harm reduction. This type of harm reduction strategy may or may not hold as much promise as alcohol substitution in persons known to become substantially more diseased with alcohol use. Such questions could be profitably researched and answered in an environment in which cannabis was available on a regulated basis.

Len's Green Thumb

During the summer of 2005, 30-year-old Len came to see me for help with his mood disorder. He had been treated as a teenager for attention deficit hyperactivity disorder (ADHD) and subsequently diagnosed with bipolar disorder, characterized by depression alternating with episodes of elevated, irritable, or expansive mood. He had been treated with stimulants, the medical treatment of choice for ADHD, which had improved his focus and concentration and decreased his irritability. He was quite sensitive to their effects and had no inclination to use excessive doses or even increase his dose over time. Before he had come to see me, Len had been treated with numerous antidepressants, mood stabilizers, and antipsychotic medications with mixed results. He reported that he had found cannabis to be more effective in stabilizing his mood than any of the prescription medications he had taken. Before coming to see me, he had been treated by his primary care physician for a period of time with dronabinol (generic for brand name drug Marinol®, or synthetic delta-9-tetrahydrocannabinol, THC) in an effort to approximate a substitution for herbal cannabis, and in fact dronabinol had been the medication that had been most helpful. Regarding his cannabis use, Len reported to me that the specific strain seemed to make a difference.

As it turned out, Len had quite a green thumb and had learned to cultivate a specific strain of cannabis for what he felt were its optimum therapeutic effects. With an adequate supply of his preferred strain, he reported effective stabilization of mood symptoms, although he achieved additional benefit from stimulant medication targeting the primary attention and concentration problems that led to his early diagnosis of ADHD. With ongoing access to cannabis—especially of a single specific strain—his need for other medications diminished significantly, and his overall functioning tended to be at its best. It has often been the case—perhaps more often than not—that Len has not had regular access to cannabis. He has never in fact grown it for the purpose of selling it to others to make money.

In my years of psychiatric practice I have treated many patients for bipolar disorder, including a small subgroup for both ADHD and bipolar disorder, with a high degree of success using standard FDA-approved medications. These medications have included primary mood stabilizers such as lithium, carbamazepine (name brands Tegretol®, Equetro®), valproate (name brand Depakote®), lamotrigine (name brand Lamictal®), and topiramate (brand name Topamax®), as well as antipsychotic medications with mood-stabilizing properties. The latter medications include many older generation medications, classic examples of which include haloperidol (brand name Haldol®) and chlorpromazine (brand name Thorazine®) and much more commonly nowadays the newer generation antipsychotics such as olanzapine (brand name Zyprexa®), aripiprazole (brand name Abilify®), quetiapine (brand name Seroquel®), and risperidone (brand name Risperdal®), to name a few. I have also on occasion had some success, with patients who either preferred natural substances or tolerated standard medicines poorly, using omega-3 fatty acids contained in fish oil preparations. Andrew Stoll, M.D., of the Harvard University Department of Psychiatry, has published research findings supporting the view that fish oil preparations high in these essential fatty acids may be helpful as adjunctive medications for patients on standard mood stabilizers who have not been able to remain symptom-free.[66]

Len has presented a challenging case. He has strong views about the superiority of his preferred herbal cannabis for mood stabilization, and we have debated the issue many times from our respective points of view. As I mentioned earlier, I do not recommend herbal cannabis as a primary treatment of choice for any psychiatric disorder, and it is rare that I would not be able to select effective psychiatric medications from within the extensive array of chemical compounds available to the modern medical practitioner. As I have also said earlier, I do listen to patients when they tell me that herbal cannabis has been helpful rather than harmful in their recovery; some patients think of their cannabis use as a much less problematic alternative to alcohol for evening relaxation, while others view it as an herbal medicine that serves as an adjunct to the medicines I do prescribe. Patients in the latter category report that herbal cannabis can be helpful for anxiety, irritability, and even disturbing thoughts and impulses.

Some patients with schizophrenia have even reported—contrary to my clinical bias based on available scientific research considered in the aggregate—that herbal cannabis is effective in decreasing their psychotic symptoms (hallucinations, or the sensing of things that are not there such as ominous or running-commentary voices, and paranoid delusions, or unfounded frightening beliefs). Also noted earlier, these reports are not entirely without credibility inasmuch as researchers in Brazil have cited evidence from the laboratory and clinical practice that at least one of the compounds in herbal cannabis, cannabidiol (CBD), has antipsychotic properties.[67]

In Len's case, I do have to admit that when he has uninterrupted access to herbal cannabis, his functioning is such that I feel less compelled to argue the superiority of my arsenal of approved medications. When he is without cannabis, I face the challenge of convincing him to work with me by accepting a sustained therapeutic trial of a standard medication. The debate continues. At times this patient is acutely suicidal. But cannabis seems to help, and more specifically it seems to work as a mood stabilizer about which the consumer is thoughtful and well informed. According to Len, the amount of CBD, as opposed to THC, seems to be important in the mood stabilizing effects he experiences with herbal cannabis use. He grows a particular strain referred to as a *blueberry*, which he uses as his primary medicinal herb, although he finds that rotating strains from time to time—using alternative strains for limited periods of time—helps preserve the effectiveness of his primary strain and maintain his mood stability.

For Len, THC produces a significant stimulating and antidepressive effect, but CBD appears to be critical for mood stabilization. This is, of course, an inference but not an unreasonable one based on Len's knowledge of *sativa* and *indica* strain variations. He maintains that *indica* strains seem to have proportionately higher—although not necessarily absolutely higher—CBD concentrations than *sativas*, and this is not out of sync with the observations of others including medicinal growers, researchers, and clinicians.[68] Since there is a broad array of cannabinoid compounds present in herbal cannabis, my focus here on THC and CBD is an oversimplification, and additional research—clinical, therapeutics research—is necessary to establish the significance of both the array and the role of the THC-to-CBD ratio as a biochemical marker or index within it. Len's ideas about the effects of various strains of cannabis, as well as their natural chemical compositions, seem congruent with observations of clinicians and scientists working closely to correlate strain-related variations in chemical composition with clinical therapeutic effects.[69]

As a musician and recording artist, Len does not find that cannabis interferes with his ability to work; in fact, he reports that he works more intently and productively when he has access to cannabis. Both dronabinol (prescription THC) and stimulants help him focus his attention on work that he values and enjoys; and for Len, as for most patients with serious mental illnesses, inherently rewarding work is an important component of recovery. He has also taken antidepressant treatment intermittently during the time I have worked with him, and he benefited most from duloxetine (brand name Cymbalta®). But he has limited tolerance for longer-term maintenance pharmacotherapy with anything other than stimulants. He has taken a number of mood-stabilizing medications, including olanzapine (Zyprexa®) and lithium during the time I have treated him, but he is more comfortable and feels safer when he can use herbal cannabis for mood stabilization—in his view, more effectively and with fewer side effects. Cannabis seems to stabilize his mood swings and helps him to maintain a baseline mood that is more euthymic (normal) than achieved with the standard mood stabilizers he has taken.

Cannabis has the added feature, for Len, of curbing his appetite for alcohol, consumption of which tends to have a destabilizing and depressive effect. There are other approved medications to help patients remain abstinent from alcohol. Most recently, acamprosate (brand name Campral®) has been approved by the FDA and is effective for that purpose. Any individual who wants help with problem drinking deserves to be considered for treatment with that medication and other therapies that may be indicated. It is well established that patients with bipolar disorder are at high risk for alcohol problems. Len has not had major problems with alcohol abuse. That does not in itself mean that cannabis use prevents him from having drinking problems; he is not inclined to drink at all, and if he does, it is not excessive. But I do know more than a handful of bipolar patients—all of whom have been stabilized on conventional psychiatric medications (for example, valproate and lithium)—who have made the observation in their own lives that they feel better when they have access to cannabis and are less likely to have problematic alcohol use. For some, access to cannabis means alcohol abstinence.

Most of my more seriously ill patients make earnest efforts to stay away from nonprescription drugs altogether, but some have made choices about alcohol use that have led them to prefer cannabis; even when patients have found cannabis helpful, they tend to avoid it because of the law. If substance use of any kind is problematic in my patients, it becomes a focus of treatment. I refer them for elements of dual diagnosis treatment, including group support that cannot be directly provided in our sessions. My patients are aware that I will always make efforts to identify, address, and adequately treat any coexisting psychiatric disorders; treatment for these conditions strengthens prospects for recovery. I find that patients as a rule collaborate effectively in medication management. They are concerned to have no more and no less medication than they need. Most are looking to feel better but not to abuse substances or to experience an unusual or altered state of consciousness as a diversion.

At some point I reached the conclusion that cannabis prohibition is one of the obstacles that interferes with Len's recovery. It may have been when I realized how much in his element he seemed when he was lecturing me about cannabis genetics. In any case, it became clear to me that Len has the natural ability, inclination, and passion to grow his own herbal medicine. He seems a natural-born cannabis connoisseur and farmer. To my mind, this is one substantive way of narrowing the gap between medical and regulatory policy reform trajectories. Why shouldn't Len be able to grow his own cannabis? Why shouldn't he be able to grow it for others for whom growing their own is not a feasible project? Why shouldn't he be compensated reasonably for this activity? Would we as a society have Len on publicly funded disability rather than earning a living putting his cannabis-farming expertise to work? He functions best when he has unrestricted access to cannabis with an opportunity to cultivate specific strains. Growing cannabis for himself and a handful of medical patients could well be a source of income that could supplement Len's earnings from his work playing and recording music. And in psychiatry, supported employment is a well-established evidenced-based practice for persons with serious mental illness.

Under current law, Len cannot grow his own medicine without putting himself at risk of arrest and prosecution. In an ideal world, he might decide to develop his talent as a cannabis grower to complement his work as a musician and recording artist. In an ideal world, such work would help him in his recovery and constitute an important component of his treatment plan. Taxpayer dollars that might have been wasted on arrest and prosecution of someone like Len could be invested instead in job coaching, which at a fraction of the cost would help him become successful in managing his work interests and determining whether he would like to become involved in the movement for safe medicinal access within communities of cannabis consumers. The commodity is in high demand, and increasing medical use by diverse patients increases the value of specific strains as patients seek products to address their specific symptom management needs. Len has knowledge and skills that equip him to participate in such an industry in a meaningful way. Such participation could be therapeutic not only by ensuring access to a preferred herbal substance for medicinal use but also by offering potentially meaningful, challenging, and rewarding work. Normalization of cannabis could facilitate Len's recovery in more than one way. This is constructive activity in the context of a larger community, and it seems to make sense economically.

Abilene and Eden

Michael Pollan writes incisively about co-evolutionary relationships between plants and animals and with special interest in the symbioses between plants and people. Charting that relationship relative to marijuana, his writing captures and elucidates the broader question of the meaning of our fear of herbal substances with the capacity for altering states of awareness. He finds human anxiety about these relationships reflected in the most ancient of stories:

"The *content* of the knowledge Adam and Eve could gain by tasting of the fruit does not matter nearly as much as its form—that is, the very fact that there was spiritual knowledge of *any* kind to be had from a tree: from nature. The new faith sought to break the human bond with magic nature, to disenchant the world of plants and animals by directing our attention to a single God in the sky. Yet Jehovah couldn't very well pretend the tree of knowledge didn't exist, not when generations of plant-worshipping pagans knew better. So the pagan tree is allowed to grow even in Eden, though ringed around now with a strong taboo. Yes, there *is* spiritual knowledge in nature, the new God is acknowledging, and its temptations are fierce, but I am fiercer still. Yield to it, and you will be punished.

"So unfolds the drug war's first battle."[70]

Maybe this war in the garden explains why things like coca leaves and opium poppies have been replaced in American culture with crack cocaine and heroin. Perhaps it also speaks to the gap between fermented grapes and distilled spirits. Alcohol alters human consciousness, arguably less sparingly and more dangerously than marijuana. War in the garden prevents us from engaging in a more thoughtful consideration of the actual nature of substances and their potential for both harms and benefits in both biological (exterior) and psychological (interior) realms. But public conversation pertaining to the American cannabis garden is now occurring. Americans are coming to realize in growing numbers that our marijuana laws represent a nation's troublesome sojourn down an unproductive, wasteful path. We find ourselves on one of Jerry Harvey's trips to Abilene: we seem to be having difficulty managing our agreement that *medicinal* cannabis use is not a criminal offense, and we aren't inclined to see *discretionary* personal use by adults in that way either.

To be clear, my policy advocacy here goes well beyond the recent position statements of the American College of Physicians (ACP) and the American Medical Association (AMA), which do not address questions of recreational, personal, or discretionary adult cannabis use. These position statements represent the most up-to-date and broadly representative statements issued by the medical profession. While the AMA statement indicated that it did not intend to endorse specific state medical marijuana laws, both statements supported protection of patients from criminalization. The ACP Position Paper includes the following: "ACP strongly urges protection from criminal or civil penalties for patients who use medical marijuana as permitted under state laws."[71] At minimum, those words should be adopted as a general statement from the medical profession and translated into federal law. A more adequate policy development would permit adult discretionary access to herbal cannabis for alternative medicinal or therapeutic use—say, for migraine, arthritis, muscle spasm, or insomnia—which is to say that herbal cannabis would become an age-restricted over-the-counter therapeutic or nutraceutical.

In keeping with the *Abilene Paradox*, we discuss the absurdity of American marijuana law in smaller groups but can't seem to create the forum for broad public conversation that translates into sensible reform. We haven't been able to talk about the issue—especially to our kids. We have "just said no." We have given up freedom of choice and speech; we are not happy about it but cannot say so. Banishing ourselves from the garden of choice and wishing we could find our way back, we wander in the desert between Abilene and Eden. Courageous souls have carried torches of reform in the moral darkness. As their courage and numbers have grown, the path has become sufficiently well-lighted for the rest of us to see. Whether that path leads to San Francisco, Amsterdam, or Oxford depends upon your issue: Compassionate care and humanity in medicine? Public health and civil rights? Or commercial enterprise, industry and business opportunity?

In a larger view, these are all our issues. We can no longer afford not to regulate the cannabis trade for reasons related to medicine, public health, and the economy. Schlosser wrote, "This war is over, if you want it." After digging deep into the disastrous charade of American marijuana law, he concluded not only that our society "is caught in the grip of a deep psychosis" but that "the government's behavior will not withstand public scrutiny for long."[72] We have already moved, in our collective mind's eye, beyond scrutiny. As we talk about drug policy, the myth of marijuana gives way to deconstruction. American drug policy has hit rock bottom, and *cannabinomics* might be a gateway back.

PART III

Cannabis and the Economy

From Reefer Madness to Recovery:
Taking Ownership
of an American Commodity

"Maybe now the message will get out there: the so-called "war" isn't working, and it's time to take a new approach!

"Legalization? Maybe, maybe not, but we shouldn't rule anything out. The bottom line is that our country is losing billions of dollars in revenue because we're too short-sighted to learn from our past."[1]

JESSE VENTURA, 2004
38TH GOVERNOR OF MINNESOTA (1999–2003)

"The budgetary implications of legalization exceed those of decriminalization for three reasons. First, legalization eliminates arrests for trafficking in addition to eliminating arrests for possession. Second, legalization saves prosecutorial, judicial, and incarceration expenses; these savings are minimal in the case of decriminalization. Third, legalization allows taxation of marijuana production and sale."[2]

JEFFREY A. MIRON, PH.D., 2005
SENIOR LECTURER IN ECONOMICS, HARVARD UNIVERSITY

IN JUNE OF 2005, economist Jeffrey A. Miron, Ph.D., published a report titled, "The Budgetary Implications of Marijuana Prohibition."[3] Miron, who has taught economics at Boston University and Harvard, was funded in part by the Marijuana Policy Project to prepare the report, which captured the attention of many of his colleagues. With the report's initial online publication, 500 economists posted online "An Open Letter to the President, Congress, Governors and State Legislatures," calling for an open and honest debate on marijuana policy. The letter's signatories included Nobel Laureates Milton Friedman, George Akerlof, and Vernon Smith. The economists wrote:

> "We...urge the country to commence an open and honest debate about marijuana prohibition. We believe such a debate will favor a regime in which marijuana is legal but taxed and regulated like other goods. At a minimum, this debate will force advocates of current policy to show that prohibition has benefits sufficient to justify the cost to taxpayers, foregone tax revenues, and numerous ancillary consequences that result from marijuana prohibition."[4]

Dollars and Sense

Using conservative assumptions that would be likely to bias results downward, Miron estimated that legalizing cannabis would lead to $13.9 billion annually in combined revenue and cost savings. This includes $7.7 billion per year in government expenditures on enforcement of prohibition, with state and local government spending accounting for $5.3 billion and federal government $2.4 billion. In addition to these savings on law enforcement expenditures, state, local, and federal governments would benefit from significant tax revenue. If cannabis were taxed like most other goods, Miron's estimated tax revenue was $2.4 billion; in the more likely scenario in which cannabis is taxed at rates comparable to those of alcohol and tobacco, the estimate came to $6.2 billion. In total, using conservative assumptions including no actual development of the industry and no accounting for the public health impact of decriminalization on communities and families, the savings come to $13.9 billion if cannabis is regulated similarly to alcohol or tobacco.

An analysis by California NORML (National Organization for Reform of Marijuana Laws) yielded an estimate of $1.5 to $2.5 billion in new revenue for the state of California under a tax-and-regulate cannabis policy.[5] The analysis uses estimates of cannabis usage that are still quite conservative. But it does include estimates of economic impact that assume legitimate development of the industry; in this regard it begins to give a clearer picture of the potential economic benefits inherent in marijuana policy reform. The California NORML analysis estimates an overall increase in economic activity of $8 to $13 billion. Extrapolating from the wine industry, this involves the creation of 36,000 to 58,000 new jobs for Californians, with $1.2 to $1.7 billion in legal wages generating additional income and business taxes for the state. Even this analysis, which points to the even greater yield of economic benefits to be expected under tax-and-regulate policy, does not include potential public health or health benefits that have additional important economic dimensions. Examples of the former would include reduced impact of criminalization on communities and naturally occurring alcohol substitution, while examples of the latter would include medicinal use as appropriate, including cases of alcohol substitution for harm reduction.

In Miron's study, estimated tax revenue under an excise-tax scenario (or taxed like alcohol and tobacco) is $6.2 billion. If this figure is used to project estimates of associated economic activity based upon the California NORML analysis, associated tax revenue estimates increase to well above the conservative estimates of Miron because of the range and quantity of revenue-generating and taxable activity under the assumption of some further development of a cannabis industry. Bruce Mirken, policy advocate with the Marijuana Policy Project, has cited a range from $10 to $40 billion as the net revenue accessible through a tax-and-regulate approach to the management of marijuana.[6] A mid-range figure of $25 billion annually would likely be a conservative estimate, with probable potential to double with any significant allowance for industry development. None of these estimates takes into account other industrial applications of hemp beyond human internal consumption.

Normalization of cannabis in American society, with tax-and-regulate integration into the American economy, has the potential to be a positive economic force. Cannabis reform, followed up with a commitment to look at the drug war as a whole in terms of opportunities to move toward a public health model for managing drug control and away from the criminalization context where nonviolent offenses are concerned, has the potential to generate substantial resources that could reasonably be directed toward the funding of healthcare. Such redirection is already implicit in early efforts to rethink policy as it relates to offenders with substance abuse problems, including those dually diagnosed with mental illness. Initiatives replacing incarceration with treatment represent a shift from criminal justice approaches to an investment in healthcare and public health.

Low Hanging Fruit

Transformation of the war on drugs from a criminal justice enterprise to a public health agenda would quite naturally begin with a rethinking and a reformation of our society's approach to the management of cannabis. Cannabis represents "low hanging fruit" for drug policy reform, and the potential fiscal impact is substantial. For comparison purposes, the upper estimate of the combined annual savings and revenue to be potentially generated by an economically integrated cannabis industry ($40 billion) exceeds the 2009 U.S. Department of Veterans Affairs (VA) medical care budget request ($38.7 billion) and is well over the total 2010 budget request for the National Institutes of Health (NIH: $31 billion). The more modest $25 billion mean figure (the midpoint between the annual savings and revenue estimates of $10 billion and $40 billion) amounts to more than five times the combined 2010 budget requests for the Substance Abuse and Mental Health Services Administration (SAMHSA: $3.4 billion) and the National Institutes of Mental Health (NIMH: nearly $1.5 billion).

Both comparisons are conservative, with only minimal allowance for expansion of a cannabis industry. Working with the more conservative $25 billion figure, the tax-and-regulate integration of cannabis into the legitimate economy could pay for the Economic Stimulus Act of 2008 over a six-year period

($152 billion) and over a ten-year period generate nearly a third of the economic stimulus package approved by Congress and signed by the President in early 2009 ($789 billion). Given that the $40 billion figure is likely still a quite conservative estimate, it would not be far-fetched to imagine that the actual figure could be well over half the cost of the 2009 stimulus package over a ten-year period.

Some have estimated that a more thoroughgoing drug policy paradigm shift—from criminalization to the "public health war" envisioned by former Baltimore mayor Kurt Schmoke[7]— could free up $70 billion or more annually,[8] an amount that approximates the 2010 discretionary budget request of the U.S. Department of Health and Human Services ($78 billion). Resources of that magnitude would go a long way reinvested in public health and nationwide healthcare reform. These figures amount to only a fraction of the mandatory federal healthcare expenditures on Medicare, Medicaid, and other mandated programs in a given year ($734 billion in 2009), but $70 billion is roughly 80 percent of the projected annual cost over a decade of the healthcare reform bill passed by the United States Senate on Christmas Eve 2009.

Once again, none of the estimates of economic trade-offs with cannabis policy reform includes assessments of medical and public health impact in the areas of medical and pharmaceutical utilization; potential reductions in alcohol-related mortality and morbidity; or the impact of decriminalization on individuals, families, and communities afflicted with the adverse health consequences of a criminalizing drug war. Moreover, none of these estimates addresses the impact of cannabis policy reform on the potential of the hemp industry in areas other than production for human consumption. Various potential industrial uses of hemp have long been known to hold significant promise.

Cannabis is low hanging fruit for an America contemplating next steps in developing a nonpunitive public health model of drug control policy. Because the issue of drug policy is so vast, far-reaching and complex, transformation cannot be achieved instantaneously. But certain things can be done. Steps toward immediate decriminalization and medical regulation of access to cannabis can be taken, even as a commission is established to determine optimum context and strategy for public regulation of cannabis and the management of the growth of related industries. We need to begin to talk about the American experience of finding ourselves on the road to Abilene, but this has been difficult because silence on the issue has been the public norm for a long time. Currently, however, there are too many factors converging on the question of how cannabis will be managed for that silence to continue.

Why is cannabis the natural starting point for drug policy reform? There are numerous reasons:

- Americans produce and use a lot of cannabis; it has been reported to be the largest cash crop in the U.S., having surpassed corn and totaling more than corn and wheat combined;
- There are roughly as many marijuana arrests as there are arrests for all other drugs combined, and most of those arrests are for possession;
- From a public health standpoint, there is no scientific basis for suggesting that the risks associated with cannabis use in the overall population come even close to the mortality, morbidity, and overall risk—with the exception of the risk of criminalization—associated with alcohol or tobacco, which are legally available and taxed and regulated;
- In fact, a critical mass of primary consumers and health-care providers—a minority, to be sure, but not a minority

that can be ignored—has found cannabis useful as an alternative to alcohol in cases where individuals experience worsening or recurrent symptoms of physical or mental illness with alcohol consumption;

- There are numerous medical uses, not acknowledged by current federal marijuana policies, that are the driving forces of the medical marijuana revolution in which at least 13 states have established provisions for medicinal access with continued building of momentum on the medical access issue;

- The groundwork for moving forward has been more than adequately laid: President Nixon's Commission, President Carter's intent to move forward on those recommendations, Judge Young's 1988 administrative law ruling on marijuana scheduling, the history and existence of the federal compassionate use program, and the state-level movements that mostly involve—but are not entirely limited to—medical use. In addition, DEA Administrative Law Judge Mary Ellen Bittner recently ruled, in the University of Massachusetts appeal to the DEA for license to grow medicinal grade cannabis, that the federal government has impeded access to medicinal grade marijuana for medical research purposes.

- FDA approval of GW Pharmaceutical's Sativex® for use as a pain reliever in treatment-resistant cancer cases seems likely within the next two to three years. But access to cannabis extracts for medicinal use should be restricted neither to treatment-resistant cases nor to cancer pain alone. Approval of Sativex® as medicine will make it possible for physicians to prescribe it for purposes other than cancer pain. But the potential applications are sufficiently broad to warrant a faster approval track and greater breadth of medicinal applications;

- There is significant potential revenue to be generated by moving in this direction at a time of crisis for healthcare and the overall economy; and
- Normalization of cannabis, as juxtaposed importantly with alcohol and tobacco, also provides an opportunity for better education and prevention in the area of substance abuse. No one wants to encourage kids to use marijuana, but everyone needs to have accurate information about the relative harmfulness of cannabis as compared with alcohol and tobacco.

As drug policy reform progresses with cannabis at the cutting edge, state and federal governments could work synergistically instead of in opposition. The current federal executive administration has already, in effect, expressed its intent to respect the interests represented by the previously proposed Hinchey-Rohrabacher amendment introduced several years in a row into the U.S. House of Representatives. Specifically, this involves limiting DEA spending—not necessarily decreasing its budget—to prevent the use of taxpayer dollars to conduct raids on dispensaries and homes of consumers trying to work within state laws to create access to cannabis for medicinal use.

The federal government could move to implement Judge Frances Young's 1988 recommendation that cannabis be rescheduled as a Schedule II controlled substance—although many knowledgeable clinical practitioners, scientists, and medicinal consumers would argue that Schedule II is overly restrictive. Those arguments have considerable merit, as evidenced most clearly by the fact that dronabinol (THC)—the most psychoactive of the constituents in marijuana, yet the only one of those chemical compounds that is already available synthetically as prescription medicine—was moved some years ago from Schedule II to Schedule III.

By comparison, stimulants like methylphenidate (Ritalin®, Concerta®, Focalin®), amphetamine (Adderall®, Dexedrine®, Vyvanse®), and methamphetamine (Desoxyn®) are Schedule II, whereas benzodiazepines such as alprazolam (Xanax®), clonazepam (Klonopin®), and diazepam (Valium®)—with anti-anxiety, antiseizure and muscle-relaxing effects—are classified under the much less restrictive Schedule IV. There would appear to be no clear medical reason for classifying either THC or herbal cannabis in a more restrictive control schedule than benzodiazepines, let alone for reclassifying THC once again to make it as restricted as methamphetamine or morphine. The current standing of cannabinoids, with THC classified as a Schedule III medicine while herbal cannabis remains in Schedule I along with heroin, represents incoherent policy.

Picking up where President Carter left off, the federal government could implement recommendations from President Nixon's Commission. Initial steps would decriminalize possession of relatively small amounts of cannabis, as well as limited cultivation for personal use. In 2009 Representative Barney Frank (D–Massachusetts) introduced proposed legislation that would decriminalize possession of up to three and one-half ounces of herbal cannabis.[9] Passage of such legislation could be the beginning of a collaborative process between federal and state governments that would work toward a rational and healthier approach to cannabis control.

To think in terms of more definitive steps forward, including struggling with the question whether herbal cannabis is best classified under a medicinal control schedule at all, a federal commission could be established and given a year to plan the regulatory framework within which first steps in economic integration would proceed. States could continue with their respective medical cannabis programs. New federal regulations could allow for grades of cannabis based on a potential spectrum of standardization parameters that would remain to be determined. For example, an herbal-genetic model might standardize herbal remedies in terms of cultivation histories. Such standardization parameters might be complementary to, or alternative to, standardization by ratio of known important compounds as has been pioneered by GW Pharmaceutical. Its product Sativex® is a highly standardized medicinal cannabis extract, available in Canada with indications for multiple sclerosis and cancer pain, and appears to be rigorously specified in terms of these and perhaps other parameters.

It would be interesting to know more about the observations of scientists at GW and others regarding relationships between variables of focus that are pharmaceutical in nature (for example, ratios of specified pharmacologically active compounds of interest) and those that are more qualitative or categorical as might be the case with specifications of herbal remedies (for example, genetic history of cultivar). Neither of these options follows the projections of the Institute of Medicine (IOM) Report, namely, that the future of cannabinoid medicine lies in the isolation and application of single cannabinoid compounds or synthetic drugs with similar or overlapping medicinal effects. Rather, these options represent two ways of thinking about herbal cannabis extracts and their quality management. In a cannabis tax-and-regulate policy environment, there might even be hierarchies of standardization including standards that come into play in establishing medicinal and therapeutic grades of cannabis production.

It seems reasonable to stipulate that GW Pharmaceutical has capabilities in medicinal cannabis standardization that would be exceeded by none. GW Pharmaceutical might well be able to market its products not only as highly standardized pharmaceuticals but also as highly specific cultivation products standardized under alternative regulatory models pertaining to herbal remedies. Interestingly, it does not seem that we are yet in a position to rule out the possibility that some degree of variation in product specifics may have value in preventing the development of tolerance to effects that may be therapeutically important. Len, for example, knows what type of cannabis he finds most consistently mood stabilizing, but he finds it helpful to rotate his primary strain with other varieties on a periodic basis; this procedure apparently helps to maintain the potency of the mood-stabilizing effects of his primary medicinal strain. I do not know the extent to which such variability may have been observed to be important in other medical areas such as pain management, but the complementary nature of the pain management effects of cannabis and opiates—and in particular the potential for a more occasional rather than continuous use of opiate compounds when cannabis is taken as the mainstay of treatment—suggests the possibility of analogous relationships among cannabis strains.

Health Economics

In no case does any of this proposed regulatory reform prevent the pharmaceutical industry from developing mono-molecular compounds or single-molecule drugs with cannabinoid activity and medicinal properties. However, in contrast to the environment implied or presumed by the 1999 IOM Report, which explicitly defers to the pharmaceutical industry over and above the healthcare consumer, a stakeholder-inclusive approach to cannabis regulation would create a landscape in which cannabinoid pharmaceutical products would actually have to demonstrate to consumers and physicians that they were preferable—for any number of reasons including effectiveness, side effects, safety, and cost—to herbal cannabis. Cannabinoid pharmaceutical development in the new consumer-driven healthcare system would be free to proceed, but as a practical matter new products would have to prove themselves in a consumer-driven medicine market.

Such a system does not undermine evidence-based practice but rather requires that the evidence take into account the experiences of those who actually have to use the medicine. In the final analysis, whether persons with AIDS, MS, hepatitis, or arthritis find oral THC or the inhaled vaporization or combustion products of whole herbal cannabis more satisfactory for relief of any of several major symptom clusters (for example, nausea, anorexia, neurological or inflammatory pain, muscle spasms, irritable mood) is a question that can be answered only with direct input from the individual consumer. I am not making the argument that there is no difference between the data we acquire through scientifically conducted basic, preclinical and clinical studies and the data acquired through real-world clinical practice and the experience of the consumer in recovery. But that difference does not define a cutoff point beyond which information is useless; rather, it delineates different kinds of data that can be weighted differently for different purposes.

For example, an insurance company might decide that it will not pay for medical marijuana use in posttraumatic stress disorder (PTSD) because it is not evidence-based practice. Fair enough. But that needn't interfere with an individual's paying for it out of pocket if he or she finds that it is more effective, better tolerated, or otherwise preferable to standard treatments that might be covered by insurance. Nor, however, should any of this information prevent a different insurance company from evaluating pharmacoeconomic and health economic data and coming to the conclusion either that (1) coverage of medical marijuana for use in PTSD is cost-effective or that (2) coverage of consumer-driven care generally is more cost-effective, whether with respect to consumer choice of cannabis as an alternative medicine or in general as a feature of inherent value to all participants—consumers, providers, and payers in a health-care system.

Naturalistic, real-world, system-level, and individual clinical follow-up observations will provide data to answer questions about both benefits and problems, on a population basis, associated with cannabis use. What is the impact on health? What is the relationship between cannabis access and health, individually and on a population basis? Will there be cost savings from reduced pharmaceutical expenditures? These are important health-economic questions, which may yield surprising answers. When Garry, the medicinal cannabis consumer introduced at the beginning of the book and discussed in Part II, and I were working in Washington with Americans for Safe Access, led by Steph Sherer and Caren Woodson, I had the opportunity to meet another medicinal cannabis patient from Portland, Oregon. He told us—and members of Congress—about his experience using herbal cannabis for a condition very much like Garry's. He suffers from rheumatoid arthritis and ankylosing spondylitis.

Unlike Garry, this individual spends the majority of his time in a wheelchair. His physician has prescribed a state-of-the-art anti-inflammatory medication that costs roughly $1,600 per month to take. But by using cannabis medicinally, the consumer finds that he can stretch a month's worth of the expensive anti-inflammatory medication to last over a period of about four months. As a result, the monthly cost of this new, pharmaceutically patented anti-inflammatory medication is reduced to $400. In addition, the consumer reports that with this approach he experiences more effective symptom relief. From his perspective, cannabis combined with the new medication is the best overall solution. Whether such a self-modified regimen would be effective for other patients is unknown. But there are other medicinal cannabis consumers who report that with cannabis as the mainstay of treatment for chronic pain and inflammation, they use fewer opiate analgesics, have less distress over side effects, and have less of a problem with tolerance to the opiate medications. The opiate pain relievers are then more likely to be effective when taken intermittently at standard doses.

If the above type of finding extends to other patients, it will have very significant economic implications within the health-care sector alone. Is there any reason to believe that it might? During the time I have known Garry, I have seen him in the aftermath of the raid on his home and have tracked his self-reported medication use during that period and in the months and years over which his access to cannabis as medicine was restored. Garry cited significant decreases in quality of life for a number of reasons after the raid. With his home-grown medicine confiscated, he spent more money on prescription pain relievers and experienced the return of unwanted side effects. Injuries he sustained in the raid—the irony of his case cutting across medical and decriminalization trajectories—make a true pharmacoeconomic analysis difficult. But by his account he was unable to optimize his use of pain-relieving medications. Growing cannabis at home in cooperation with a handful of other patients, he kept down the overall cost of his prescription pain relievers and at the same time felt much better.

The health-economic dimensions of cannabis as alternative medicine will in time be subject to analysis by insurance companies, services researchers, and increasing numbers of policy analysts. Some of this work may have been done already, but I have yet to see systematic, aggregate, or population-based figures examining the potential pharmacoeconomics or health economic cost offsets of cannabis therapeutics. While the overall economic arguments for normalizing the cannabis trade are compelling enough in their own right, the health economics of cannabis—a field of scientific inquiry awaiting development by economists and health professionals—will prove to be incisive.

Will access to medicinal cannabis affect patient healthcare utilization? Will frequency of visits to emergency rooms, urgent care clinics, and other indicators of healthcare utilization be likely to decrease as a result of a shift of some fraction of alcohol consumers from personal use of alcohol to personal use of cannabis? Will some potential cases of alcoholism be prevented as a result of choices made in early adulthood for cannabis as an alternative for personal use? Under current policy, an adult can choose cannabis as an alternative to alcohol only at peril of arrest and prosecution. As Steve Fox, Paul Armentano, and Mason Tvert of the SAFER organization have reflected in the subtitle of their 2009 book, marijuana policy in the United States is, quite literally, *driving people to drink!*[10]

Denver voters supported the SAFER Alcohol-Marijuana Equalization Initiative in 2005, and 41 percent of Colorado voters supported taking the initiative statewide in 2006. The logic of the SAFER initiative is so coherent that the unfolding of something like it as law across the country seems inevitable. This issue is a public health platform. Therapeutic use of cannabis could be regulated at federal and state levels, and medical guidelines could be developed. Permissible uses of cannabis under a health-oriented, as opposed to an abuse-oriented, concept could range from clinical symptom reduction (for example, pain, muscle spasms, nausea) and prevention (for example, migraines, seizures, chronic PTSD symptoms, alcohol problems, and possibly some cyclic mood disorders) to nonspecific herbal therapy as an adjunctive component of broader and more comprehensive stress management strategies.

I have already stated that as a psychiatrist, I do not at this time advocate use of cannabis as first-line or primary treatment for any psychiatric disorder. However, I believe we cannot rule out the possibility that cannabis may be of adjunctive or secondary benefit for an unknown number of psychiatric patients with mood and/or anxiety disorders, not necessarily because it serves as primary pharmacotherapy but because it helps the individual avoid consumption of alcohol, which is not uncommonly much more problematic and destabilizing. Time will tell whether more specific medicinal applications in behavioral health will emerge based on scientific support for current consumer claims and the shepherding of herbal cannabis medicinal products through the relevant regulatory approval processes.

Based on the known, widespread American interest in cannabis availability for adult personal use, it seems reasonable to integrate medical access and broader policy trajectories (decriminalization generally, the SAFER approach, and tax-and-regulate proposals along the lines of Nevada's 2006 Question 7) by way of an expanded medicinal availability on an age-restricted basis. The SAFER approach as contextualized here is fundamentally a public health proposal, poised on a civil rights platform, that makes medicinal and therapeutic use possible without specifying exactly how that is to be regulated (some cannabinoid medicines may in fact warrant classification in a highly restrictive control schedule, while others may be appropriate for age-restricted over-the-counter access). I would suggest that FDA approval of GW Pharmaceutical's Sativex® be accomplished on a fast track, without limiting its intended use to terminal illness or tertiary intervention targeted at esoteric disease states. It should subsequently be studied and evaluated as to its suitability for release over-the-counter on an age-restricted basis. Although such access may or may not be appropriate in the case of Sativex® or any other specific product, the matter now warrants serious consideration.

Physicians and healthcare consumers need language with which to have public conversation in these areas; the language of cannabis therapeutics is surfacing as states line up to be the next to pass a new, second-generation medical marijuana law. The language of cannabis therapeutics is not the same as the language of drug abuse and addiction, but the latter has for years been the only officially recognized language for discussing marijuana in the U.S.—the port of entry for legal access to marijuana for research in the U.S. being through the National Institute on Drug Abuse (NIDA). Federal drug policy reform can begin by supporting a language within which therapeutic aspects of cannabis can be discussed. There is every reason for such support to be bipartisan in nature; medicinal cannabis has, in the past, been a bipartisan issue. The 1978 medical provision amending the Illinois Cannabis Control Act of 1971 is a case in point: introduced with bipartisan sponsorship, the bill passed by an overwhelming majority.

New Gold Standard?

It seems reasonable to surmise, given the limited information available for comparison, that GW Pharmaceutical sets a new gold standard for cannabis products. The politics of that fact alone would seem to require and dictate some negotiated privilege with respect to entry into the legitimate medicinal cannabis market. But entry onto the playing field by American cannabis manufacturers operating under state law must also be ensured and facilitated by federal policy. This important point warrants reinforcement: our federal government currently actively denies American cannabis producers the opportunity to enter into business in the open marketplace, in which the demand for cannabis—for medicinal and personal use—is quite high. It does so by maintaining a federal monopoly on production in addition to the prohibitive Schedule I control classification, predicated on the belief that cannabis can be understood only as a substance of abuse. At the same time, it actively works with a British company to set the stage for importing whole herbal cannabis-based medicinal extracts at prices yet to be determined.

The medicinal cannabis extract that is first in line for FDA approval, Sativex®, is not a single-molecule cannabinoid medicine as envisioned by the IOM report. It is not even a simple mixture of two cannabinoid molecules or chemical compounds, as described by reporters and physicians unfamiliar with GW Pharmaceutical's production methodology. GW Pharmaceutical CEO Geoffrey Guy, M.D., has described the medicinal cannabis extract production process as involving an effort to preserve the entire array of naturally occurring chemical compounds found in herbal cannabis—so that the use of GW's liquid cannabis extracts as medicine involves exposure to the same groups of molecules found in the natural cannabis plant.[11] Production of Sativex® or other medicinal cannabis extracts, according to GW Pharmaceutical methods as described by the company's CEO, does not involve the combining of two isolated chemical compounds; rather, the product is standardized according to a ratio of those compounds within the naturally occurring cannabinoid array.

To be clear, this is medical marijuana knocking at the front door of the American healthcare system as federally regulated through the FDA. The medication under consideration and currently being researched is an herbal cannabis extract. The extract is highly standardized, using a specific index, but it is an extract that is described by the company's CEO as attempting to preserve the full array of naturally occurring groups of molecules. There are potentially other ratios or indices based on the same two chemical compounds and potentially other relevant compounds. Is anyone else making similar extracts? No and yes. No—at least I am unaware of reports of other clinical trials of liquid herbal cannabis extracts for possible FDA approval. But yes, you can find similar liquid extracts in medical marijuana dispensaries in California. But then again, no, the producers of those extracts in California are not presenting rigorous data on either composition or clinical efficacy as GW Pharmaceutical has done. On the other hand—yes, some of these extracts might be as well-produced and even as effective as the GW medication, but no one knows because those products haven't been studied.

The implications of accelerated and impending cannabis policy reform, at state and local levels, for a company such as GW Pharmaceutical—manufacturing essentially the only recognized cannabis-based medicinal extracts—need to be understood and addressed. Regulatory requirements in the distribution of FDA-approved pharmaceuticals, herbal medicines or remedies, and dietary supplements must ensure that Americans are not denied business opportunities in the marketplace. Medicinal growers in California and other states are no doubt working on ways to achieve and improve standardization of their products. There must be opportunities for business entry into the market of high-grade medicinal cannabis extracts, as well as standardization and regulatory processes that support trade at standards of quality control appropriate for herbal remedies. Such standards, together with a taxonomy of appropriate levels of cannabis regulation, could be established by a new stakeholder-inclusive cannabis regulatory commission charged with planning and implementing regulation of the cannabis trade. The plan would include a time line with reasonably specifiable goals and an intended outcome clear in its concept but appropriately flexible in its details.

The cannabis industry in California, or anywhere else in the United States, isn't capable of competing on the open market because herbal cannabis is not a legal American commodity. So maybe the American home-grown medicinal cannabis extracts are as good as those produced by GW Pharmaceutical, and maybe they are not; in fact we don't know. We can't know under current restrictions because only one company—a company from outside the United States—has been able to position itself in the pharmaceutical market with an herbal cannabis product. But rather than help position American entrepreneurs for participation in the medicinal cannabis market competition process, American federal government has responded to the medical marijuana movement by attempting—unsuccessfully—to quash local cannabis supply initiatives by deploying aggressive quasi-military law enforcement teams against American citizens.

Cannabis Crisis, Ownership Opportunity

License to provide cannabis for consumers—according to various potential parameters of specificity and standardization—should be based on quality control, not on who's got control. You don't have to look far to find people who are discouraged by observations about relationships between the pharmaceutical industry and processes governing drug approval and regulation. Nor will it be hard to find individuals who have turned to complementary and alternative medicine because they have struggled with side effects of FDA-approved medications. If there are questions about relative product performance of extracts produced under less stringent and well-controlled laboratory conditions than those established by GW Pharmaceutical, those questions should be empirically researched. That is, differently branded products including both medicinal cannabis extracts and raw herbal cannabis itself can be compared to one another.

The quality of herbal cannabis is undoubtedly variable. It may be clean or contaminated, relatively ripe or immature, potent or weak, one strain or another, relatively rich or poor in relevant cannabinoid compounds, relatively effective for this or that problem—say, pain relief or mood stabilization—with this or that aroma, at relatively high or low cost, and relatively high or low in consistency from one batch to another. All of these ways of assessing product quality and better informing consumers become available in a commercial environment. Individuals might grow their own cannabis strains—with greater or lesser technical sophistication—at home for personal use, but if they sought to market and distribute them to others they would have to meet regulatory and trade requirements. Violations of regulatory standards, including licensing requirements, can be prosecuted and penalized as such. Wherever feasible—for example, with regulatory violation only and no human harm—financial penalties can be used instead of incarceration. Fines have potential to enhance public revenue; imprisonment drains it.

Some law enforcement officials might choose to work in roles that help establish aspects of the infrastructure of a cannabis therapeutics program. One such role would be security; other roles would be establishing and operationalizing reasonable regulatory requirements. Many other law enforcement personnel would be free of the make-work of marijuana prosecution. Officials at every level of law enforcement could focus on more important matters. Instead of thinking about how to eradicate drugs, they could focus on reducing crime. They could begin to develop strategies through which the resources freed up by virtually eliminating marijuana arrests could be used to focus on making communities safer.

Although such projects as this must be executed carefully and deliberately, it is clear that the benefits of decriminalizing the war on drugs in favor of some form of combined medical and public health management strategy extend beyond cannabis. The 10,000-member organization LEAP (Law Enforcement Against Prohibition) has called for a rethinking of drug prohibition across the board, with various members arguing for the superior safety and fiscal responsibility of regulation over criminalization. Yet with cannabis as a reasonable first step, the problems and opportunities associated with transition from a criminal justice to a public health model of drug control policy will likely become rapidly apparent in the early stages of implementation. Cannabis is the obvious pilot project for any systematic transition from a criminalization model to a public health model of drug control.

The linking of cannabis policy with broader drug control policy reform adds to the transformative potential in both arenas. The low-hanging-fruit quality of marijuana creates an incentive for relatively rapid movement on cannabis inasmuch as resources freed up with cannabis decriminalization can be invested in planning and implementation of reasonable next steps in a transition to public health management of substance-related problems. Ultimately, the logic of this process cascades toward taxation and regulation, with law enforcement geared toward regulatory violations with an emphasis on consumer protection. In the case of distilled spirits or hard liquor, the purchaser must be at least 21 years of age, and the manufacturer is required to represent the product according to established standards of accuracy under laws governing the responsibilities of vendors to their customers. Repeal of alcohol prohibition made it far less likely that a customer might purchase something even more toxic—for example, methyl alcohol (or methanol) instead of the ethyl alcohol (or ethanol) that is acceptable for beverages. In fact, historically, repeal of alcohol prohibition was at least partially driven by concerns about consumption of unknown alcoholic substances with more severe toxicities. For example, methanol intoxication has been well known to be associated with neurological and retinal damage and even blindness.

The DEA has recently undertaken a process of revising the language governing the derivation of the Schedule III medication dronabinol (brand name Marinol®, or THC); in anticipation of its patent expiration, would-be manufacturers have pointed out that extraction of this cannabinoid component from the natural whole plant is less expensive than its current means of production by synthesis in the laboratory. The DEA's proposed rule change would accommodate this finding by allowing the medication to be extracted from natural herbal cannabis. Such a rule revision will, in turn, pave the way—intentionally or not—for the entry of standardized medicinal cannabis extracts produced through processes such as those employed by GW Pharmaceutical in the manufacture of Sativex®. In short, the rescheduling of cannabis—ironically, as the vehicle for THC—is underway but hidden as inexplicit just like our nation's long journey to Abilene. The question is whether federal government will continue to *attempt* to prevent Americans from owning their home-grown commodity. There would appear to be no plausible medical justification for doing so and clear economic reasons for not doing so.

Whether there may be financial conflicts of interest—for example, key policymakers holding stock in GW Pharmaceutical—is unknown to me but might warrant further investigation if current marijuana policy continues much longer. It stands to reason that stockholders in a company that makes the only medicinal cannabis extracts available could have an economic interest in restricting entry of other herbal cannabis products into the medicinal market—including whole herbal cannabis if it is a legitimate competitor. *The current federal mo-*

nopoly on marijuana production ensures that GW Pharmaceutical will have no legitimate American competitors. The holding of such stock by government employees with a disproportionate stake in marijuana prohibition as a policy agenda and influence over the political process driving it might create a conflict of interest. At this point it may not matter, because the market position and technical accomplishments of GW Pharmaceutical as a leader in cannabis neuroscience and creator of a new gold standard will have to be acknowledged and accommodated in the rolling out of a regulatory structure and market participation process.

The availability of oral tinctures and sprays in California medicinal cannabis dispensaries operating under supportive state law (Proposition 215) raises a fascinating question. How long will those businesses—dispensaries and their suppliers—have to wait before they can put these products into the mainstream market? GW Pharmaceutical is knocking on the door of the United States pharmaceutical market with a much more highly standardized but similar product. It may be useful for anti-marijuana crusaders to emphasize the differences between Sativex® and California-grown medicinal tinctures, but in some contexts it may be appropriate to emphasize the similarities.

It seems reasonable, in my view, to stipulate up front that GW Pharmaceutical makes the best standardized medicinal cannabis extracts in the world—the enterprise is made easier when there are no legal competitors—but they don't make the only medicinal cannabis extracts in the world. Some California producers of medicinal cannabis tinctures are moving toward increasing standardization of their production. Is there any reason to think that alternatives to GW Pharmaceutical—with equal, more or less similar, or even superior quality control—are not possible? Whether there are any dispensaries capable of delivering products of comparable standardization at the current time is unknown to me, but cannot be ruled out. In the United States, prohibition, a federal monopoly, and aggressive government enforcement have retarded the development of cannabis therapeutics, and, as a result, Americans have suffered. To clarify, the issue is not just about lack of medicinal cannabis access on the part of potential consumers or even about the economic desirability of taxing the sale of medical marijuana in California or other states. More than that, *the problem involves depriving Californians and other American entrepreneurs of the right to compete on the open cannabinoid medicine market.*

It is an insufficient response to this critique to cite development of synthetic cannabinoid molecules that may be underway by the pharmaceutical industry, because American consumers have made it clear that they also want access to alternative medicines including whole herbal cannabis products. A California company or entrepreneur cannot present an herbal cannabis extract to the FDA as GW Pharmaceutical has done, because doing that work in the United States is against the law. For that reason alone it is only a matter of time until the law—fundamentally at odds with American values of individual liberty and opportunity—is changed. The prohibitive Marihuana Tax Act of 1937 was ruled unconstitutional by the U.S. Supreme Court before being superseded by the Controlled Substances Act of 1970.[12] Courts have ruled in favor of cannabis consumers using a medical defense and accessing the federal compassionate use program (for example, Robert Randall), and it has now been more than 20 years since *Judge Young of the DEA ruled that marijuana, by federal law, belongs in a control schedule that permits medical use.*

Various analyses and commentators, including the findings of economist Jeffrey Miron and of California NORML, have identified significant potential economic gains to be realized through taxation and regulation of herbal cannabis. However, there are numerous potential economic benefits that haven't even been touched by these estimates. Health economic and public health benefits are among them. But in the current economic environment, it is important to underscore that the potential economic gains associated with cannabis change involve the correction of an imbalanced and economically detrimental federal monopoly that not only works against consumers and consumer-driven healthcare but also stifles entrepreneurship through arbitrary restraint of trade and a de facto exportation of business opportunity overseas. Now the U.S. prepares, as it moves through Phase III Sativex® trials for treatment of cancer pain, to invite a British company to sell Americans products—at an unknown but possibly exorbitant cost—that have undeniable similarities with those available under state-authorized access but home-grown and manufactured beneath the regulatory radar and the cloud of criminalization.

Professor Lyle Craker, a biologist at the University of Massachussetts at Amherst, applied for and was denied federal permission to grow research grade cannabis in his laboratory in order to study the medicinal properties of various strains.[13] On the appeal for the license to grow cannabis for research purposes, DEA Administrative Law Judge Mary Ellen Bittner ruled in favor of Craker and the University of Massachusetts and cited a shortage of marijuana available for medical research purposes.[14] Meanwhile, some California buyers' organizations have collected their own naturalistic data by attempting to correlate identifiable characteristics of various strains of herbal cannabis with the therapeutic benefits reported by medicinal consumers; the Wo/Men's Alliance for Medical Marijuana (WAMM) made notable progress in this area before their operation was raided in the early part of the first decade of the 21st century. Even now, some medicinal cannabis providers operating under state law are making strategic decisions about investing in equipment (for example, gas chromatography and mass spectrometry) that can be used to refine their quality control efforts and improve standardization. Such investments, and perhaps other strategies, could increase the likelihood of their being able to compete with suppliers such as GW Pharmaceutical.

Sativex® would appear to represent nothing less than a new gold standard in pharmaceutical grade alternative medicine. But other vendors must be allowed to compete in the open market, and although the historical complexity of this transition compels us to acknowledge the strategic position of GW in this market, the setting of regulatory parameters for cannabis is a process that needs to include input from alternative practitioners and from consumers. Cannabis regulation requires representation from a broader stakeholder constituency. Provisions must be made for the possibility that regulation would extend at minimum to approximate THC concentration and standard cultivar information and be open to the development of sophisticated quantitative indices of standardization along the lines of those developed by GW Pharmaceutical (for example, the approximately 1:1 ratio of CBD to THC that characterizes Sativex®).

The labeling of cannabis products by strain or THC concentration is simplistic by comparison to the sophistication of the standardization process represented by Sativex®. Nonetheless, such labels can be useful in identifying variables associated with positive or negative individual responses in terms of both therapeutic and adverse effects. Simple identification of approximate THC concentration may be sufficient to redirect some cannabis users to less potent forms of the herb with favorable results for those individuals. That means neither that THC concentration alone will be important or adequate in determining appropriate cannabinoid treatment for most individuals nor that all individuals with schizophrenia or vulnerability to psychosis will be adversely affected by THC; clinical accounts from patients indicate otherwise.

GW pharmaceutical researchers have experimented to some degree with medicinal cannabis extracts standardized to other THC-to-CBD ratios. Whether any of those products have the ability to consistently relieve symptoms of psychotic mental illness remains to be determined, and the question should be researched. It would be helpful for some persons with behavioral health problems to be able to avoid consumption of cannabis products that historically have exacerbated their symptoms or have known potential to do so, and in some cases the process may be as simple as making distinctions among cannabis strains in terms of their relative potency as determined by THC concentration. A regulated cannabis market would make this possible. Whether recommended by a physician or not, some persons with schizophrenia or other psychotic illness may choose to use cannabis because it has other effects that are relatively reliable in their experience. In particular, some patients with histories of serious mental illness report that the effects of cannabis in their experience include decreased anxiety or irritability and elimination of outbursts of rage and violent behavior.

Some persons with such symptoms, but without a history of psychosis, will be so cogent in their reports of therapeutic benefit from cannabis that the risk benefit analysis will be easy. Patients treated for mood disorders should be advised by their physicians to stay away from strains that make them feel worse, just as we generally advise them to abstain from alcohol. But to suggest that abstinence from all forms of cannabis is imperative for individuals with mood or anxiety disorders—as though the medical risks for them were comparable to those associated with alcohol—would be a gross misrepresentation of our actual experience with and knowledge of these substances. Practically speaking, we physicians often counsel patients in that way—

which is justifiable only because of the behavioral health risks of criminalization; marijuana is less a "gateway" drug than a substance subject to "gateway" laws.

It is important for patients with any psychiatric illness to be aware that the fact that alcohol is legal does not make it safer *for them*. Even when it comes to schizophrenia or other psychotic mental illness, not all persons suffering from such disorders find that their condition is worsened by cannabis. For such individuals there is no basis for suggesting that alcohol is less harmful to their health. In clinical practice, alcohol is much more consistently a factor in the exacerbation of mood and anxiety disorders than cannabis; for many individuals cannabis use may be more often associated with symptom relief than worsening of mental illness.

In fact, there is abundant reason to believe that generally of the two, alcohol is the more dangerous to health both physically and behaviorally for many if not most consumers. Still, it is important for the consumer to be able to make choices (not just between pharmaceuticals and herbal remedies but between cannabis and alcohol for personal use). Why not consider using a more rigorous licensure process to achieve a balance between the relaxation of ineffective drug access restrictions and the implementation of controls that send more appropriate and constructive public health messages? Under such a licensure scenario, legal infractions could lead to revocation, suspension, or other restriction of such licensure. Domestic violence, impaired driving, or other patterns of use that risk harm to self or others (including overconsumption) could be managed with even greater attention to outcomes, with vigilance directed toward the prevention of dangerousness rather than social stigmatization.

Cannabis regulation should address available forms of cannabis or cannabis-containing products and level of assurance to the consumer about product description, content, and consistency. It should be possible to purchase whole herbal cannabis or to grow it oneself for personal use and not for sale. It should also be possible to purchase refined products such as tinctures and edibles standardized according to agreed-upon criteria. For example, tinctures, edibles, and higher-grade whole herbal cannabis could hypothetically be required to meet "Grade A" criteria, while whole herbal cannabis might also be available as a "Grade B" variety. The former would be held to greater standards of consistency, while the latter might be based only on strain, regulated qualitatively but within established purity and potency parameters. Pharmaceutical or medicinal grade might then be a class above "Grade A" and manufactured with highly specific indices of standardization as has been the case for the work of GW Pharmaceutical specifically with Sativex® as well as with similarly prepared products standardized to different THC-to-CBD ratios. All of these ideas would be most appropriately entertained and evaluated by a stakeholder-inclusive regulatory process.

Healthcare and Federal Renewal

In addition to initiating a broader regulatory process, the federal government could choose to embrace the cannabis therapeutics concept by making it available as indicated, on a physician's recommendation, to veterans through the Department of Veterans Affairs (VA) healthcare system. Without a doubt, some portion of veterans returning from war will request it. Among reported psychiatric uses of cannabis, PTSD was the single largest diagnostic group in a large San Francisco Bay Area clinical practice specializing in medicinal cannabis consultation and recommendation.[15]

Implementation of medicinal cannabis access for veterans who have appropriate medical needs (which should include PTSD as well as physical trauma) could proceed first in states that now allow it. The VA hospital system, with its affiliated satellite clinics, could establish a registry of those seeking access to cannabis on a medicinal basis. Through its affiliate universities, VA could rapidly establish laboratories such as that proposed by Professor Lyle Craker of the University of Massachusetts. Using the existing Veterans Integrated Service Network (VISN) structure, VA could become instrumental in a federal effort to develop regionally sensitive federal-state collaborative regulatory frameworks. VISN-based implementation could facilitate the building of bridges across states, while working with state legislatures to be sure that implementation steps are in sync with state law.

In partnership with its academic affiliates, VA could take a lead role in developing medicinal grade cannabis and begin pioneering research on cannabis and health at many levels. Cannabis taxation and regulation, together with a commitment to begin the public health reformation of the war on drugs, have the potential to make a sizable contribution to the funding of healthcare nationally. The VA system could be one of the beneficiaries of the new revenue generated through these processes and perhaps contribute to the development of the cannabis therapeutics industry through its research. For some time now—at least a decade—VA has been poised to expand into markets beyond veterans. A national healthcare reform agenda with integrity will prioritize VA expansion at the outset and ensure that VA is funded at the level necessary to do the job of which it is highly capable. Future expansion of VA to become an open federal healthcare system could be built upon the excellence achieved in its response to the growing need for medical care among returning veterans.

To further sketch out this scenario, VA could provide the backbone of a future integrated federal healthcare system that would open its doors to families and other individuals and compete in the healthcare marketplace by virtue of its excellence. This move would expand the role of VA in education and public health research and mark a new era in which federally-operated healthcare services are evaluated based on performance in a consumer-driven system rather than caricatured in the armchair strategic planning discussions of policymakers pandering to special interests. Expansion of the federally operated healthcare sector would create a multitude of new jobs and training opportunities in areas that include not only the entire spectrum of healthcare professions and biomedical research activities but also law enforcement and secure facilities management as well. Substantial numbers of jobs in the prison industry could be reconfigured as union jobs in areas and aspects of the healthcare industry that are compatible with individual employee training, background, and interests. Additional training geared toward facilitating such transitions could be built into the reinvestment process. Veterans would receive preference for these jobs; a systematic effort would be made to find opportunities for returning warriors to find meaningful work in areas of healing and service that are in keeping with their overall needs and interests.

Cannabis change will bring substantial new revenue into the system and likely bring other cost-saving benefits yet to be appreciated. Interest in medicinal cannabis access through the VA Healthcare System could provide an opportunity for the federal government to step up to the plate and facilitate forward movement rather than repeating its pattern of obstruction. The federal government could indeed take steps to catalyze appropriate development of therapeutic and public health policy reforms that bring cannabis back into the healthcare mainstream. The federal government could take ownership of cannabis therapeutics and respond constructively to the predictable increase in demand for medicinal access that will occur with the return of America's wounded warriors. The infusion of resources associated with medicinal cannabis development would help jumpstart federal Health and Human Services agencies for the reconfiguration necessary to accommodate healthcare expansion and a newly invigorated operational role of federal government in establishing healthcare access.

Toward a 21st Century New (Drug) Deal

How would the federal government move forward with cannabinomics? To uphold the Constitution and protect civil rights, it would support a legislative and administrative framework within which people who found therapeutic value in cannabis could gain safe access to quality products. At this point that means, at the very least, not interfering with state implementation of medical cannabis programs. Given the substantial demand represented by these programs, it also means—at the very least—following Judge Young's 1988 recommendation for rescheduling, so that federal government is not left in an untenable position (although in fact it has been in an untenable position for many years with its compassionate use program, which will be unnecessary with rescheduling). Of course, the question remains exactly how cannabis should be scheduled, and we will return to that issue shortly.

How far should the notion of therapeutic value be extended? If the alcohol problem is taken seriously, there is no reason why therapeutic use of cannabis should not be extended to harm reduction substitution for alcohol, at least for individuals with alcohol-related problems. But if cannabis is available as an alternative to alcohol based not only on a medical recommendation but also on a preferable safety profile, then why shouldn't the safer alternative be available to adults generally? Is there any reason why it should be necessary to have debilitating alcohol-related disease in order to qualify for cannabis substitution? There would appear to be no medical or public health justification for such a restriction.[16]

Change of the sort advocated in this book usually requires trade-offs and compromises. Libertarians will argue that the Constitution, civil rights, and economic opportunity are reasons enough to open up the cannabis market and to proceed with a revamping of drug control policy generally. Democrats will agree with the importance of civil rights but will be concerned that public health implications are addressed to protect consumers. From prevention, education, and political messaging standpoints, a proposal to treat marijuana differently will be most intelligible if it is articulated in relation to other contemporary drug policy and drug use concerns. Those concerns include therapeutic cannabis access (consumer-driven healthcare), drug war violence and malignant criminalization (public health and civil rights), and economic waste (misspent funds and lost tax revenue), as well as our need for public policy that supports better management of alcohol-related problems. (The predictable objection by some that using cannabis instead of alcohol is simply substituting one addiction for another is, in the absence of other case-specific information, merely a knee-jerk response of questionable usefulness.)

The following series of possible steps is offered in an effort to envision a path forward on cannabis change that entails responsible stewardship of a popular home-grown commodity, while being responsive to other substance-related concerns. It attempts to open doors to a healthier future, while instituting controls that send appropriate messages about health and safety. To facilitate *cannabinomics*, federal government could:

1. Establish a broad-based and stakeholder-inclusive regulatory process, possibly involving a new cannabis regu-

latory commission, to address and accommodate the full range of possibilities for regulated cannabis access including not only trade requirements for cannabis as a commodity but also specific limits (and licensure provisions) for home-growing for personal use only without license for sales;

2. Become a buyer of herbal cannabis, calling for growers to present samples of their products for no-risk analysis to facilitate systematic study of strains currently traded in the domestic underground;

3. Conduct and/or fund a real-world population-based study of the public health impact of regulated cannabis access;

4. Create a pilot program granting medicinal cannabis access to veterans through the VA healthcare system (such access should include provisions for whole herbal cannabis regulated by strain or genetic history, as well as medicinal extracts standardized more quantitatively); such a program would be responsive to a growing movement represented by Kalamazoo-based "Veterans for Medical Marijuana Access";

5. Facilitate a fast-track FDA approval of GW Pharmaceutical's product, Sativex®, not as a tertiary intervention for esoteric disease states but for broader prescription usage for relief of pain, muscle spasms, and possibly anxiety; fund or otherwise facilitate research into the feasibility of revising the FDA standing of Sativex® to that of an age-restricted over-the-counter (OTC) herbal remedy for relief of pain, muscle tension, stress, and for some individuals insomnia;

6. Use its regulatory authority to guide the entry of similar products into the medicinal-grade cannabis market (for example, GW Pharmaceutical has reportedly worked

with medicinal extract formulations that have differing THC-to-CBD ratios) and support further research to determine what other standardization parameters may be appropriate for the regulation of whole herbal cannabis at other levels of production refinement (for example, strain or potency);

7. Modify statutes as required, in connection with Items #1 and 6 above, to ensure that American entrepreneurs have the opportunity to enter the marketplace with similar products, under regulations agreed upon by stakeholders;

8. Set minimum public health requirements, for implementation at the state level, that may need to be satisfied for individuals to grow limited amounts of cannabis for personal use but not for sale (for example, user's license or home-grower's permit);

9. Fund public service implementation, research, and system transformation grants to law enforcement to facilitate the transition from marijuana criminalization to cannabis regulation; include funding for research to improve technology used in impairment testing and to move from reliance on blood levels or urine screening to the use of hand-held electronic devices to screen for behavioral evidence of impairment;

10. Collaborate supportively with state and local governments on implementation projects; and

11. Consider federal legislation and rulemaking to establish parameters within which states can experiment with new licensure processes governing access to age-restricted substances including alcohol and tobacco. Given our current level of scientific and medical knowledge—in particular, our ability to recognize and disentangle substance use disorders, addictive behaviors, and psychiatric

illnesses and their co-existence or co-morbidity—consideration should be given to conceptualizing the use of potentially intoxicating substances as a privilege subject to licensure rather than a right based on age alone. One approach to such a licensure process might be structured in the following way:

a. At the age of 18 an individual would be entitled to apply for a personal age-restricted substances license that permits purchase and personal use of beer, wine, cannabis, and tobacco.[17] Such a model could rely upon the medicinal cannabis concept to facilitate the transition to cannabis regulation by requiring a physician's (or nurse practitioner's) clearance. The process could involve a deliberate and intentional transition through a medical clearance model to a regulated public health model.

b. As with the acquisition of a driver's license, approval of the application could be contingent upon passing a relatively simple and straightforward test. Such a test would not only reinforce existing laws prohibiting driving under the influence but also address such issues as the relative potency of different forms of alcohol, the potential of alcohol to impair both judgment and physical organ functioning (for example, its potential effects on the stomach, brain, and liver), basic information on alcohol metabolism and its potential for interaction with other drugs including prescription medicines and cannabis, and information on standard drink sizes. Instructional materials preparing applicants for the test would include raising awareness of the fact that cannabis can potentiate or magnify the effects of alcohol and would caution the licensee against combining the two.[18]

c. Such a license could be included as one category on a standard driver's license or state identification card.

d. Subsequent to the issuance of an initial license, at a designated age to be determined but likely somewhere between 19 and 21, the age-restricted substances license-holder would be eligible to apply for an upgrade of their licensure privileges to entitle them to purchase, possess, and consume stronger forms of alcohol—high proof spirits such as vodka, scotch or gin—and perhaps other age-restricted substances the regulation of which remains to be worked out. For example, Bolivian President Evo Morales Ayma recently made a plea to the international community for tolerance regarding the traditional practice of chewing coca leaves.[19] Coca leaves might well rank below hard liquor on the hierarchy of access to age-restricted substances. On a strict medical safety basis, such a ranking may be appropriate. But that is the kind of question that a stakeholder-inclusive regulatory process, with a purview expanded beyond the task of cannabis regulation, would be able to address.

In time we will figure out how to regulate the home-grown commodity in our own backyard. Then we will have to ask ourselves what we have learned that may be applicable to broader, more complex, and more difficult global drug war problems. We will be able to build upon our learning from the work of cannabis policy reform to inform approaches to the regulation of other aspects of the current underground drug trade, both domestic and international. For example, the federal purchasing of cannabis from domestic growers might provide a model for similar responses to the coca and/or opium trade.[20] Numerous potential solutions and strategies could be entertained, but further speculation on the matter is neither necessary at this time nor the primary focus of this book.

Physicians, their patients, and the general public rely upon government regulation to ensure that medicines are safe, effective, and reliable in their composition. A century ago, there was relatively little involvement of government with quality control of medicines and little regulation of medical education. By the beginning of the 20th century, it was clear that both pharmaceuticals and medical education could benefit from more rigorous standards of quality and consistency. The so-called "patent" medicines included proprietary mixtures of compounds with known medicinal properties that could be dangerous— especially where opiate-containing products were concerned— because of specific combinations of compounds they contained or because consumers were inadequately informed about safe dosing. A century later, physicians, patients, and commercial producers have all benefited enormously from improved regulation, and there seems little question but that medical treatment is more sophisticated and pharmaceuticals more reliable and safe than in times long past. This is not to say that there are not problems with our regulatory system; this book has offered a general case to the contrary and taken the position that in many ways our system has failed.

Cannabis prohibition was not an idea conceived by the medical profession. Nor did it begin at the federal level, even though it culminated in the federal Marihuana Tax Act of 1937. Cannabis prohibition began locally and with state laws and probably represented a response to racial tensions closely associated with the Mexican Revolution and its impact on the American

Southwest. The anti-marijuana bias that ensued was later catapulted forward by Nixon's war on drugs. The Reagan "Just Say No" approach fortified the platform for scapegoating cannabis users for the so-called drug problem against which the so-called drug war has been waged. Self-interested and self-righteous individuals and groups with minimal sensitivity to those who think differently and little motivation to educate themselves have promulgated a level of intolerance that has no place in American democracy. Politicians in particular, and especially our leaders at the federal level who ought to be educated well enough to know better, have proliferated punitive, extreme, and irrational drug criminalization policies out of ignorance, cynicism, or both.

Unfortunately, we Americans have colluded with our leaders through our silence, allowing them to experience an inauthentic and unwarranted sense of success. In reality, they have failed miserably by adopting an anti-marijuana campaign as a proxy or substitute for the broader war on drugs, while scapegoating drugs more generally for broader social problems including lack of education and narrow-minded intolerance. In make-believe attempts to measure the outcomes of misguided runaway lawmaking, government officials create an illusion of policy effectiveness by amassing marijuana arrest statistics that scapegoat cannabis itself for both drug problems and broader social policy failures by repeating the mantra that marijuana is a gateway drug. If there is such a thing as a gateway *drug*—in contrast to obvious gateway *laws*—it is alcohol, because it impairs judgment and restraint much more consistently. In the early 21st century, American government is in desperate need of face-saving policy overhaul strategies in numerous areas; cannabis policy is one with tremendous upside potential.

The strategic conversation begins by separating out specific drugs and asking not what is meant by "legalization," but rather whether there are strategies for managing the respective problems more wisely. With regard to cannabis that question is posed by *cannabinomics*—that is, how should America proceed with the management of cannabis? We can no longer afford *not* to regulate the cannabis trade, just as we could no longer afford *not* to regulate sale of alcohol at the time of the Great Depression. In fact it is probably the case that globally we can no longer afford *not* to regulate other drug trade. Which drug trade? That remains to be determined, and a variety of scenarios and rationales could be sketched out. At one level, such a question might translate into whether individuals with heroin addiction should be permitted to access the drug with clean needles in medically supervised settings rather than dealing on the streets. More systemically, it could mean American intervention in the broader opium market (for example, Afghanistan) as a buyer and the study of regulatory alternatives in that market that might facilitate harm reduction by shifting substance use away from its most potent and dangerous forms. In addition, on a global scale it has been estimated that as many as 10 million people suffer from chronic pain without the benefit of needed medications that can be derived from opium.[21] Many such patients in Africa suffer the chronic neurologic pain of AIDS. However, the starting point in contemplating nonmilitary, noncriminalizing interventions is with American home-grown cannabis.

At this moment in history we have the opportunity to begin a paradigm shift that could yield significant economic and technological advantages long term and act as an immediate economic stimulus. Why now? Because the grassroots medical cannabis movement has built enough momentum for us to take notice nationally; the need to envision nonviolent alternatives to the drug war is now pressing; the logic of the SAFER campaign is inescapable; and medicinal whole plant cannabis extracts are already here, working their way in the door as a valuable new addition to the American pharmacopoeia, with GW Pharmaceutical's Sativex® leading the way.

Three Trajectories Revisited

This book has been intended as an invitation to reflect. It has been offered as an interpretation of where we are as Americans in general on the issue of whether grown-ups can use cannabis, or marijuana, responsibly. With a physician's recommendation, approval, or clearance? As a healthier choice over alcohol for many people? As an alternative tonic? Or as a matter of civil rights and the United States Constitution? It doesn't really matter where one enters the discussion, because the various points of entry converge. Freedom of choice is healthy, and so is respect for differences. Medical science is of little value if it obliterates the individual patient in the process. But if you require other arguments for the issue to become compelling, then pick your point of entry. We can pick up the thread of the discussion in a San Francisco, Amsterdam, or Oxford mode.

San Francisco

People with AIDS need it, and so do people with cancer. People on various chemotherapies need it, and others with serious pain syndromes find that it offers an important pain-relieving alternative that helps them decrease their use of prescription opiate pain relievers while improving their effectiveness (for example, by avoiding tolerance and constipation). The herb seems practically engineered for symptomatic treatment of MS, and it is the genius of GW Pharmaceutical to recognize this and take their product Sativex® to market in Canada. People have the right to make personal healthcare choices, and this may include a preference for some medicines, remedies, or therapeutic alternatives over others. Some people in recovery from psychiatric and substance abuse problems also report benefit from cannabis, specifically because of its anti-anxiety and mood-elevating effects. Reports of improved sleep, decreased irritability, decreased depressive-type negative thoughts, improved mood stability, and sustained abstinence from alcohol are abundant if largely anecdotal.

Posttraumatic stress disorder (PTSD), especially when it involves polytrauma, may turn out to be another condition—like MS—for which cannabis seems almost tailored. Patients with both disorders report cannabis-related improvement in well-defined symptoms along multiple dimensions recognized as part of the medical illness or syndrome. For PTSD, approved medications prescribed appropriately can substantially decrease symptoms of the disorder; this is known from research and clinical experience, and treatment guidelines have been compiled and published. However, many if not most cases of PTSD will require more than one medication for psychiatric stabilization, even when the first medication tried is one with an FDA-indication specifically for PTSD. Beyond medication management, psychotherapy can be effective in the psychological management of traumatic memories and associated symptoms.

When some patients with PTSD or other behavioral health problems report that cannabis has been helpful in their recovery—for example, by helping them sleep better and/or redirecting them away from alcohol use that has made their condition worse—they need to be heard. More than that, consumers need to be supported in communicating that kind of information to their healthcare provider. Responses such as, "marijuana is a substance of abuse" or "that's just addictive behavior" are, by themselves and without more than cannabis use as their basis, of little therapeutic value or medical relevance. Referral for substance abuse treatment may be helpful if marijuana abuse is an issue, but there are cases in which cannabis use may not be problematic at all—except to the degree that the activity is criminalized; substance abuse treatment for many patients will more often be relevant and useful when it supports their efforts to remove alcohol from their lives. Marijuana may be more of a solution than a problem for some individuals with PTSD or other anxiety and mood disorders. And *cannabis* may be the solution to their marijuana problem, with *cannabinomics* the alternative to marijuana policies that perpetuate the public health disaster of criminalization.

There may be good reasons for counseling some patients against cannabis use. One such reason might be that the individual's functioning has clearly declined with cannabis use; under such circumstances it would be appropriate to advise an individual against it. Physically, excessive smoking causes problems. Fortunately, cannabis use does not depend on excessive smoking or smoking at all necessarily. Less smoking is generally better. Some will need to abstain from cannabis because of difficulty managing their intake. But if we maintain that managing personal cannabis intake is more difficult for responsible adults than managing alcohol or tobacco intake we delude ourselves. It is appropriate for adults to be in the position of deciding for themselves whether cannabis use has therapeutic value in their case, and for that reason it is appropriate that herbal cannabis be accessible more broadly than for narrowly defined, esoteric, tertiary disease states.

Herbal cannabis is most appropriately regulated as an over-the-counter (OTC), age-restricted herbal medicine or remedy with prescription herbal cannabis preparations also available as an option for more sophisticated or highly standardized products. Such products may be developed to further refine the medicinal use of cannabis, so that individuals for whom some of the subjective effects—psychoactive properties or a feeling of being "high"—are undesirable or produce impairment. But the desirability of further medicinal refinement is not an adequate reason to prohibit access for those individuals who find herbal cannabis use helpful now. These ideas are nothing more than derivatives of a consumer-driven healthcare philosophy and a person-centered approach to recovery.

Amsterdam

Too many people are locked up for drug use. We need to be thoughtful about sorting out the different drugs that people seek and trying to determine the best approach for reducing the harms associated with drug use. Drug use is obviously an accepted human activity: coffee, a glass of wine, prescription and over-the-counter (OTC) medications, chocolate. Which kinds of drug use and drug-related activities are most harmful, and which ones least so? Can we structure our laws in such a way that we begin to sort this out? What if it were easy to access cannabis in comparison with more dangerous drugs?

Serious consideration should be given to the notion that people in general would be better off with earlier age-restricted access to cannabis than to alcohol; a modification of that concept involves splitting alcoholic beverages into forms with lower and higher alcohol content so that, for example, an individual might be eligible for an age-restricted substances license that permits him or her to purchase beer, wine, cannabis, and tobacco at the age of 18 but be required to demonstrate responsible use of that license before being eligible to add to it the purchase of distilled spirits or hard liquor. The age at which the latter occurs could be 21, as it is now in the United States, or there may be reasons for lowering it.

Oxford

Cannabis clearly has medicinal properties, or people wouldn't have been using it as medicine for so many different ailments throughout history. But the modern practice of medicine requires precision to the greatest extent possible, and it must be supported by scientific findings demonstrating the efficacy of its recommended treatments. For the renaissance of medicinal cannabis to come to fruition, medicinal cannabis extracts must be subjected to rigorous clinical trial methods so that they can be evaluated and approved according to the same standards that govern the introduction of other medications into the pharmaceutical marketplace.

Sativex® may well be effective in a variety of pain syndromes and appropriate for approval as medicine more broadly. Given the reported use of cannabis to target behavioral as well as physical symptoms, Sativex® may well have therapeutic applications in anxiety disorders such as PTSD, and it could be suitable for nonprescription use in relieving stress and promoting alcohol abstinence and harm reduction. However broad the use of Sativex®, other medicinal cannabis extracts, or whole herbal cannabis as medicine, it makes little sense to forgo the economic benefits of taxation or the quality improvement achievable with regulation. But Californians and other Americans have ideas about this, too. Why should they be forced to peddle their products underground? A British company is knocking on the door of the FDA with an excellent product, GW Pharmaceutical's Sativex® or the new "Oxford Gold." If Californians are prohibited from developing similar products, or from coming out of the closet with the products they have already developed, then American business opportunity and jobs are being de facto exported overseas. Neither medicinal consumers nor local entrepreneurs should be deprived of the benefits of a normalized, economically integrated cannabis industry.

Economic circumstances in the first decade of the 21st century invite comparisons with the Great Depression. With the New Deal came something less talked about but far from negligible economically—repeal of alcohol prohibition. In addition to the common plight and burden of harsh economic times, the America that embraced the New Deal had, like ours, grown weary of prohibition-era violence and the public health hazards of nonregulation of a popular ingestible substance. Given the current state of our knowledge of cannabis and alcohol, our decision to move from prohibition to regulation should be easier than theirs. And given the known industrial applications and possibilities with cannabis, the upside potential seems far greater.

In this 21st century the task of cannabinomics now presents itself, whether the work begins with medical patients in San Francisco, policy reformers in Amsterdam, or entrepreneurs in Oxford. The realities of our time prompt us to reckon with the fact that drug criminalization, which never really works anyway, is unaffordable. Cannabis change is the low hanging fruit of drug policy reform, and medical marijuana is so ripe it's falling off the trees in front of us. As Americans embrace the task of cannabis management and take ownership of this home-grown commodity, conversations in *cannabinomics* have the potential to help us better tend the garden in our own backyard.

ACKNOWLEDGEMENTS

IN JULY OF 2006 Judge James P. Gray of the Orange County, California, Superior Court spoke on drug policy reform in downtown Chicago. My copy of his book, *Why Our Drug Laws Have Failed and What We Can Do About It* (Temple University Press, 2001), bears the inscription, "It's OK to discuss drug policy" above his autograph. Judge Gray spoke compellingly that evening, and one of his statements inscribed itself with equal clarity and simplicity on my memory: "Prohibition never works as well as regulation." These two quotes could well serve as bookends for the ideas and observations found in the following pages. I thank Judge Gray for his inspirational call for drug policy reform.

I am indebted to the Administrative Office of the Illinois Courts for inviting me to speak at its 2007 Advanced Judicial Academy, held on the campus of the University of Illinois at Springfield. In particular, I am grateful to Justice Michael Gallagher of the Illinois Appellate Court, who as chairman of the planning committee personally extended me the invitation. Justice Gallagher read an early draft of this work following the Academy meeting. Justice Joy Cunningham, also on the planning committee, read several drafts and provided both critical and encouraging commentary. I deeply appreciate the gift of her interest in this work; her feedback helped make the book better and reinforced my sense of the project's importance. I thank the 100-plus Illinois judges who attended the one-week Academy for a stimulating exchange of ideas that became a catalyst to the book's progress, especially regarding Part II. For passing my name on to Justice Gallagher and for his longstanding support and friendship, I thank James L. Cavanaugh, Jr., M.D., Professor of Psychiatry at Rush University and founder of the Isaac Ray Center and the Section on Psychiatry and the Law.

It has been my good fortune to have come to know the Honorable Paul P. Biebel, Jr., Presiding Judge of the Criminal Division of the State of Illinois Circuit Court of Cook County, and I am grateful to him for lending his ear on several occasions—as I ranted about the counterproductive nature of drug policy in relation to mental illness, substance abuse, and their co-occurrence. I thank Jack Cole, Norm Stamper, and the members of the LEAP organization (Law Enforcement Against Prohibition) generally for their courageous and timely leadership in drug policy reform. I thank Judge Arthur Burnett for the privilege of making his acquaintance, beginning with a stimulating conversation over lunch at the 2005 International Drug Policy Conference in Long Beach, California, and leading to his enlisting my participation in the work of the National African American Drug Policy Coalition to help form the Illinois Drug Policy Coalition. Among the valuable exchanges of ideas that developed in connection with my involvement in that work, conversations with Congressman Danny Davis and [then] Illinois Senate President Emil Jones stand out as especially significant. I thank Illinois Assistant State's Attorney John Fairman and other members of the steering committee of the Illinois Drug Policy Coalition, including Deborah Fortier, Reanetta Hunt, Stephen Stern, and George Williams for the opportunity to collaborate with them on that initiative.

Robert Vyverberg, Ed.D. and Lorrie Rickman Jones, Ph.D, graced me with their support when, as state mental health director in Illinois (2003-2005), I was increasingly drawn to meta-level discussions about the contribution of drug laws to defining the contexts within which mental health policy and program development are conceptualized. Pastor Frederick Aigner, Ph.D., retired President and CEO of Lutheran Social Services of Illinois and a compassionate leader and friend, was a supportive dialogue partner in some of the same areas. His genuine curiosity about my work in this area helped improve the book through several revisions.

Physicians on the front lines of the medicinal cannabis movement and/or drug policy reform more generally who have been sources of learning and encouragement include many known to me only through their writing (salient are Lester Grinspoon, M.D., Andrew Weil, M.D., Gregory Carter, M.D., and the late Tod Mikuriya, M.D.). Most notable among those who have made a direct impact on my work in this area is David Bearman, M.D., son of a pharmacist who made tincture of cannabis by the textbooks in the old days, with whom I have had the pleasure of working closely on numerous occasions and from whom I have learned much. Other physicians who—through their medical knowledge, research, and/or patient advocacy—have made a direct impact on my work in this area include Frank Lucido, M.D., Donald Abrams, M.D., Mark Ware, M.D., John Halpern, M.D., Charles Grob, M.D., Bruce Doblin, M.D., Ethan Russo, M.D., David Ostrow, M.D., Ph.D., Joan Cummings, M.D., and Sue Hurtado, M.D.

Other physicians, not particularly associated with the drug policy reform movement but supportive in various ways specific to this project include Carl Wahlstrom, M.D., Andrew Stoll, M.D., Joseph A. Flaherty, M.D., Bennett Leventhal, M.D., Stephen Hunt Dinwiddie, M.D., Stephen Soltys, M.D., Carl

Bell, M.D., Shastri Swaminathan, M.D., Paul Rodenhauser, M.D., Morris Goldman, M.D., David A.S. Garfield, M.D., Fred Sierles, M.D., JSSR Van, M.D., John Lancas, M.D., and Jesus Bucardo, M.D. I thank Daniel J. Luchins, M.D., for his longstanding collegial support and friendship and for his critical feedback on an early draft of the manuscript.

Sunil Aggarwal, Ph.D. deserves special thanks, not just for his encouraging resonance with the ideas expressed herein but also for his emergence as an effective leader in the policy transformation envisioned at the core of this book—even before his graduation from medical school. Dr. Aggarwal, whose doctoral dissertation in community health elucidated the medical geography of cannabis therapeutics activity in the state of Washington, has resolutely led the effort to update the American Medical Association's position on the issue for the 21st century. Other scholars and policy advocates who have made a direct helpful impact on my work here include Rick Doblin, Ph.D., Dale Gieringer, Ph.D., Robert Melamede, Ph.D., of the University of Colorado; Mitch Earleywine, Ph.D., of the State University of New York; Harriet de Wit, Ph.D., of the University of Chicago; and Rush University College of Nursing Dean Melanie Dreher, Ph.D.

My thanks to Matthew Atwood for bringing the medical marijuana movement to my attention and, along with George Pappas, Bryan Brickner, Diana Brickner, Dan Linn, John Walker, and others involved with Illinois NORML and IDEAL Reform, sparking my interest in learning more about the medicinal uses of cannabis and the experiences of patient consumers. Additional thanks go to Steph Sherer and Caren Woodson of Americans for Safe Access; Kathleen Kane-Willis and Jennifer Janichek of the Illinois Consortium on Drug Policy; Mason Tvert, Paul Armentano, and Steve Fox of the SAFER organization; and Bruce Mirken of the Marijuana Policy Project.

If Judge Gray's words can be seen as bookends, in a sense highlighting the contours of this work, then the trial of "ganja guru" Ed Rosenthal was an event that seems to have fueled or supercharged its writing. When I first read the news of the 2003 federal trial in a Chicago newspaper, it seemed to jump out from the page and brought to my mind simultaneously the images of flare and beacon—signaling in either case that something important was occurring and it warranted my attention. Rosenthal, a recognized expert on cannabis cultivation, had been deputized by Oakland officials to provide cannabis for the city's medicinal program and to operate under state law. But after his West Oakland growing operation was raided by the Drug Enforcement Administration (DEA), Rosenthal was tried in federal court in San Francisco on multiple counts of marijuana possession and cultivation.

The case drew national attention—to the extent possible for a nation still reeling from a major terrorist assault and focused on a new war—in connection with what *The Examiner* termed a "jury revolt." After Rosenthal's conviction, members of the jury protested the requirement under federal law, as administered by U.S. District Judge Charles Breyer, that they reach a verdict without considering any evidence pertaining to medicinal cannabis or the California state law under which Rosenthal understood himself to be operating. The front page of *The Examiner* featured juror Marni Craig expressing dismay that the jurors "were manipulated and controlled" in the federal trial process. Judge Breyer barred all evidence pertaining to medical marijuana use from the courtroom during the trial with the result that the jury had no access to evidence of Rosenthal's work in its local context.

After the jury had convicted Rosenthal and had access to the embargoed evidence, seven jurors protested that they had been misled and called for a new trial. Craig said, "It was a nightmare for us once we realized what we had done here." Jury foreman Charles Sackett apologized "for having participated in so unfair a court trial." In the end, Judge Breyer exercised unexpected leniency, limiting the sentence to a single day of jail time served. Under federal sentencing guidelines, Rosenthal faced a mandatory minimum of five years and possibly as many as 60 behind bars. The trial of Ed Rosenthal was for me a lightning rod that exposed the ugliness of what federal law had become under the influence of intolerant and authoritarian influences in legislative and executive branches of government. Yet another front-page article at the time of the trial featured Rosenthal with his daughter Justine and the headline quote "My dad's a hero." A couple of years later I would meet Ed Rosenthal in person, but well before that time I formed the lasting impression that Justine was right.

The Rosenthal case is one of many that can easily engender outrage. I am grateful to Eric Schlosser for giving us accounts of many others in his book *Reefer Madness* (Houghton Mifflin, 2003) and similarly to Judge Rudolph J. Gerber, retired from the Arizona Court of Appeals, for case descriptions in his book *Legalizing Marijuana: Drug Policy Reform and Prohibition Politics* (Praeger, 2004).

Heartfelt thanks are extended to all of the consumers whose case material I am privileged to use in the book. With the exceptions of Julie Falco, the most prominent and dynamic advocate in Illinois, and Garry Silva, whose leadership represents a major contribution to achieving full statewide implementation in California, the names of medicinal consumers have been changed, and I will not enumerate further here. Many Illinoisans thank Senator John Cullerton [now Senate President] for his sponsorship of medical cannabis legislation in the Illinois Senate several years in a row, and I am grateful to have had opportunities to work with him in that effort.

Others who provided feedback on early versions of the manuscript include Steven A. Holmes, JoAnna LaForce, Katherine Brash, Carrie Bartholme, my brother Patrick Fichtner, film maker Jed Riffe, and my editor Ann Kepler. To Ann Kepler I presented an amply reworked, restructured and retitled manuscript nearly two years after she reviewed the first one—which she felt was practically ready for publication at that time. Ann's thoroughness, organization, efficiency, and finesse greatly facilitated my progress through the last several months of the manuscript's preparation, and I am grateful for that. I thank Jim Kepler for guiding me through the publication process with encouragement, specific information, and strategic options for getting the book out. I thank Tom Kepler for his work on graphic design, website development, and typesetting. Attorney Richard Schell's assistance in several areas has been invaluable in the final few months prepublication. I am indebted to Ethan Nadelman, Ph.D., Executive Director of the Drug Policy Alliance, as well as Benjamin Leitch and Samuel Inglese for reading the manuscript in near-final form prior to its going to press. Eric Sterling, J.D., President of the Criminal Justice Policy Foundation, also read the final manuscript, and I deeply appreciate his agreeing to write the foreword to *Cannabinomics*.

I cannot fully express the depths of my gratitude to my partner in life Dr. Linda Grossman, who put up with my need to focus on little else during the book's writing, offered words of encouragement and emotional support throughout the process, and critically read more versions of this manuscript than anyone else. Professor, clinical psychologist, forensic expert, and reviewer for numerous academic journals, she is a tough critic who knows the difference between rigorous experimental science and the kind of anecdotal case report data that form the backbone of much of my work in this book. I am also tremendously grateful to Linda's brother, my brother-in-law Steve

Grossman, for reading numerous drafts of every section of the manuscript. Steve's belief in this project, listening skill, capacity for critical thinking, political awareness, and consistent availability for exchange of ideas shaped the work in important ways. Ongoing conversations with my other brother-in-law, Gerry Grossman, have also influenced my thinking on drug policy and shaped the content of this work.

Linda and I have been blessed with two wonderful sons, Aaron and Justin, who are sources of boundless joy for us both. I am deeply appreciative of their participation in many more than their fair share of drug policy discussions, their emotional and intellectual support throughout the book's writing, and their weathering of the toll that my pursuit of that activity took on our family life. Most of all, I thank Aaron, Justin, and their fellow musicians for filling my life with music of such beauty that I am transported by it to a state of peace and wellness lacking nothing.

NOTES

Introduction

1. *Washington Post*, June 6, 1971; cited in Gerber RA. *Legalizing Marijuana: Drug Policy Reform and Prohibition Politics*. Westport, CT: Praeger, 2004.

2. For examples, see the following: Baum D. *Smoke and Mirrors: The War on Drugs and the Politics of Failure*. Boston: Little, Brown & Company, 1996; Masters B (Editor). *The New Prohibition: Voices of Dissent Challenge the Drug War*. St. Louis: Accurate Press, 2004; Gray JP. *Why Our Drug Laws Have Failed and What We Can Do About It*. Philadelphia: Temple University Press, 2001; Robinson MB, Scherlen RG. *Lies, Damned Lies, and Drug War Statistics: A Critical Analysis of Claims Made by the Office of National Drug Control Policy*. Albany: State University of New York Press, 2007; Earleywine M (Editor). *Pot Politics: Marijuana and the Costs of Prohibition*. Oxford: Oxford University Press, 2007; Rowe TC. *Federal Narcotics Laws and the War on Drugs: Money Down a Rat Hole*. New York: Haworth Press, 2006. An Open Letter from Lawyers and Judges, posted by the Voluntary Committee of Lawyers at www.vcl.org and quoted by Gray, JP (2001: 3-4), includes the following statement: "As Congress and state legislatures enact more punitive and costly drug control measures, we conclude with alarm that the war on drugs now causes more harm than drug abuse itself."

3. See Wallace-Wells B. How America lost the war on drugs. *Rolling Stone*, December 13, 2007; Lawson G. The War Next Door. *Rolling Stone*, November 13, 2008; Serrano RA, Quinones S. Mexico drug wars spill across the border. *Los Angeles Times*, November 16, 2008; Quinones S. 23 seconds of the Mexican drug war. *Los Angeles Times*, December 7, 2008; McKinley Jr JC. Two Sides of a Border: One Violent, One Peaceful. *New York Times*, January 23, 2009; Quinones S. Phoenix, kidnap-for-ransom capitol. *Los Angeles Times*, February 12, 2009; Lawson G. The Making of a Narco State. *Rolling Stone*, March 4, 2009; Editors, How to Stop the Drug Wars, *The Economist*, March 4, 2009; Quinones S. Senators take their concerns to

the border. *Los Angeles Times*, March 31, 2009; Quinones S. State of War. *Foreign Policy*, March/April, 2009.

4. Stolberg SG. Obama's twist on town hall; top Internet query was about marijuana. *New York Times*, March 27, 2009.

5. See Yamamura K. Schwarzenegger says 'time for debate' on legal marijuana. *Sacramento Bee*, May 5, 2009.

6. Former Brazilian President Fernando Enrique Cordoso, along with Ernesto Zedillo of Mexico and Cesar Gaviria of Colombia, reporting with the Latin American Commission on Drugs and Democracy in February of 2009 called for a public health approach to drug use problems. See Goodman J. Cordoso, Gaviria, Zedillo Urge Obama to Decriminalize Marijuana. *Bloomberg.com*, February 11, 2009.

7. Associated Press, South Carolina sheriff considering criminal charges against Michael Phelps over pot pipe pic. *Mlive.com*, February 3, 2009.

8. Christie J. California government declares fiscal emergency over budget. *Reuters*, July 1, 2009. Available at: http://www.reuters.com/article/politicsNews/idUSTRE5601F220090701

9. See Stateman, A. Can Marijuana Help Rescue California's Economy? Time.com, March 13, 2009; Smith FA. A neglected revenue source for California—marijuana. *San Francisco Chronicle*, January 13, 2009.

10. See Gettman J. Marijuana Production in the United States (2006). The Bulletin of Cannabis Reform, December, 2006. http://www.drugscience.org/bcr/index.html

11. See McKinley Jr. JC. Two Sides of a Border: One Violent, One Peaceful. *New York Times,* January 23, 2009.

12. Harvey J. *The Abilene Paradox*. San Francisco: Jossey-Bass, 1988.

13. Ibid.: 15.

14. Ibid.: 15.

15. Harvey (*The Abilene Paradox*) illustrates use of the Abilene paradox as a frame of reference in organizational consultation, finding that the inability to manage agreement can be a critical obstacle in attempting to move a group, organization, or social system forward. The CEO, or group leader, may be especially prone to being used by the group to keep from confronting the underlying agreement of its members. Is this different from the behavior of elected officials in our social and political systems? Any executive team can orchestrate a trip to Abilene for its organization, but it is only able to maintain the journey for as long as the underlying problem—invariably involving the management of agreement—remains unaddressed, which it will be for as long as no one talks about it. This dynamic, familiar to students of group behavior, may perhaps be formulated in a variety of ways and is sometimes referred to as "groupthink" (see Stahl S. Editor's Note: Speak Your Mind and Skirt Abilene. *Information Week*, October 4, 2004). Harvey's story of his family's trip to Abilene in the grit and grime of that sweltering hot west Texas desert day captures well the feel of a group's pursuing a course of action despite agreement that it doesn't make sense. Perhaps it also captures the sense of a group's need to get up and do something even though the only proposed course of action is ill conceived.

16. In the years prior to the prohibitive Marihuana Tax Act passed by Congress in 1937, extracts from *Cannabis sativa* and *Cannabis indica* were used as medicines for a number of indications including chronic pain, muscle cramps, and migraine headaches. The increase in popular use of marijuana in the 1960s spawned a renaissance of interest in its medical applications beginning with the discovery of its effectiveness in alleviating nausea for cancer patients receiving chemotherapy and gained substantial momentum in the late 1980s with its application for the same purpose in patients receiving anti-retroviral chemotherapy for AIDS. It was also discovered by AIDS patients and their physicians that cannabis was helpful not only for appetite stimulation but also for relief of pain associated

with neurological deterioration characteristic of the disease, HIV neuropathy.

17. Medical education does not necessarily deviate from such cultural norms—and would not deviate in matters of law pertinent to the practice of medicine—so that without additional study of the history of medicine an allopathic medical education (leading to the M.D. degree) would not generally guarantee any knowledge on the part of physicians regarding medicinal applications of cannabis. Medical education does, on the other hand, ensure at least minimal acquaintance with substance abuse problems, and what doctors generally understand about marijuana has been derived from within that context. Be that as it may, the renaissance of interest in whole plant cannabis as medicine has continued to grow even as federal government efforts to quash it have been stepped up.

18. The "bizarre public discussion" comment was made by Tom Riley as spokesman for ONDCP Director John Walters. See Harris, G. "F.D.A. Dismisses Medical Benefit From Marijuana." *New York Times*, April 21, 2006.

19. Quote is from Baum D. *Smoke and Mirrors: The War on Drugs and the Politics of Failure*. Boston: Little, Brown & Company, 1996; Baum is quoted in Cermak TL. Addiction Medicine Perspective on the Medicalization of Marijuana. *Journal of Psychoactive Drugs*. 1998; 30(2):155-162.

20. Grinspoon L. *Marihuana, the Forbidden Medicine (Revised and Expanded Edition)*. New Haven: Yale University Press, 1997: xii.

21. Sullum J. *Saying Yes*. New York: Jeremy P. Tarcher/Putnam, 2003: 14. Jacob Sullum is a senior editor of the libertarian monthly magazine *Reason*, a syndicated columnist, and author of several books.

22. When, in 1988 as Mayor of Baltimore, Kurt Schmoke called for a national debate on the drug war, it precipitated strong reactions and engendered controversy. Schmoke writes, "Many of my political supporters encouraged me to drop the subject… but, as Mr. Buckley

argued to the New York Bar Association, *dropping the subject of the war on drugs means dropping any hope of solving some of America's most difficult social problems*" [italics mine]. See Buckley WF, Schmoke K, McNamara J, Sweet RW. The War on Drugs is Lost. In Gray M (Editor). *Busted: Stone Cowboys, Narco-Lords, and Washington's War on Drugs.* New York: Thunder's Mouth Press/Nation Books, 2002: 203, from an article originally published in the *National Review*, July 1, 1996.

23. Editors, *Foreign Policy*, September-October, 2007.

24. See Nadelman EA. An End to Marijuana Prohibition. *National Review*, July 12, 2004. Also see Walters JP. No Surrender: The drug war saves lives. *National Review*, September 27, 2004; and Nadelman EA. The Future of An Illusion: On the drug war, believe your own eyes. *National Review*, September 27, 2004.

25. See websites for Marijuana Policy Project. Available at: www.mpp. org/search/search.jsp?query=marijuana+polls and the National Organization for the Reform of Marijuana Laws (NORML) and at: www. googlesyndicatedsearch.com/u/norml?q=marijuana+polls&x=9&y=1

26. Ibid.

27. Figure (71 percent) based on poll results released in October, 2008, before the passage of Question 2 in the November election (65 percent voted in favor), drawn from a statewide sample of 400 persons who were asked if they would vote to replace criminal penalties with a simple fine for the possession of an ounce or less of marijuana. See Marijuana Policy Project Website at: http://mpp.convio.net/site/MessageViewer?em_id=16601.0

28. See Yamamura K. Schwarzenegger says 'time for debate' on legal marijuana. *Sacramento Bee*, May 5, 2009.

29. See Grim R. Holder Vows to End Raids on Medical Marijuana Clubs. *Huffington Post*, March 29, 2009, at: www.huffingtonpost. com/2009/02/26/holder-vows-to-end-raids_n_170119.html

30. Representative Barney Frank (D-Massachusetts) introduced the Personal Use of Marijuana By Responsible Adults Act of 2009 (HR 2943) to remove federal criminal penalties for the possession of less than 100 grams (about 3.5 ounces) and for the not-for-profit transfer of up to one ounce. Representative Frank introduced the Medical Marijuana Patient Protection Act (HR 2835) to reschedule cannabis for medical prescriptive use.

31. As many as 35 states passed laws to permit access to cannabis on a medical basis in the late 1970s, 1980s, and into the early 1990s (see Grinspoon L, Bakalar JB. *Marihuana, the Forbidden Medicine.* 1997: 17. Illinois was one of the earliest states to do so. But in 1996 California passed the first of a new generation of medical cannabis laws by popular vote in the state's initiative process. I use the distinction between "first generation" and "second generation" laws to contrast the intent of the earlier laws with that of the later laws. First generation medical cannabis legislation was intended for implementation cooperatively and in tandem with federal "compassionate use" provisions. The later, second generation laws have been passed largely through popular initiative but also legislatively, as proactive expressions of the will of local communities in light of a perceived lack of constructive responsiveness to their concerns on the part of the federal government. Californians have been willing to fight a sustained uphill battle for the freedoms of local communities against aggressive federal opposition.

32. See Gleick J. *Chaos: Making a New Science.* New York: Penguin Books, 1987. For more contemporary social science and futurist applications of chaos theory and the concept of weak signals, see Smyre R. Why Weak Signals? Available at: www.charlotteviewpoint.org/default.aspx?viewpoint=110&objld=12

33. Chaos theory is a branch of mathematics concerned with the behavior of dynamic systems, and it has been found to have applications in a wide range of sciences including meteorology, biology, chemistry, and physics.

34. See, for example, Wheatley MJ. *Leadership and the New Science: Discovering Order in a Chaotic World.* San Francisco: Berrett-Koehler Publishers, 1999.

35. Judge James Gray has pointed out (personal communication) that state medical cannabis laws are really a form of strictly regulated and controlled distribution; I refer to these laws as a selective form of decriminalization to emphasize that their implementation hinges not only on the rules and regulations for accessing and distributing cannabis but also on a decision at the state level to forgo use of state resources to enforce federal laws that extend to activities for which the state has chosen not to apply criminal sanctions.

36. See Part I, p. 240 and Endnote #6.

37. The SAFER organization, discussed in more detail in Part II, was established to promote policy change that recognizes the potential relative harmfulness of marijuana as compared with alcohol. The SAFER acronym stands for Safer Alternative For Enjoyable Recreation. See Fox S, Armentano P, Tvert M. *Marijuana is Safer: So Why Are We Driving People to Drink?* White River Junction, Vermont: Chelsea Green Publishing Company, 2009; also see SAFER, Alcohol vs. Marijuana, at: www.saferchoice.org/content/view/24/53/

38. *Gonzales v. Raich* et al., U.S. Supreme Court, June 6, 2005 (545 U.S. 1-18, 2005).

39. See Joy JE, Watson Jr SJ, Benson JA (Editors, for the Institute of Medicine). *Marijuana and Medicine: Assessing the Science Base.* Washington, DC: National Academy Press, 1999; Mack A, Joy J. *Marijuana as Medicine? The Science Beyond the Controversy.* Washington, DC: National Academy Press, 2000; Plasse TF, Gorter RW, Krasnow SH, Lane M, Shepard KV, Wadleigh RG. Recent clinical experience with dronabinol. *Pharmacol Biochem Behav. 1991;* 40:695-700; Iversen LL. *The Science of Marijuana.* Oxford: Oxford University Press, 2000; Plasse T. Antiemetic Effects of Cannabinoids. In Grotenhermen F, Russo E (Editors). *Cannabis and Cannabinoids: Phar-*

macology, *Toxicology, and Therapeutic Potential.* New York: Haworth Integrative Healing Press, 2002: 165-180.

40. See Abel EL. *Marijuana: The First Twelve Thousand Years.* New York: Plenum Press, 1980; Grinspoon L, Bakalar JB, *Marihuana, the Forbidden Medicine.* New Haven: Yale University Press, 1997; Gieringer D, Rosenthal E, Carter GT. *Marijuana Medical Handbook.* Oakland, CA: Quick American, 2008.

41. *Lancet* Editors. Alcohol misuse needs a global response. *Lancet.* 2009; 373:433, 2009.

42. Zuardi AW, Crippa JAS, Hallak JEC, Moreira FA, Guimaraes FS. Cannabidiol, a Cannabis sativa constituent, as an Antipsychotic Drug. *Brazilian Journal of Medical and Biological Research.* 2006; 39(4):421-429; Zuardi AW, Guimaraes FS, Guimares VMC, Del Bel EA. Cannabidiol: Possible Therapeutic Application. In Grotenhermen F, Russo E (Eds). *Cannabis and Cannabinoids: Pharmacology, Toxicology, and Therapeutic Potential.* New York: Haworth Integrative Healing Press, 2002: 359-369; Zuardi AW, Shirakawa I, Finkelfarb E, Karniol IG. Action of cannabidiol on the anxiety and other effects produced by delta 9-THC in normal subjects. *Psychopharmacology.* 1982; 76(3): 245-250; Zuardi AW, Morais SL, Guimaraes FS, Mechoulam R. Antipsychotic Effect of Cannabidiol. *J Clin Psychiatry.* 1995; 56(10): 485-486; also see McPartland JM, Russo EB. Cannabis and Cannabis Extracts: Greater Than the Sum of Their Parts? In Russo EB, Grotenhermen F (Editors). *Handbook of Cannabis Therapeutics: From Bench to Bedside.* New York: Haworth Press, 2006: 171-204; Grotenhermen F. Clinical Pharmacodynamics of Cannabinoids. In Russo EB, Grotenhermen F (Editors). Ibid: 117-170.

43. D'Souza DC, Perry E, MacDougall L, Ammerman Y, Cooper T, Wu Y, Braley G, Gueorguieva R, Krystal JH. The Psychotomimetic Effects of Intravenous Delta-9-Tetrahydrocannabinol in Healthy Individuals: Implications for Psychosis. *Neuropsychopharmacology.* 2004; 29: 1558-1572.

44. Gladwell M. *The Tipping Point.* New York: Little, Brown and Company, 2002; quotes excerpted from pages 9-13.

Part I

1. Grinspoon L. Whither Medical Marijuana. In Gray M (Editor). *Busted: Stone Cowboys, Narco-Lords, and Washington's War on Drugs.* New York: Thunder's Mouth Press/Nation Books, 2002: 273.

2. Carter G. Foreword. In Armentano P. *Emerging Clinical Applications for Cannabis and Cannabinoids: A Review of the Recent Scientific Literature 2000-2006.* Washington, DC: NORML Foundation, 2007: 6.

3. See Grinspoon, L. *Marihuana Reconsidered.* Cambridge: Harvards University Press, 1971; Grinspoon L, Bakalar JB, *Marihuana, the Forbidden Medicine* New Haven: Yale University Press, 1993; Revised and Expanded Edition, 1997. Both books use the spelling "marihuana," which was the common spelling in federal government documents at the time the Marihuana Tax Act of 1937 was passed. The two spellings are interchangeable with "marijuana" now more common. Webster's Dictionary (1970) refers to the word, spelled either way, as an "Americanism."

4. Cannabis remained on the United States Pharmacopoeia, or national formulary of approved medicines, through 1941.

5. Grinspoon L, Bakalar JB. *Marihuana, the Forbidden Medicine,* 1997: xi.

6. The U.S. National Commission on Marihuana and Drug Abuse, appointed by President Nixon and chaired by a former Republican Governor of Pennsylvania, Raymond P. Shafer, issued its first report in 1972, and the recommendations were endorsed by the American Medical Association, the American Bar Association, the American Association for Public Health, the National Education Association, and the National Council of Churches. The commission issued its second and final report in 1973. See Gray JP. *Why Our Drug Laws Have Failed and What We Can Do About It.* Philadelphia: Temple University Press, 2001: 255-257.

7. *Washington Post,* June 6, 1971. Cited in Gerber RJ. *Legalizing Marijuana: Drug Policy Reform and Prohibition Politics.* Westport, CT: Praeger, 2004: 24.

8. *Washington Post,* March 1973, at A4, quoting an address of the president on crime and drug abuse, broadcast on radio from Camp David, October 15, 1972 (White House Press Release of this date). Cited in Gerber RJ. Ibid.: 25.

9. Judge Rudolph J. Gerber writes, "Nixon's final word on the drug menace, especially marijuana, was the creation of the Drug Enforcement Administration (DEA) to prosecute, as he told Congress in 1973, an 'all-out global war on the drug menace' threatening the country from within, just as Communism did from without" (Gerber, ibid.: 26). Nixon's marijuana legacy was to formalize the federal government's commitment to a drug war labeling all cannabis users as criminals. In so doing, he set the federal bureaucracy on an untenable course that would only gradually come to be widely recognized for what it was—a collision course with medicine, science, public health, common sense, and the basic principles of freedom and tolerance upon which our country was founded. Although cannabis was federally prohibited before America reached the middle of the 20th century, Nixon's insistence on its prohibition as the new federal Controlled Substances Act (1970) was crafted turned out to be a costly decision that denied potential benefits to consumers, created new crimes, incurred new law enforcement costs, quashed opportunities for research, and relinquished the economic benefits of a potentially legitimate industry.

10. For a more detailed historical review including additional medical references from the late 19th and early 20th centuries, see Grinspoon L, Bakalar, JB. *Marihuana, the Forbidden Medicine*: 1-22.

11. See Rowe TC. Federal *Narcotic Laws and the War on Drugs: Money Down a Rathole.* New York: Haworth Press, 2006; also see Herer J. *The Emperor Wears No Clothes.* Austin, TX: Ah Ha, 2000.

12. At the present time, in consideration of economic incentives for maintaining prohibition, one might ask about the alcohol industry, the tobacco industry, the pharmaceutical industry, the drug testing industry, and the prison industry. Each of those industries could potentially benefit from maintaining cannabis prohibition.

13. Grinspoon L, Bakalar JB. *Marihuana, the Forbidden Medicine,* 1997.

14. In the Matter of Marijuana Rescheduling Petition, Drug Enforcement Administration, Docket No. 86-22, September 6, 1988 (Opinion, Recommended Ruling, Findings of Fact, Conclusions of Law and Decision of Administrative Law Judge Francis L. Young).

15. Quoted in Gerber RJ. *Legalizing Marijuana: Drug Policy Reform and Prohibition Politics*: 102.

16. See Zimmer L, Morgan JP. *Marijuana Myths, Marijuana Facts: A Review of the Scientific Evidence.* New York: Lindesmith Center, 1997; also see Joy J, Watson S, Benson J (Institute of Medicine). *Marijuana and Medicine: Assessing the Science Base.* Washington, DC: National Academy Press, 1999.

17. See Grinspoon L, Bakalar JB. *Marihuana, the Forbidden Medicine*: 48-58. For a more recent and extensive discussion and summary of cases from the Compassionate IND program, see Russo EB, Mathre ML, Byrne A, Velin R, Bach PJ, Sanchez-Ramos J, Kirlin KA. Chronic Cannabis Use in the Compassionate Investigational New Drug Program: An Examination of Benefits and Adverse Effects of Legal Clinical Cannabis. In Russo EB, Grotenhermen F (Editors). *Handbook of Cannabis Therapeutics: From Bench to Bedside*: 399-447.

18. See Russo EB, Mathre ML, Byrne A, Velin R, Sanchez-Ramos J, Kirlin KA. Ibid.

19. See Zimmer L, Morgan JP. *Marijuana Myths, Marijuana Facts*; also Joy J, Watson S, Benson J. *Marijuana and Medicine: Assessing the Science Base.*

20. Joy J, Watson S, Benson J. Ibid.

21. Vaporizers currently used for cannabis inhalation heat the plant material to temperatures high enough to release active cannabinoid compounds without plant combustion, so that there is little or no tar—a presumptive carcinogen—in the vapor; tar has been implicated as a carcinogen from tobacco studies. There is no compelling direct evidence of similar effects even with smoked cannabis, but vaporization addresses that concern by minimizing tar exposure. Liquid medicinal cannabis extracts are produced and used in the United States, though not as legal commodities, in some states with medical cannabis laws. A legally manufactured pharmaceutical grade medicinal cannabis extract is produced by GW Pharmaceutical of Oxford, England, and is available for use in Canada with indications of multiple sclerosis and cancer pain. This product, patented as Sativex®, is currently being researched in the United States for possible FDA approval.

22. American Medical Association, Council on Scientific Affairs. Featured Report: Medical Marijuana (A-01) Full Text, 22 pages. Published in 2001. Available at: www.ama-assn.org/ama/pub/category/print/13625.html

23. Canadian Senate's Special Committee on Illegal Drugs, 2002.

24. American College of Physicians. Supporting Research into the Therapeutic Role of Marijuana. Philadelphia: American College of Physicians; 2008: Position Paper. (Available from American College of Physicians, 190 N. Independence Mall West, Philadelphia, PA 19106). Also available, with Addendum, at: www.acponline.org/advocacy/where_we_stand/other_issues/medmarijuana.pdf

25. Produced and directed by Jed Riffe, *Waiting to Inhale: Marijuana, Medicine and the Law*. Jed Riffe Films, LLC, 2006.

26. Chapkis W, Webb R. *Dying to Get High: Marijuana as Medicine*. New York: New York University Press, 2008.

27. See Russo E, Guy GW. A Tale of Two Cannabinoids: The Therapeutic Rationale for Combining Tetrahydrocannabinol and Canna-

bidiol. *Medical Hypotheses.* 2006; 66(2): 234-246; McPartland JM, Russo EB. Cannabis and Cannabis Extracts: Greater Than the Sum of Their Parts? In Russo EB, Grotenhermen F (Editors). *Handbook of Cannabis Therapeutics: From Bench to Bedside.* New York: Haworth Press, 2006: 171-204; Grotenhermen F. Clinical Pharmacodynamics of Cannabinoids. In Russo EB, Grotenhermen F (Editors). *Handbook of Cannabis Therapeutics: From Bench to Bedside,* 2006: 117-170.

28. Captured on video clip in *Waiting to Inhale,* Jed Riffe Films, 2006.

29. In America's federal system, states license the practice of medicine, whereas the federal government regulates controlled substances and other medicines. Some would argue that the latter activity already oversteps the federal government's legitimate reach, but in either case McCaffrey's threats involved a conflict over states' rights.

30. U.S. Court of Appeals, Ninth Circuit, October 29, 2002 decision in *Conant v. Walters,* No. 00-17222 (formerly *Conant v. McCaffrey*), written by Chief Judge Mary M. Schroeder, quoted in Liptak A. Medical Marijuana Wins a Court Victory. *New York Times,* October 30, 2002.

31. Kassirer JP. Federal Foolishness and Marijuana. *New Engl J Med.* 1997; 336: 366-367.

32. American Medical Association, Council on Scientific Affairs. Medical Marijuana (A-01), 2001. Available at: www.ama-assn.org/pub/category/print/13625.html

33. This remark pertains primarily to my clinical findings listening to what patients have told me about their experiences with cannabis, but for additional examples see: www.rxmarijuana.com/comments_and_observations.htm; also Grinspoon L, Bakalar J. *Marihuana, the Forbidden Medicine,* 1997. For other sources also see: Gieringer D, Medical Use of Cannabis: Experience in California. In Grotenhermen F, Russo E (Editors). *Cannabis and Cannabinoids: Pharmacology, Toxicology, and Therapeutic Potential.* New York: Haworth Integrative

Healing Press, 2002: 143-151; Gieringer D, Rosenthal E, Carter GT. *Marijuana Medical Handbook: Practical Guide to the Therapeutic Uses of Marijuana.* Oakland, CA: Quick American, 2008; Russo E, Grotenhermen F (Editors). *Handbook of Cannabis Therapeutics: From Bench to Bedside.* New York: The Haworth Press, 2006; and Bello J. *The Benefits of Marijuana: Physical, Psychological and Spiritual.* Boca Raton, Florida: Lifeservices Press, 2000.

34. Schmoke K. Forging a New Consensus in the War on Drugs. In Masters B (Editor). 2004: 60.

35. For an overview of cannabis use in multiple sclerosis (MS) and a brief general synopsis of MS and its standard treatment, see Petro DJ. Cannabis in Multiple Sclerosis: Women's Health Concerns. In Russo EB, Grotenhermen F (Editors). *Handbook of Cannabis Therapeutics: From Bench to Bedside.* 2006: 363-379; also see Gieringer D, Rosenthal E, Carter GT. *Marijuana Medical Handbook.* Oakland, CA: Quick American, 2008: 73-75; for a more extensive general discussion of MS and its treatment, see Ropper AH, Samuels MA. *Adams & Victor's Principles of Neurology,* Ninth Edition. Chapter 36: Multiple Sclerosis and Allied Demyelinating Diseases. New York: McGraw-Hill, 2009; for consumer-oriented general information on MS, see the website of the National Multiple Sclerosis Society at www.nationalmssociety.org/index.aspx or the Mayo Clinic at www.mayoclinic.com/health/multiple-sclerosis/DS00188.

36. Bearman D. *Demons, Discrimination and Dollars: A Brief History of the Origins of American Drug Policy.* Goleta, CA: Prosperity Press, 2008: 97.

37. Harry J. Anslinger, Director of the Bureau of Narcotics from 1932 to 1962, championed the cause of marijuana prohibition by sounding an alarm to members of Congress. He maintained case files that included newspaper clippings—often drawn from publications owned by William Randolph Hearst—that he used for his speeches and articles and from which he read liberally in his testimony before Congress in support of the 1937 Marihuana Tax Act. He submitted material on

"Marijuana Users—Musicians, 1933-1937," reported to have included the following: "Most marijuana smokers are Negroes, Hispanics, Filipinos, and entertainers. Their satanic music, jazz, and swing result from marijuana usage. This marijuana causes white women to seek sexual relations with Negroes" (see Gerber RJ. *Legalizing Marijuana: Drug Policy Reform and Prohibition Politics.* 2004: 9; Bearman, ibid: 95). Anslinger's "Reefer Madness" campaign, including the propaganda film by that name, claimed that marijuana led to insanity and violence. Ironically, Anslinger later claimed not only that marijuana legalization would lead to "slaughter on the highways" but also that marijuana also produced "pacifism and communist brainwashing" in its users (see Gerber, ibid.: 19; Bearman, ibid.: 101).

At the time of the passage of the Marihuana Tax Act, Dr. William Woodward of the American Medical Association (AMA) argued that the known medical applications and history of safe use warranted preservation of access to cannabis as medicine. Dr. Woodward pointed out that there were no data demonstrating harms of marijuana sufficient to warrant its federal prohibition; that the rhetoric of Anslinger's antimarijuana campaign was drawn from selected newspaper articles of the day; and that consultation with relevant and appropriate public agencies revealed no record that marijuana or cannabis problems had been identified as salient or significant sources of social disruption, health problems, or criminality. Woodward, a physician and lawyer whose distinguished career included representation of the AMA on health policy issues, was apparently not well received by the House Ways and Means Committee, and he was told: "You ought to come here with some constructive proposals rather than criticisms, rather than trying to throw obstacles in the way of something that the Federal Government is trying to do" (see Grinspoon L, Bakalar JB. *Marihuana, the Forbidden Medicine.* 1997: 10-11, citing the U.S. Congress, House Ways and Means Committee, Hearings on HR 6385: Taxation of Marihuana, 75th Cong., 1st sess., 1937: 117).

38. For general information on fibromyalgia, see the Centers for Disease Control and Prevention, Arthritis Types Overview, Fibromyalgia, at: www.cdc.gov/ARTHRITIS/arthritis/fibromyalgia.htm;

or Mayo Clinic Staff, Fibromyalgia, at: www.mayoclinic.com/health/ fibromyalgia/DS00079; for general information on Sjogren's Syndrome, see: www.nlm.nih.gov/medlineplus/sjogrenssyndrome.html, www.sjogrensworld.org/brain_fog.htm, and www.sjogrens.org. For anecdotal reports and summaries of consumers using cannabis for fibromyalgia symptoms, see: www.rxmarijuana.com/comments and observations.htm. For summary information and case documentation on cannabis use by individuals with chronic pain, inflammation, and autoimmune conditions (including multiple sclerosis [MS]), see Gieringer D, Rosenthal E, Carter GT. *Marijuana Medical Handbook: Practical Guide to the Therapeutic Uses of Marijuana.* Oakland, CA: Quick American, 2008: 62-80; Gieringer D. Medical Use of Cannabis: Experience in California. In Grotenhermen F, Russo E (Editors). *Cannabis and Cannabinoids: Pharmacology, Toxicology, and Therapeutic Potential.* New York: Haworth Integrative Healing Press, 2002: 143-151; Grinspoon L, Bakalar JL. *Marihuana, the Forbidden Medicine,* 1997; and for a more recent overview of cannabinoids in chronic pain, see Russo EB. Cannabinoids in the management of difficult to treat pain. *Ther Clin Risk Manag.* 2008; 4(1): 245-259. Available at: www.pubmedcentral.nih.gov/articlerender. fcgi?artid=2503660

39. *Waiting to Inhale,* Jed Riffe Films, 2006.

40. Despite its prohibition during the 20th century, cannabis has been available legally and used as medicine in the U.S. for more of this nation's history than not. Cannabis was probably used medicinally in the U.S. at least as far back as 1840 and was cultivated for hemp fiber long before that. Bearman writes: "Hemp is a very versatile plant. Hemp was used to make fabric, lighting oil, fuel oil, incense, medicine, paper (all the drafts of the Constitution were written on hemp paper). Hemp is a food, an important source of protein for human and animal consumption. It also is rich in Omega 3 fatty acids…The hemp fibers extracted from cannabis were used mainly for textiles, rope, canvas, and paper" (Bearman, D. *Demons, Discrimination and Dollars*).

41. See Bergstrom J. Marijuana Smoking Does Not Cause Lung Cancer. *Anderson Valley Advertiser* (CA), July 6, 2005. The article covers the 15th annual meeting of the International Cannabinoid Research Society, Clearwater, Florida, June 24-27, 2005, and includes summaries of both Tashkin's study on marijuana use and lung cancer, and Abrams's research on cannabis for the management of pain in AIDS neuropathy. Bergstrom writes: "After Abrams's presentation, a questioner bemoaned the difficulty of 'separating the high from the clinical benefits.' Abrams responded: 'I'm an oncologist as well as an AIDS doctor and I don't think that a drug that creates euphoria in patients with terminal diseases is having an adverse effect.'"

42. See Grinspoon L, Bakalar JB. *Marihuana, the Forbidden Medicine*, 1997; Grinspoon L. In Ratsch, C. *Marijuana Medicine*, 2001; Grinspoon L. In Gray M. *Busted: Stone Cowboys, Narco-Lords, and Washington's War on Drugs*, 2002; Grinspoon L. *O'Shaughnessy's: Journal of the California Cannabis Research Medical Group*, 2003; Grinspoon L. *Boston Globe*, 2007.

43. Abrams DI, Jay CA, Shade SB, Vizoso H, Reda H, Press S, Kelly ME, Rowbotham MC, Petersen KL. Cannabis in painful HIV-associated neuropathy: A randomized placebo-controlled trial. *Neurology*. 2007; 68: 515-521.

44. Video clip of interview with Dr. Abrams in *Waiting to Inhale*, Riffe J.

45. Kassirer JP. Federal Foolishness and Marijuana. *New Engl J Med*. 1997; 336: 366-367.

46. The first article mentioned: Abrams DI, Hilton JF, Leiser RJ, Shade SB, Elbeik TA, Aweeka FT, Benowitz NL, Bredt BM, Kosel B, Aberg JA, Deeks SG, Mitchell TF, Mulligan K, Bacchetti P, McCune JM, Schambelan M. Short-Term Effects of Cannabinoids in Patients with HIV-1 Infection: A Randomized, Placebo-Controlled Clinical Trial. *Ann Intern Med*. 2003; 139: 258-266; the second article, cited above (note 43).

47. United States Department of Justice, Drug Enforcement Administration. In the Matter of Lyle E. Cracker, Ph.D. (Docket No. 05-16). Opinion and Recommended Ruling, Findings of Fact, Conclusions of Law, and Decision of the Administrative Law Judge. Mary Ellen Bittner, Administrative Law Judge, February 12, 2007.

48. United States Department of Justice, Drug Enforcement Administration. Lyle E. Cracker, Ph.D., Denial of Application (Docket No. 05-16). Michele M. Leonhart, Deputy Administrator, January 7, 2009.

49. American Medical Association, Annual Meeting, Orlando, Florida, November 9, 2008.

50. The studies referred to include: Soderpalm AHV, Schuster A, de Wit H. Antiemetic Efficacy of Smoked Marijuana: Subjective and Behavioral Effects on Nausea Induced by Syrup of Ipecac. *Pharmacology, Biochemistry and Behavior.* 2001; 69: 343-350; Abrams DI, Hilton JF, Leiser RJ, Shade SB, Elbeik TA, Aweeka FT, Benowitz NL, Bredt BM, Kosel B, Aberg JA, Deeks SG, Mitchell TF, Mulligan K, Bacchetti P, McCune JM, Schambelan M. Short-Term Effects of Cannabinoids in Patients with HIV-1 Infection: A Randomized, Placebo-Controlled Clinical Trial. *Ann Intern Med.* 2003; 139: 258-263; Haney M, Rabkin J, Gunderson E, Foltin RW. Dronabinol and marijuana in HIV(+) smokers: acute effects on caloric intake and mood. *Psychopharmacology.* 2005; 181: 170-178; Abrams DI, Jay CA, Shade SB, Vizoso H, Reda H, Press S, Kelly ME, Rowbotham MC, Petersen KL. Cannabis in painful HIV-associated neuropathy: A randomized placebo-controlled trial. *Neurology.* 2007; 68: 515-521; Abrams DI, Vizoso HP, Shade SB, Jay C, Kelly ME, Benowitz NL. Vaporization as a Smokeless Cannabis Delivery System: A Pilot Study. *Clinical Pharmacology & Therapeutics.* 2007; 82: 572-578; Haney M, Gunderson EW, Rabkin J, Hart CL, Vosburg SK, Comer SD, Foltin RW. Dronabinol and marijuana in HIV-positive marijuana smokers. Caloric intake, mood, and sleep. *J Acquir Defic Syndr.* 2007; 45(5): 545-554; Wallace M, Schulteis G, Atkinson JH, Wolfson T, Lazzaretto D, Bentley H, Gouaux B, Abramson I.

Dose-dependent Effects of Smoked Cannabis on Capsaicin-induced Pain and Hyperalgesia in Healthy Volunteers. *Anesthesiology.* 2007; 107(5): 785-796; Corey-Bloom J, Wolfson T, Gamst A, Jin S, Marcotte T, Bentley H, Gouaux B. Short-term Effects of Medicinal Cannabis on Spasticity in Multiple Sclerosis. Poster presented at the 60th Annual Meeting of the American Academy of Neurology, Chicago, Illinois, 2008. Available at: http://www.cmcr.ucsd.edu/geninfo/jcb_aan_poster.pdf; Ellis RJ, Toperoff W, Vaida F, van der Brande G, Gonzales J, Gouaux B, Bentley H, Atkinson JH. Smoked Medicinal Cannabis for Neuropathic Pain in HIV: A Randomized, Crossover Clinical Trial. *Neuropsychopharmacology.* 2008; 1-9, published online, 8/6/08; and Wilsey B, Marcotte T, Tsodikov A, Millman J, Bentley H, Gouaux B, Fishman S. A Randomized, Placebo-Controlled, Crossover Trial of Cannabis Cigarettes in Neuropathic Pain. *Journal of Pain.* 2008; 9(6): 506-521.

51. See Klausner MS. Feds should stop harassing sick patients who have the legal right to use cannabis. *Los Angeles Times*, January 26, 2007.

52. Grotenhermen F. Practical Hints. In Grotenhermen F, Russo E (Editors). *Cannabis and Cannabinoids: Pharmacology, Toxicology, and Therapeutic Potential.* New York: Haworth Integrative Healing Press, 2002: 349.

53. Herzlinger R. *Who Killed Healthcare? America's $2 Trillion Medical Problem—And the Consumer-Driven Cure.* New York: McGraw-Hill, 2007.

54. See Brooke L. A Brief History of the Transdermal Cannabinoid Patch. *Hempire*, Premier Issue, July/August 2009: 27. Distributed at the First Annual THC Expo, Los Angeles Convention Center, June, 2009.

55. See Abrams DI, Vizoso HP, Shade SB, Jay C, Kelly ME, Benowitz NL. Vaporization as a Smokeless Cannabis Delivery System: A Pilot Study. *Clinical Pharmacology & Therapeutics*, 2007; 82: 572-578; also see Gieringer D, St. Laurent J, Goodrich S. Cannabis Vaporizer

Combines Efficient Delivery of THC with Effective Suppression of Pyrolytic Compounds. *J Cannabis Ther.* 2004; 4.

56. See Grotenhermen F. Clinical Pharmacodynamics of Cannabinoids. In Russo EB, Grotenhermen F (Editors). *Handbook of Cannabis Therapeutics: From Bench to Bedside.* New York: Haworth Press, 2006: 117-170.

57. See McPartland JM, Russo EB. Cannabis and Cannabis Extracts: Greater Than the Sum of Their Parts? In Russo EB, Grotenhermen F (Editors). *Handbook of Cannabis Therapeutics: From Bench to Bedside.* New York: Haworth Press, 2006: 171-204.

58. Joy JE, Watson Jr SJ, Benson JA (Editors). *Marijuana and Medicine: Assessing the Science Base.* Institute of Medicine. Washington, DC: National Academy Press, 1999.

59. See Ligresti A, Di Marzo V. Endocannabinoid-Based Molecules as Potential Therapeutic Drugs. In Onaivi ES, Sugiura T, Di Marzo V (Editors). *Endocannabinoids: The Brain and Body's Marijuana and Beyond.* Boca Raton, FL: Taylor & Francis, 2006; Grotenhermen F. Clinical Pharmacodynamics of Cannabinoids. In Russo E, Grotenhermen F (Editors). *Handbook of Cannabis Therapeutics: From Bench to Bedside.* New York: The Haworth Press, 2006: 117-170; Gieringer D, Rosenthal E, Carter GT. *Marijuana Medical Handbook.* Oakland, CA: Quick American: 51-73.

60. Russo E, Guy GW. A Tale of Two Cannabinoids: The Therapeutic Rationale for Combining Tetrahydrocannabinol and Cannabidiol. *Medical Hypotheses.* 2006; 66(2): 234-246.

61. For example, see www.rxmarijuana.com; also see Americans for Safe Access website, at: www.safeaccessnow.org.

62. For example, see Notcutt W, Price M, Miller R, Newport S, Phillips C, Simmons S, Sansom C. Initial experiences with medicinal extracts of cannabis for chronic pain: Results from 34 'N of 1' studies. *Anaesthesia.* 2004; 59: 440-452.

63. See Fichtner CG, Luchins DJ, Malan RD, Hanrahan P. Real-World Pharmacotherapy with Novel Antipsychotics. *Journal of Practical Psychiatry and Behavioral Health.* 1999; 5: 37-43.

64. See Kinzie JD, Leung P. Clonidine in Cambodian patients with post-traumatic stress disorder. *J Nerv Ment Dis.* 1989; 177: 546-550; Perry BD, Giller EL, Southwick SM. Altered platelet alpha-2-adrenergic receptor affinity states in post-traumatic stress disorder. *Am J Psychiatry.* 1987; 144: 1511-1512.

65. See Grinspoon L, Bakalar, JB. *Marihuana, the Forbidden Medicine.* New Haven: Yale University Press, 1997; also see Russo E. Migraine. In Grotenhermen F, Russo E (Editors). *Cannabis and Cannabinoids: Pharmacology, Toxicology, and Therapeutic Potential.* New York: Haworth Integrative Healing Press, 2002: 187-193; Gieringer D, Rosenthal E, Carter GT. *Marijuana Medical Handbook.* Oakland, CA: Quick American, 2008: 67-69.

66. For a recent example of pharmacogenetic research in psychiatry, specifically studying genetic variables that may provide information about the likelihood of lithium's sustained effectiveness as a mood stabilizer in patients with bipolar disorder, see Perlis RH, Smoller JW, Ferreira MAR, McQuillin A, Bass N, Lawrence J, Sachs GS, Nimgaonkar V, Scolnick EM, Gurling H, Sklar P, Purcell S. A Genomewide Association Study of Response to Lithium for Prevention of Recurrence in Bipolar Disorder. *Am J Psychiatry.* 2009; 166: 718-725; also see an editorial addressing the issue more broadly: Nurnberger Jr JI. New Hope for Pharmacogenetic Testing. *Am J Psychiatry.* 2009; 166: 635-638; for a comprehensive and detailed overview of similar approaches to the study of the endocannabinoid system, with particular attention to genetic variables associated with marijuana use, see Onaivi ES, Ishiguro H, Zhang PW, Lin Z, Akinshola BE, Leonard CM, Chirwa SS, Gong J, Uhl GR. Endocannabinoid Receptor Genetics and Marijuana Use. In Onaivi ES, Sugiura T, Di Marzo V (Editors). *Endocannabinoids: The Brain and Body's Marijuana and Beyond.* Boca Raton, FL: Taylor & Francis, 2006: 57-118. The methods of pharmacogenetics might eventually help explain why some patients report

cannabis to be effective as a substitute for alcohol and may even find that their interest in alcohol is greatly diminished or eliminated when they have access to cannabis.

67. Joy JE, Watson Jr SJ, Benson JA (Editors). *Marijuana and Medicine: Assessing the Science Base.* Institute of Medicine. Washington, DC: National Academy Press, 1999.

68. Joy JE. Ibid.

69. Ibid.

70. See Tashkin DP. Respiratory Risks from Marijuana Smoking. In Grotenhermen F, Russo E (Editors). *Cannabis and Cannabinoids: Pharmacology, Toxicology, and Therapeutic Potential.* New York: Haworth Integrative Healing Press, 2002: 325-335.

71. See Bergstrom J. Marijuana Smoking Does Not Cause Lung Cancer. *Anderson Valley Advertiser* (CA), July 6, 2005. Ibid, for a general summary of the trajectory of Dr. Tashkin's research; for a more detailed summary of specific research findings, see Tashkin DP. Respiratory Risks from Marijuana Smoking. In Grotenhermen F, Russo E (Editors). *Cannabis and Cannabinoids: Pharmacology, Toxicology, and Therapeutic Potential.* New York: Haworth Integrative Healing Press, 2002: 325-335. For subsequent research on the question of an association between marijuana use and cancer, not only failing to find a significant positive correlation but actually finding a statistically significant negative association, see note 72.

72. Liang C, McClean MD, Marsit C, Christensen B, Peters E, Nelson HH, Kelsey KT. A Population-Based Case-Control Study of Marijuana Use and Head and Neck Squamous Cell Carcinoma. *Cancer Prev Res*, July 28, 2009. Epub ahead of print, available at: www.ncbi.nlm.nih.gov/pubmed/19638490. A previous report, with less adequate statistical and population control measures, found increased risk of head and neck cancer associated with marijuana use: Zhang Z-F, Morgenstern H, Spitz MR, Tashkin DP, Yu G-P, Marshall JR, Hsu TC, Schantz SP. Marijuana Use and Increased Risk of

Squamous Cell Carcinoma of the Head and Neck. *Cancer Epidemiology Biomarkers & Prevention.* 1999; 8: 1071-1078.

73. See Maccarrone M. Involvement of the Endocannabinoid System in Cancer. In Onaivi ES, Sugiura T, Di Marzo V (Editors). *Endocannabinoids: The Brain and Body's Marijuana and Beyond.* 2006: 451-466; Parolaro D, Massi P, Rubino T, Monti E. Endocannabinoids in the immune system and cancer. *Prostaglandins, Leukotrienes and Essential Fatty Acids.* 2002; 66: 319-332; Melck D, Bisogno T, De Petrocellis L, Beaulieu P, Rice AS, Di Marzo V. Cannabimimetic eicosanoids in cancer and inflammation: an update. *Advances in Experimental Medicine and Biology.* 2002; 507: 381-386; Galve-Roperh I, Sanchez C, Cortes ML, Gomez del Pulgar T, Izquierdo M, Guzman M. Anti-tumoral action of cannabinoids: Involvement of sustained ceramide accumulation and extracellular signal-regulated kinase activation. *Nature Medicine.* 2000; 3: 313-319. Carracedo A, Gironella M, Lorente M, Garcia S, Guzman M, Velasco G, Iovanna JL. Cannabinoids Induce Apoptosis of Pancreatic Tumor Cells via Endoplasmic Reticulum Stress-Related Genes. *Cancer Res.* 2006; 66: 6748-6755; Caffarel MM, Sarrio D, Palacios J, Guzman M, Sanchez C. Delta(9)-Tetrahydrocannabinol Inhibits Cell Cycle Progression in Human Breast Cancer Cells through Cdc2 Regulation. *Cancer Res.* 2006; 66: 6615-6621; Ligresti A, Moriello AS, Starowicz K, Matias I, Pisanti S, De Petrocellis L, Laezza C, Portella G, Bifulco M, Di Marzo V. Anti-Tumor Activity of Plant Cannabinoids with Emphasis on the Effect of Cannabidiol on Human Breast Carcinoma. *J Pharmacol Exp Ther.* 2006; 318: 1375-1387.

74. See Dasgupta P, Rizwani W, Pillai S, Kinkade R, Kovacs M, Rastogi S, Banerjee S, Carless M, Kim E, Coppola D, Haura E, Chellappan S. Nicotine induces cell proliferation, invasion and epithelial-mesenchymal transition in a variety of human cancer cell lines. *International Journal of Cancer.* 2008; 124: 36-45.

75. The argument can be made that because cannabis has been prohibited, unlike tobacco and alcohol, studies may not have been sufficiently large to demonstrate an increased risk statistically. However,

the Kaiser-Permanente studies of marijuana use, mortality, and cancer incidence have analyzed data on a population of 65,171 medical care program enrollees and found no clear relationship between cannabis use and cancer; see Sidney S, Beck JE, Tekawa IS, Quesenberry CP, Friedman GD. Marijuana use and mortality. *American Journal of Public Health.* 1997; 87(4): 585-590, and Sidney S, Quesenberry CP Jr, Friedman GD, Tekawa IS. Marijuana use and cancer incidence. *Cancer Causes Control.* 1997; 8: 722-728. In addition, other studies since that time, including case-control human studies, have suggested the possibility of an effect in the other direction, that is, a protective effect; see Liang et al, 2009, cited above in note 72, and, for examples of basic science research, Carracedo et al, 2006, Caffarel et al, 2006, and Ligresti et al, 2006, cited in note 73.

76. Mitchell SW. The Case of George Dedlow. *Atlantic Monthly,* 1866; Mitchell SW. *The Injuries of Nerves.* New York: Dover, 1872/1965.

77. Sacks O. *Musicophilia: Tales of Music and the Brain.* New York: Alfred A. Knopf, Inc., 2007.

78. Ibid.: 260.

79. Ibid.: 260.

80. For diagnostic criteria for posttraumatic stress disorder (PTSD) see American Psychiatric Association, *Diagnostic and Statistical Manual of Mental Disorders,* Fourth Edition. Washington, DC: American Psychiatric Association, 1994: 424-429.

81. See Mikuriya T. Cannabis as a Substitute for Alcohol. *O'Shaughnessy's: Journal of the California Cannabis Research Medical Group,* Summer, 2003: 5-8; also see Mikuriya TH. Dependency and Cannabis. In Grotenhermen F, Russo E (Eds). *Cannabis and Cannabinoids: Pharmacology, Toxicology, and Therapeutic Potential.* New York: Haworth Integrative Healing Press, 2002: 225-230.

82. Hampson AJ, Axelrod J, Grimaldi M. Cannabinoids as Antioxidants and Neuroprotectants. United States Patent, US 6,630,507

B1, October 7, 2003. Reprinted in *Hempire* Magazine, Premier Issue, July/August 2009. Distributed at the First Annual THC Expo, Los Angeles Convention Center, June, 2009.

83. Ibid.

84. Buzzell C. The 2007 Esquire 100. No. 10: Medical Pot and the Iraq Veteran. *Esquire.* Available at: www.esquire.com/features/esquire-100/essay1007

85. Ibid.

86. Marsicano G, Wotjak CT, Azad SC, Bisogno T, Rammes G, Cascio MG, Hermann H, Tang J, Hofmann C, Zieglgansberger W, et al. The endogenous cannabinoid system controls extinction of aversive memories. *Nature.* 2002; 418: 530-534.

87. In the documentary film, *Waiting to Inhale* (Jed Riffe Films, 2005), Corral summarizes the consumer-driven process used by WAMM to evaluate the quality and effects of their herbal cannabis.

88. The approach of GW Pharmaceutical to the cultivation of medicinal grade herbal cannabis and the production of herbal cannabis extracts is summarized briefly by Chief Executive Officer Geoffrey W. Guy, M.D., in a video interview included in the Jed Riffe film *Waiting to Inhale* (2005).

Part II

1. Gerber RJ. *Legalizing Marijuana: Drug Policy Reform and Prohibition Politics*. Westport, CT: Praeger, 2004: xvi.

2. Stamper N. Foreward. In Fox S, Armentano P, Tvert M. *Marijuana is Safer: So Why Are We Driving People to Drink?* White River Junction, Vermont: Chelsea Green Publishing, 2009: x-xi.

3. Lawson, G. The War Next Door. *Rolling Stone*, November 13, 2008; also see Lawson, G. *Rolling Stone*, March 19, 2009.

4. *Los Angeles Times*, Mexico Under Siege, Serrano and Quinones, November 16, 2008; Quinones, December 7, 2008; *The Atlantic*, The Border of Madness, Caputo P, December 2009.

5. Bogan J, Dolan KA, Helman C, Vardi N. The Next Disaster. *Forbes Magazine*, December 22, 2008.

6. Riverside County District Attorney's Office, White Paper. Medical Marijuana: History and Current Complications, September 2006: 2. Available at: www.rivcoda.org/News/press_releases.html

7. See Russo EB, Mathre ML, Byrne A, Velin R, Bach PJ, Sanchez-Ramos J, Kirlin KA. Chronic Cannabis Use in the Compassionate Investigational New Drug Program: An Examination of Benefits and Adverse Effects of Legal Clinical Cannabis. In Russo EB, Grotenhermen F (Editors). *Handbook of Cannabis Therapeutics: From Bench to Bedside*. New York: The Haworth Press, 2006: 399-447.

8. Quoted in Hoffman A. Judge rejects counties' challenge to California marijuana law. Associated Press, San Diego, California, December 6, 2006. At: www.sfgate.com/cgi-bin/article.cgi?file=/news/archive/2006/12/06/state/n171545S10.DTL

9. Scientific studies provide information about effectiveness based on overall trends in multiple-patient samples, typically large numbers. When a medical treatment produces positive results in scientific studies and the findings of early studies are later replicated, the

overall sample of the population studied grows and with it the case for having confidence in and recommending the treatment—provided its safety is acceptable. Such data are in turn critical in making treatment decisions (selecting treatments known to be beneficial). However, findings from scientific studies cannot yet predict whether the individual patient in question will respond favorably. Nor can they predict whether the individual patient will tolerate the medication well or experience troublesome side effects. Use of combination medication regimens is common in many branches of medicine. The database for doing so, documenting combined effectiveness and potential adverse effects to facilitate a risk-benefit analysis, is more substantial in some fields than others. Minimization of uncomfortable side effects, as well as total medication burden, is usually seen as a positive outcome. In the case of pain management, strategies to minimize tolerance to medications may be an important part of the treatment plan.

10. Klausner MS. *Los Angeles Times,* January 26, 2007.

11. Schlosser E. *Reefer Madness: Sex, Drugs, and Cheap Labor in the American Black Market.* Boston: Houghton Mifflin Company, Mariner Books Edition, 2004: 74.

12. Weil A, Rosen W. *From Chocolate to Morphine* (Revised Edition). Boston: Houghton Mifflin, Mariner Books Edition, 2004: 205.

13. Illinois Criminal Justice Information Authority, 2003 data.

14. McVay DA (Editor). *Drug War Facts (Sixth Edition).* Common Sense for Drug Policy. Printed in Canada, 2007: 177.

15. Numerous sources support this assertion. For some poignant examples, see Schlosser E. *Reefer Madness: Sex, Drugs, and Cheap Labor in the American Black Market.* Boston: Houghton Mifflin, Mariner Books Edition, 2004: 13-74, 223-228.

16. Mauer M. *Race to Incarcerate (Revised and Updated).* The Sentencing Project. New York: The New Press, 2006: 20.

17. Ibid.: 20.

18. Kane JL. Policy is Not a Synonym for Justice. In Masters B (Editor). *The New Prohibition: Voices of Dissent Challenge the Drug War.* St. Louis: Accurate Press, 2004: 45.

19. Mauer M. Race to Incarcerate. 2006: 30.

20. Ibid.: 30.

21. Ibid.: 30-35.

22. Ibid.: 162.

23. Ibid. 162.

24. Kane-Willis K, Janichek J, Clark D. *Intersecting Voices: Impacts of Illinois' Drug Policies.* Chicago: Illinois Consortium on Drug Policy, Institute for Metropolitan Affairs, Roosevelt University, 2006.

25. Ibid.: 1.

26. Ibid.: 2, 52.

27. Ibid. Quantitative descriptions include further calculations based on data provided in the Roosevelt University report.

28. Ibid. Quantitative descriptions include further calculations based on data provided in the Roosevelt University report.

29. For example, see Byrne F, Schauffler R, Lightman L, Finigan M, Carey S. California Drug Courts: A Methodology for Determining Costs and Avoided Costs. *Journal of Psychoactive Drugs, SARC Supplement.* 2004; 2: 147-156.

30. The proposal to close two prisons in Illinois met with resistance from the American Federation of State, County, and Municipal Employees (AFSCME), which represents many unionized workers across the state. Thinking strategically about future reforms, the creation of new jobs through expansion of healthcare services, as well as the establishment of new regulatory processes and structures as an alternative to the drug war, could be helpful in achieving col-

laborative relationships with organizations such as AFSCME and the employees they represent. Collectively our priorities as Americans overlap: AFSCME leadership was reported not long ago to have approved a resolution expressing general support for access to cannabis on a medicinal basis (see American Federation of State, County and Municipal Employees, 2006; available at www.afscme. org/resolutions/11367.cfm). Movement on drug policy reform will require support for workforce development to ensure that the skills of those who have helped implement the drug war agenda—a failure of policy, not workforce—are directed toward critical public health, healthcare, and law enforcement needs we all share.

31. See Drug Policy Alliance. Proposition 36: Improving Lives, Delivering Results. A Review of the First Four Years of California's Substance Abuse and Crime Prevention Act of 2000. March, 2006. Available at: www.drugpolicy.org/library/Prop360306.cfm.

32. Cronkite W. Why I Support DPA, and So Should You. Letter in support of the Drug Policy Alliance, February 23, 2006. Available at the Drug Policy Alliance website, Lindesmith Library: www.drug-policy.org/library/cronkite022306.cfm

33. See Fox S, Armentano P, Tvert M. *Marijuana is Safer: So Why Are We Driving People to Drink?* White River Junction, Vermont: Chelsea Green Publishing Company, 2009; also see www.saferchoice.org

34. Grinspoon quote from *Waiting to Inhale.* Jed Riffe Films, 2005.

35. See Pope Jr HG, Gruber AJ, Hudson JI, Huestas MA, Yurgelun-Todd D. Neuropsychological Performance in Long-term Cannabis Users. *Arch Gen Psychiatry.* 2001; 58: 909-915; Pope Jr HG, Gruber AG, Yurgelun-Todd D. Residual Neuropsychologic Effects of Cannabis. *Curr Psychiatry Rep.* 2001; 3: 507-512; Pope Jr HG, Yurgelun-Todd D. The Residual Cognitive Effects of Heavy Marijuana Use in College Students. *JAMA.* 1996; 275(7): 521-527; Earleywine M. *Understanding Marijuana: A New Look at the Scientific Evidence.* Oxford: Oxford University Press, 2002: 67-95.

36. See Cermak TL. Cannabis: The Effect of THC on Our Endogenous Cannabinoid Neural System. CSAM Addiction Review Course, October 25, 2008. Available at: www.csam-asam.org/pdf/misc/Cermak - Cannaabis.pdf; also see Hasin DS, Keyes KM, Alderson D, Wang S, Aharonovich E, Grant BF. Cannabis Withdrawal in the United States: results from NESARC. *J Clin Psychiatry.* 2008; 69:1354-1363; Budney AJ, Hughes JR, Moore BA, Novy PL. Marijuana Abstinence Effects in Marijuana Smokers Maintained in their Home Evironment. *Arch Gen Psychiatry.* 2001; 58: 917-924; Budney AJ, Hughes JR, Moore BA, Vandrey R. Review of the Validity and Significance of Cannabis Withdrawal Syndrome. *Am J Psychiatry.* 2004; 161:1967-1977; Roffman RA, Stephens RS (Editors). *Cannabis Dependence: Its Nature, Consequences and Treatment.* Cambridge, UK: Cambridge University Press, 2006.

37. See Cermak TL, 2008. ibid; also see Gieringer D, Rosenthal E, Carter GT. *Marijuana Medical Handbook: Practical Guide to the Therapeutic Uses of Marijuana.* Oakland, CA: Quick American, 2008: 27-28.

38. See House of Commons, Science and Technology Committee. Drug Classification: Making a Hash of It? Fifth Report of Session 2005-06. London: The Stationery Office Limited, July 31, 2006.

39. Booth M. *Cannabis: A History.* London: Doubleday, 2003.

40. National Institute on Alcohol Abuse and Alcoholism. Parents—Spring Break Is Another Important Time to Discuss College Drinking. NIAAA Spring Break Fact Sheet 2007, NIH Publication No. 05-5642. Rockville, MD: National Institutes of Health, March, 2007.

41. Bédard M, Dubois S, Weaver B. The impact of cannabis on driving. *Can J Public Health.* 2007; 98(1): 6-11.

42. Laumon B, Gadegbeku B, Martin J-L, Biecheler M-B. Cannabis intoxication and fatal road crashes in France: population-based case-control study. *British Medical Journal* doi:10.1136/bmj.38648.617986.1F, December 2, 2005.

43. See Smiley A. Marijuana: On-Road and Driving Simulator Studies. *Alcohol, Drugs, and Driving.* 1986; 2: 121-134; Chesher GB, Longo M. Cannabis and Alcohol in Motor Vehicle Accidents. In Grotenhermen F, Russo E (Editors). *Cannabis and Cannabinoids: Pharmacology, Toxicology, and Therapeutic Potential.* New York: Haworth Integrative Healing Press, 2002: 313-323.

44. See Earleywine M. *Understanding Marijuana: A New Look at the Scientific Evidence.* Oxford: Oxford University Press, 2002: 210-214.

45. See Grotenhermen F, Leson G, Berghaus G, Drummer OH, Krüger H-P, Longo M, Moskowitz H, Perrine B, Ramaekers J, Smiley A, Tunbridge R. Developing Science-Based Per Se Limits for Driving under the Influence of Cannabis: Findings and Recommendations by an Expert Panel. International Association for Cannabis Medicine, September, 2005. Available at: www.canorml.org/healthfacts/DUICreport.2005.pdf

46. Cermak TL. *Marijuana: What's a Parent to Believe?* Center City, Minnesota: Hazeldon, 2003.

47. See Jeffries D, Jeffries L. *Jeffrey's Journey: Healing a Child's Violent Rages.* Oakland, CA: Quick American, 2005; Sterling EE. *Maryland Medical Marijuana Criminal Defense Manual, Revised.* Silver Spring, Maryland: The Criminal Justice Policy Foundation, 2004: 11.

48. President Jimmy Carter. Speech delivered to Congress, August 2, 1977.

49. Information on Senate Bill 1381. Available at: www.ilga.gov

50. Information available at: www.ilga.gov

51. Gieringer D. Medical Use of Cannabis: Experience in California. In Grotenhermen F, Russo E (Editors): *Cannabis and Cannabinoids: Pharmacology, Toxicology, and Therapeutic Potential.* New York: Haworth Integrative Healing Press, 2002: 143-151; also see Mikuriya T. Cannabis Eases Post-Traumatic Stress. *O'Shaughnessy's: The Journal of*

Cannabis in Clinical Practice, Spring, 2006:11-12.

52. For example, see www.rxmarijuana.com/comments and observations.htm

53. D'Souza DC, Perry E, MacDougall L, Ammerman Y, Cooper T, Wu Y, Braley G, Gueorguieva R, Krystal JH. The Psychotomimetic Effects of Intravenous Delta-9-Tetrahydrocannabinol in Healthy Individuals: Implications for Psychosis. *Neuropsychopharmacology.* 2004; 29:1558-1572.

54. See Weil A, Rosen W. *From Chocolate to Morphine* (Revised Edition). Boston: Houghton Mifflin Company, 2004: 144.

55. Arseneault L, Cannon M, Poulton R, Murray R, Caspi A, Moffitt TE. Cannabis Use in Adolescence and Risk for Adult Psychosis: Longitudinal Prospective Study. *British Medical Journal.* 2002; 325:1212-1213; Henquet C, Krabbendam L, Spauwen J, Kaplan C, Lieb R, Wittchen H-U, van Os J. Prospective Cohort Study of Cannabis Use, Predisposition for Psychosis, and Psychotic Symptoms in Young People. *British Medical Journal (BMJ)*, doi:10.1136/bmj.38267.664086.63 (published 1 December 2004); Zammit S, Allebeck P, Andreasson S, Lundberg I, Lewis G. Self reported cannabis use as a risk factor for schizophrenia in Swedish conscripts of 1969: A historical cohort study. *British Medical Journal.* 2002; 325: 1199-1201; Patton GC, Coffey C, Carlin JB, Degenhardt L, Lynskey M, Hall W. Cannabis Use and Mental Health in Young People: Cohort Study. *British Medical Journal.* 2002; 325: 1195-1198; Rey JM, Tennant CC. Cannabis and Mental Health. *British Medical Journal.* 2002; 325: 1183-1184; Moore THM, Zammit S, Lingford-Hughes A, Barnes TRE, Jones PB, Burke M, Lewis G. Cannabis use and risk of psychotic or affective mental health outcomes: a systematic review. *Lancet.* 2007; 370: 319-328; Ben Amar M, Potvin S. Cannabis and Psychosis: What is the Link? *Journal of Psychoactive Drugs.* 2007; 39(2): 131-142; Arseneault L, Cannon M, Witton J, Murray RM. Causal Association Between Cannabis and Psychosis: Examination of the Evidence. *British Journal of Psychiatry.* 2004; 184:110-117; Henquet C, Murray R, Linzen D,

van Os J. The environment and schizophrenia: the role of cannabis use. *Schizophr Bull.* 2005; 31: 608-612.

56. See Gieringer D. Medical Use of Cannabis: Experience in California. In Grotenhermen F, Russo E (Editors). *Cannabis and Cannabinoids: Pharmacology, Toxicology, and Therapeutic Potential.* New York: Haworth Integrative Healing Press, 2002: 143-151; also see Mikuriya T. Cannabis as a Substitute for Alcohol. *O'Shaughnessy's: Journal of the California Cannabis Research Medical Group,* Summer 2003: 5-8; Mikuriya T. Cannabis Eases Post-Traumatic Stress. *O'Shaughnessy's: The Journal of Cannabis in Clinical Practice,* Spring, 2006:11-12.

57. Ben Amar M, Potvin S. Cannabis and Psychosis: What is the Link? *Journal of Psychoactive Drugs.* 2007; 39(2):131-142; Moore THM, Zammit S, Lingford-Hughes A, Barnes TRE, Jones PB, Burke M, Lewis G. Cannabis use and risk of psychotic or affective mental health outcomes: a systematic review. *Lancet.* 2007; 370:319-328; Hall W. Is cannabis use psychotogenic? *Lancet.* 2006; 367:193-195; Nordentoft M, Hjorthoj C. Cannabis use and risk of psychosis in later life. *Lancet.* 2007; 370: 293-294; Macleod J, Smith GD, Hickman M. Does cannabis use cause schizophrenia? *Lancet.* 2006; 367: 1055; Malik AR, D'Souza DC. Gone to Pot: The Association Between Cannabis and Psychosis. *Psychiatric Times,* April 1, 2006; Macleod J, Oakes R, Copello A, Crome I, Egger M, Hickman M, Oppenkowski T, Stokes-Lampard H, Smith GD. Psychological and social sequelae of cannabis and other illicit drug use by young people: a systematic review of longitudinal, general population studies. *Lancet.* 2004; 363: 1579-1588.

58. Moore THM, Zammit S, Lingford-Hughes A, Barnes TRE, Jones PB, Burke M, Lewis G. Cannabis use and risk of psychotic or affective mental health outcomes: a systematic review. *Lancet.* 2007; 370: 319-328.

59. For example, see Andrew EM, Gray NS, Snowden RJ. The relationship between trauma and beliefs about hearing voices: a study of

psychiatric and nonpsychiatric voice-hearers. *Psychological Medicine.* 2008; 38(10):1409-1417; also see Ritsher JB, Lucksted A, Otilingam PG, Grajales M. Hearing voices: Explanations and implications. *Psychiatric Rehabilitation Journal.* 2004; 27: 219-227.

60. See Grinspoon L, Bakalar, JB. *Marihuana, the Forbidden Medicine.* New Haven: Yale University Press, 1997; Grinspoon L, Bakalar JB. The Use of Cannabis as a Mood Stabilizer in Bipolar Disorder: Anecdotal Evidence and the Need for Clinical Research. *J Psychoactive Drugs.* 1998; 30(2): 171-7; Gieringer D, Rosenthal E, Carter GT. *Marijuana Medical Handbook: Practical Guide to the Therapeutic Uses of Marijuana.* Oakland, CA: Quick American, 2008: 80-89; Gieringer D. Medical Use of Cannabis: Experience in California. In Grotenhermen F, Russo E (Editors). *Cannabis and Cannabinoids: Pharmacology, Toxicology, and Therapeutic Potential.* New York: Haworth Integrative Healing Press, 2002: 143-151.

61. See Gieringer D, Rosenthal E, Carter GT. *Marijuana Medical Handbook: Practical Guide to the Therapeutic Uses of Marijuana.* Oakland, CA: Quick American, 2008: 80-89; Gieringer D. Medical Use of Cannabis: Experience in California. In Grotenhermen F, Russo E (Editors). *Cannabis and Cannabinoids: Pharmacology, Toxicology, and Therapeutic Potential.* New York: Haworth Integrative Healing Press, 2002: 143-151.

62. Denson TF, Earleywine M. Decreased Depression in Marijuana Users. *Addictive Behaviors.* 2006; 31(4): 738-742.

63. Shedler J, Block J. Adolescent Drug Use and Psychological Health. *American Psychologist.* 1990; 45(5): 612-630.

64. Dalman C, Allebeck P, Gunnell D, Harrison G, Kristensson K, Lewis G, Lofving S, Rasmussen F, Wicks S, Karlsson H. Infections in the CNS During Childhood and the Risk of Subsequent Psychotic Illness: A Cohort Study of More Than One Million Swedish Subjects. *Am J Psychiatry.* 2008; 165: 59-65.

65. Ibid.

66. Stoll AL, Severus WE, Freeman MP, Rueter S, Zboyan HA, Diamond E, Cress KK, Marangell LB. Omega -3 fatty acids in bipolar disorder: A preliminary double-blind, placebo-controlled trial. *Arch Gen Psychiatry.* 1999; 56: 407-412; also see Stoll AL. *The Omega-3 Connection.* New York: Simon & Schuster (Fireside Edition), 2002.

67. See Zuardi AW, Crippa JAS, Hallak JEC, Moreira FA, Guimaraes FS. Cannabidiol, a *Cannabis sativa* constituent, as an Antipsychotic Drug. *Brazilian Journal of Medical and Biological Research.* 2006; 39(4): 421-429; Zuardi AW, Guimaraes FS, Guimares VMC, Del Bel EA. Cannabidiol: Possible Therapeutic Application. In Grotenhermen F, Russo E (Eds). *Cannabis and Cannabinoids: Pharmacology, Toxicology, and Therapeutic Potential.* New York: Haworth Integrative Healing Press, 2002: 359-369; Zuardi AW, Morais SL, Guimaraes FS, Mechoulam R. Antipsychotic Effect of Cannabidiol. *J Clin Psychiatry.* 1995; 56(10): 485-486; also see Fride E, Russo E. Neuropsychiatry: Schizophrenia, Depression, and Anxiety. In Onaivi ES, Sugiura T, Di Marzo V (Editors). *Endocannabinoids: The Brain and Body's Marijuana and Beyond.* Boca Raton, FL: Taylor & Francis, 2006: 371-382.

68. See, for example: Gieringer D, Rosenthal E, Carter GT. *Marijuana Medical Handbook: Practical Guide to the Therapeutic Uses of Marijuana.* Oakland, CA: Quick American, 2008: 215-224; Conrad C. *Hemp for Health: The Medicinal and Nutritional Uses of Cannabis Sativa.* Rochester, Vermont: Healing Arts Press, 1997; also see: McPartland JM, Russo EB. Cannabis and Cannabis Extracts: Greater Than the Sum of Their Parts? In Russo EB, Grotenhermen F (Editors). *Handbook of Cannabis Therapeutics: From Bench to Bedside.* New York: Haworth Press, 2006: 171-204; Russo E, Guy GW. A Tale of Two Cannabinoids: The Therapeutic Rationale for Combining Tetrahydrocannabinol and Cannabidiol. *Medical Hypotheses.* 2006; 66(2): 234-246; Russo EB, McPartland JM. Cannabis is More than Simply Delta(9)-Tetrahydrocannabinol. *Psychopharmacology* (Berl). 2003; 165(4): 431-432.

69. See, for example, McPartland JM, Russo EB. Cannabis and Cannabis Extracts: Greater Than the Sum of Their Parts? In Russo

EB, Grotenhermen F (Editors). *Handbook of Cannabis Therapeutics: From Bench to Bedside.* New York: Haworth Press, 2006: 171-204; Russo E, Guy GW. A Tale of Two Cannabinoids: The Therapeutic Rationale for Combining Tetrahydrocannabinol and Cannabidiol. *Medical Hypotheses.* 2006; 66(2): 234-246; Russo EB, McPartland JM. Cannabis is More than Simply Delta(9)-Tetrahydrocannabinol. *Psychopharmacology* (Berl). 2003; 165(4): 431-432; Grotenhermen F. Clinical Pharmacodynamics of Cannabinoids. In Russo EB, Grotenhermen F (Editors). *Handbook of Cannabis Therapeutics: From Bench to Bedside.* New York: Haworth Press, 2006: 117-170; Zuardi AW, Crippa JAS, Hallak JEC, Moreira FA, Guimaraes FS. Cannabidiol, a *Cannabis sativa* constituent, as an Antipsychotic Drug. *Brazilian Journal of Medical and Biological Research.* 2006; 39(4): 421-429; Zuardi AW, Guimaraes FS, Guimares VMC, Del Bel EA. Cannabidiol: Possible Therapeutic Application. In Grotenhermen F, Russo E (Editors). *Cannabis and Cannabinoids: Pharmacology, Toxicology, and Therapeutic Potential.* New York: Haworth Integrative Healing Press, 2002: 359-369; Zuardi AW, Shirakawa I, Finkelfarb E, Karniol IG. Action of cannabidiol on the anxiety and other effects produced by delta 9-THC in normal subjects. *Psychopharmacology.* 1982; 76(3): 245-250.

70. Pollan M. *The Botany of Desire.* New York: Random House, 2001: 176.

71. American College of Physicians. Supporting Research into the Therapeutic Role of Marijuana. Philadelphia: American College of Physicians; 2008: Position Paper: 9. (Available from American College of Physicians, 190 N. Independence Mall West, Philadelphia, PA 19106); American Medical Association, Report on the Use of Cannabis for Medicinal Purposes, 2009, and House of Delegates Resolution, Houston, Texas, 2009. In point of clarification, this quote from the American College of Physicians (ACP) position paper is in no way intended to suggest that ACP as an organization supports a broader decriminalization agenda; the position paper is clear in its intent to support a medicinal cannabis research agenda

primarily and secondarily calls for protection—as quoted here—for patients using cannabis with the approval of their physician under state medical marijuana laws. I have argued here, especially in Part II, that medicinal or therapeutic use of cannabis is in fact sufficiently broad to extend into the realm of harm reduction by substitution for alcohol and, furthermore, that acknowledgement of that concept in fact becomes an argument not only for decriminalization for adult personal use but for regulation in order to achieve better quality control for consumers. The ACP position paper does not address the broader issues of cannabis decriminalization or regulation; I quote it here to underscore the developing consensus that there are at least some uses of cannabis, in particular when such use is supported by a patient's physician, for which criminalization is misguided and inappropriate.

72. Schlosser E. *Reefer Madness: Sex, Drugs, and Cheap Labor in the American Black Market*. 74.

Part III

1. Ventura J. Foreward. In Masters B (Editor). *The New Prohibition: Voices of Dissent Challenge the Drug War*. St. Louis: Accurate Press, 2004: vii.

2. In Miron JA. The Budgetary Implications of Marijuana Prohibition. At: www.prohibitioncosts.org. Published online, June, 2005.

3. Originally prepared as a report to the Marijuana Policy Project and published online at www.prohibitioncosts.org, June, 2005; also see Egan D, Miron JA. The Budgetary Implications of Marijuana Prohibition. In Earleywine M (Editor). *Pot Politics: Marijuana and the Costs of Prohibition*. Oxford: Oxford University Press, 2007: 17-39.

4. At: www.prohibitioncosts.org.

5. See California NORML. CA NORML Analysis Finds Marijuana Legalization Could Yield California $1.5-$2.5 Billion Per Year. Available at: www.canorml.org/background/CA_legalization.html

6. The range of $10 to $40 billion as the cost of marijuana prohibition was given by Bruce Mirken, Director of Communications for the Marijuana Policy Project, in an interview with Rachel Maddow on MSNBC, March 11, 2009. This broad range covers estimates consistent with the work of economist Jeffrey Miron (note 2 above) as well as the analysis of California NORML (note 5 above).

7. See Schmoke K. Forging a New Consensus in the War on Drugs. In Masters B (Editor). *The New Prohibition: Voices of Dissent Challenge the Drug War*. St. Louis: Accurate Press, 2004: 59-66. Schmoke wrote: "What I'm suggesting is yes, indeed, in this century there needs to be a war on drugs, but that war on drugs should be primarily a public health war, rather than a criminal justice war" (p. 62).

8. On the estimated annual cost of the existing war on drugs, see Cole J. End Prohibition Now. In Masters B. (Editor). Ibid.: 35.

9. Representative Barney Frank (D-Massachusetts) introduced the Personal Use of Marijuana By Responsible Adults Act of 2009 (H.R. 2943) on June 18, 2009. The bill would remove federal criminal penalties for the possession of less than 100 grams (about 3.5 ounces) and for the not-for-profit transfer of up to one ounce.

10. Fox S, Armentano P, Tvert M. *Marijuana is Safer: So Why Are We Driving People to Drink?* White River Junction, Vermont: Chelsea Green Publishing Company, 2009.

11. Video clip of interview with Geoffrey Guy, M.D., in Jed Riffe's film, *Waiting to Inhale*.

12. In *Leary v. United States*, 395 U.S. 6 (1969), Dr. Timothy Leary challenged the constitutionality of the Marihuana Tax Act of 1937 on the grounds that compliance with the act required self-incrimination and therefore violated the Fifth Amendment, and the U.S. Supreme Court overturned Leary's conviction for possession of marijuana on that basis. The Marihuana Tax Act was shortly thereafter superseded by the Comprehensive Drug Abuse Prevention and Control Act (Controlled Substances Act, CSA) passed by Congress in 1970.

13. United States Department of Justice, Drug Enforcement Administration. Lyle E. Cracker; Denial of Application (Docket No. 05-16), December 10, 2004.

14. United States Department of Justice, Drug Enforcement Administration. In the Matter of Lyle E. Cracker, Ph.D. (Docket No. 05-16). Opinion and Recommended Ruling, Findings of Fact, Conclusions of Law, and Decision of the Administrative Law Judge. Mary Ellen Bittner, Administrative Law Judge, February 12, 2007.

15. See Gieringer D. Medical Use of Cannabis: Experience in California. In Grotenhermen F, Russo E (Editors). *Cannabis and Cannabinoids: Pharmacology, Toxicology, and Therapeutic Potential.* New York: Haworth Integrative Healing Press, 2002: 143-151.

16. Some opponents of cannabis regulation argue that marijuana potentiates the effects of alcohol—makes it more intoxicating—when

the two are used together. That is true. But given the known health effects of the two substances, that is a better argument for prohibition of alcohol than of cannabis. Since alcohol prohibition will not be reinstated under any circumstances at this point in history, the best response on this issue is education.

17. Some have suggested lowering the drinking age as a possible response to some of the problem drinking on college campuses. Legal access to at least some alcoholic beverages for college students could facilitate a more deliberate effort to work with them on principles of responsible alcohol consumption.

18. Anecdotal observations suggest that individuals under the influence of alcohol may fail to judge or anticipate the impact of using cannabis at the same time, while cannabis consumers are often less interested in alcohol and may be more mindful of its undesirable effects.

19. Ayma EM. Let Me Chew My Coca Leaves. *New York Times*, March 14, 2009.

20. See the March 4, 2009, issue of *The Economist*. The editors present a series of articles in an issue titled: How to Stop the Drug Wars.

21. Sterling E (moderator). After Prohibition: Imagining Alternative Drug Regimes, Present and Future. Presentation and Panel Discussion, International Drug Policy Reform Conference, Albuquerque, New Mexico, November 14, 2009.

BIBLIOGRAPHY

Abel EL. *Marijuana: The First Twelve Thousand Years.* New York: Plenum Press, 1980.

Abrams DI. Medical Marijuana: Tribulations and Trials. *Journal of Psychoactive Drugs.* 1998; 30(2): 163-169.

Abrams DI, Child CC, Mitchell TF. Marijuana, the AIDS Wasting Syndrome, and the U.S. Government. *New Engl J Med.* 1995; 333: 671.

Abrams DI, Hilton JF, Leiser RJ, Shade SB, Elbeik TA, Aweeka FT, Benowitz NL, Bredt BM, Kosel B, Aberg JA, Deeks SG, Mitchell TF, Mulligan K, Bacchetti P, Mccune JM, Schambelan M. Short-Term Effects of Cannabinoids in Patients with HIV-1 Infection: A Randomized, Placebo-Controlled Clinical Trial. *Ann Intern Med.* 2003; 139: 258-266.

Abrams DI, Jay CA, Shade SB, Vizoso H, Reda H, Press S, Kelly ME, Rowbotham MC, Petersen KL. Cannabis in painful HIV-associated neuropathy: A randomized placebo-controlled trial. *Neurology.* 2007; 68: 515-521.

Abrams DI, Vizoso HP, Shade SB, Jay C, Kelly ME, Benowitz NL. Vaporization as a Smokeless Cannabis Delivery System: A Pilot Study. *Clinical Pharmacology & Therapeutics.* 2007; 82: 572-578.

Advisory Committee on Drug Dependence. Cannabis. London: Her Majesty's Stationery Office, 1969.

Aggarwal S, Carter GT, Steinborn JJ. Clearing the air: What the latest Supreme Court decision regarding medical marijuana really means. *American Journal of Hospice & Palliative Medicine.* 2005; 22(5): 327-329.

Agurell S, Halldin M, Lindgren J-E, Ohlsson A, Widman M, Gillespie H, Hollister L. Pharmacokinetics and Metabolism of Delta(1)-Tetrahydrocannabinol and Other Cannabinoids with Emphasis on Man. *Pharmacological Reviews.* 1986; 38(1): 21-43.

Bibliography

Albrecht AT, Herrick C. *100 Questions & Answers About Bipolar (Manic-Depressive) Disorder.* Sudbury, Massachusetts: Jones and Bartlett Publishers, 2007.

Alcalay M. Medical Marijuana and Children. In Jeffries D, Jeffries L. *Jeffrey's Journey.* Oakland, California: Quick American, 2005: 78-81.

Aldington S, Harwood M, Cox B, Weatherall M, Beckert L, Hansell A, Pritchard A, Robinson G, Beasley R, on behalf of the Cannabis and Respiratory Disease Research Group. Cannabis use and risk of lung cancer: a case-control study. *Eur Respir J.* 2008; 31: 280-286.

American College of Physicians. Supporting Research into the Therapeutic Role of Marijuana. Philadelphia: American College of Physicians; 2008: Position Paper. (Available from American College of Physicians, 190 N. Independence Mall West, Philadelphia, PA 19106.) Also available, with Addendum, at: www.acponline.org/advocacy/where_we_stand/other_issues/medmarijuana.pdf

American Federation of State, County and Municipal Employees (AFSCME). Supporting the Legalization of Medical Marijuana. Resolution No: 93, 37th Annual International Convention, August 7-11, 2006, Chicago, Illinois. Available at: www.afscme.org/resolutions/11367.cfm

American Medical Association, Council on Scientific Affairs. Featured Report: Medical Marijuana (A-01) Full Text, 22 pages. www.ama-assn.org/ama/pub/category/print/13625.html

American Medical Association. Report on the Use of Cannabis for Medicinal Purposes, 2009.

American Psychiatric Association, *Diagnostic and Statistical Manual of Mental Disorders*, Fourth Edition. Washington, DC: American Psychiatric Association, 1994.

Americans for Safe Access. Government Pressed to Defend Medical Marijuana Policies with Sound Science or Face Federal Lawsuit. May 2, 2006. www.safeaccessnow.org

American Thoracic Society. Study Finds No Link Between Marijuana Use and Lung Cancer. Summary of study by Tashkin et al. presented at the American Thoracic Society International Conference on May 23, 2007. Available at: www.thoracic.org/sections/publications/press-releases/conference/articles.

Amodia DS, Cano C, Eliason MJ. An Integral Approach to Substance Abuse. *Journal of Psychoactive Drugs.* 2005; 37(4): 363-371.

Andreas P, Nadelman E. *Policing the Globe: Criminalization and Crime Control in International Relations.* Oxford: Oxford University Press, 2006.

Andreasson S, Allebeck P, Engstrom A, Rydberg U. Cannabis and Schizophrenia: A Longitudinal Study of Swedish Conscripts. *Lancet,* September 26, 1987: 1483-1486.

Andrew EM, Gray NS, Snowden RJ. The relationship between trauma and beliefs about hearing voices: a study of psychiatric and non-psychiatric voice-hearers. *Psychological Medicine.* 2008; 38(10): 1409-1417.

Arendt M, Rosenberg R, Foldager L, Perto G, Munk-Jorgensen P. Cannabis-induced psychosis and subsequent schizophrenia-spectrum disorders: follow-up study of 535 incident cases. *Br J Psychiatry.* 2005; 187: 510-515.

Armentano P. Cannabis, Mental Health and Context: The Case For Regulation. National Organization for the Reform of Marijuana Laws. www.norml.org

Armentano P. Cannabis Smoke and Cancer: Assessing the Risk. NORML Library. http://www.norml.org/index.cfm?Group_ID=6891

Bibliography

Armentano P. *Emerging Clinical Applications for Cannabis and Cannabinoids: A Review of the Recent Scientific Literature 2000-2006.* Washington, DC: NORML Foundation, 2007.

Armentano P, Stroup K. Your Government Is Lying to You (Again) About Marijuana. In Masters B (Editor). *The New Prohibition: Voices of Dissent Challenge the Drug War.* St. Louis: Accurate Press, 2004: 153-170.

Arseneault L, Cannon M, Poulton R, Murray R, Caspi A, Moffitt TE. Cannabis Use in Adolescence and Risk for Adult Psychosis: Longitudinal Prospective Study. *British Medical Journal.* 2002; 325: 1212-1213.

Arseneault L, Cannon M, Witton J, Murray RM. Causal Association Between Cannabis and Psychosis: Examination of the Evidence. *British Journal of Psychiatry.* 2004; 184:110-117.

Ashton CH, Moore PB, Gallagher P, Young AH. Cannabinoids in Bipolar Affective Disorder: A Review and Discussion of Their Therapeutic Potential. *Journal of Psychopharmacology.* 2005; 19(3): 293-300.

Ayma EM. Let Me Chew My Coca Leaves. *New York Times,* March 14, 2009.

Bagshaw SM, Hagen NA. Medical Efficacy of Cannabinoids and Marijuana: A Comprehensive Review of the Literature. *J Palliat Care.* 2002; 18(2): 111-122.

Baker D, Pryce G, Giovannoni G, Thompson AJ. The Therapeutic Potential of Cannabis. *Lancet Neurol.* 2003; 2(5): 291-298.

Baum D. *Smoke and Mirrors: The War on Drugs and the Politics of Failure.* Boston: Little, Brown & Company, 1996.

Bearman D. *Demons, Discrimination and Dollars.* Goleta, California: Prosperity Press, 2008.

Bearman D. PTSD and Cannabis: A Clinician Ponders Mechanism

of Action. *O'Shaughnessy's: The Journal of Cannabis in Clinical Practice*, Spring, 2006: 9-10.

Bédard M, Dubois S, Weaver B. The impact of cannabis on driving. *Can J Public Health*. 2007; 98(1): 6-11.

Bello J. *The Benefits of Marijuana: Physical, Psychological and Spiritual* (Revised Edition). Boca Raton, Florida: Lifeservices Press, 2000.

Belville R. NBC, CBS, ABC, & FOX Happy to Profit from Marijuana, as Long as Nobody Talks About Legalizing It. National Organization for the Reform of Marijuana Laws (NORML). AlterNet August 4, 2009. Available at: www.alternet.org/story/141773/

Ben Amar M. Cannabinoids in Medicine: A Review of Their Therapeutic Potential. *Journal of Ethnopharmacology*. 2006; 105:1-25.

Ben Amar M, Potvin S. Cannabis and Psychosis: What is the Link? *Journal of Psychoactive Drugs*. 2007; 39(2):131-142.

Berlach DM, Shir Y, Ware MA. Experience with the Synthetic Cannabinoid Nabilone in Chronic Noncancer Pain. *Pain Medicine*. 2006; 7: 25-29.

Berman JS, Symonds C, Birch R. Efficacy of Two Cannabis Based Medicinal Extracts for Relief of Central Neuropathic Pain from Brachial Plexus Avulsion: Results of a Randomised Controlled Trial. *Pain*. 2004; 112: 299-306.

Bernadette H. Cannabinoid Therapeutics: High Hopes for the Future. *Drug Discov Today*. 2005; 10(7): 459-462.

Block RI. Does Heavy Marijuana Use Impair Human Cognition and Brain Function? *JAMA*. 1996; 275(7): 560-561.

Bock AW. *Waiting to Inhale*. Santa Ana, California: Seven Locks Press, 2000.

Boire RG, Feeney K. *Medical Marijuana Law*. Berkeley, California: Ronin Publishing, 2006.

Bibliography

Bolger T. Reefer Relief: The ongoing battle to legalize medical marijuana. *Long Island Press*, March 23, 2006.

Bolla KI, Brown K, Eldreth D, Tate K, Cadet JL. Dose-related Neurocognitive Effects of Marijuana Use. *Neurology.* 2002; 59: 1337-1343.

Booth, M. *Cannabis: A History.* London: Doubleday, 2003.

Bostrom BA. Gonzales v Raich. In the Supreme Court of the United States. *Issues Law Med.* 2005; 21: 47-56.

Bowers, MB. Family History and Early Psychotogenic Response to Marijuana. *Journal of Clinical Psychiatry.* 1998; 59(4): 198-199.

Brunswick M. Medical Marijuana May Soon Be Reality. *Star Tribune* (Minnesota), March 3, 2007.

Buckley WF, Schmoke K, McNamara J, Sweet RW. The War on Drugs is Lost. In Gray M (Editor). *Busted: Stone Cowboys, Narco-Lords, and Washington's War on Drugs.* New York: Thunder's Mouth Press/Nation Books, 2002; partial reprint of an article originally published in the *National Review*, July 1, 1996.

Budney AJ, Hughes JR, Moore BA, Novy PL. Marijuana Abstinence Effects in Marijuana Smokers Maintained in their Home Evnironment. *Arch Gen Psychiatry.* 2001; 58: 917-924.

Budney AJ, Hughes JR, Moore BA, Vandrey R. Review of the Validity and Significance of Cannabis Withdrawal Syndrome. *Am J Psychiatry.* 2004; 161: 1967-1977.

Buxton J. *The Political Economy of Narcotics: Production, Consumption, & Global Markets.* Nova Scotia: Fernwood Publishing, 2006.

Buzzell C. The 2007 Esquire 100. No. 10: Medical Pot and the Iraq Veteran. *Esquire.* Available at: www.esquire.com/features/esquire-100/essay1007

Byrne A. The Recurring Terror of Combat. *O'Shaughnessy's: The Journal of Cannabis in Clinical Practice*, Spring, 2006: 6-7.

Byrne F, Schauffler R, Lightman L, Finigan M, Carey S. California Drug Courts: A Methodology for Determining Costs and Avoided Costs. *Journal of Psychoactive Drugs, SARC Supplement.* 2004; 2: 147-156.

Caffarel MM, Sarrio D, Palacios J, Guzman M, Sanchez C. Delta(9)-Tetrahydrocannabinol Inhibits Cell Cycle Progression in Human Breast Cancer Cells through Cdc2 Regulation. *Cancer Res.* 2006; 66: 6615-6621.

Calhoun SR, Galloway GP, Smith DE. Abuse Potential of Dronabinol (Marinol). *Journal of Psychoactive Drugs.* 1998; 30(2): 187-196.

California NORML. CA NORML Analysis Finds Marijuana Legalization Could Yield California $1.5-$2.5 Billion Per Year. Available at: www.canorml.org/background/CA_legalization.html

Cami J, Farre M. Drug Addiction. *New Engl J Med.* 2003; 349: 975-986.

Campbell FA, Tramer MR, Carroll D, Reynolds DJ, Moore RA, McQuay HJ. Are Cannabinoids an Effective and Safe Treatment Option in the Management of Pain? A Qualitative Systematic Review. *BMJ.* 2001; 323: 13-16.

Campos P. In reviewing some drugs, FDA practices twisted science. Scripps Howard News Service, April 27, 2006.

Canadian Government Commission of Inquiry. The Non-Medical Use of Drugs. Ottawa, Canada: Information Canada, 1970.

Canal Zone Committee. The Panama Canal Zone Military Investigations, 1925.

Capler R, Lucas P. Guidelines for the Community-Based Distribution of Medical Cannabis in Canada. British Columbia Compassion Club Society and Vancouver Island Compassion Society, May 2006, 22 pages.

Caputo P. The Border of Madness. *The Atlantic,* December 2009.

Carlini EA. The Good and the Bad Effects of (-) Trans-Delta-9-Tetrahydrocannabidiol (Delta 9-THC) on Humans. *Toxicon.* 2004; 44(4): 461-467.

Carracedo A, Gironella M, Lorente M, Garcia S, Guzman M, Velasco G, Iovanna JL. Cannabinoids Induce Apoptosis of Pancreatic Tumor Cells via Endoplasmic Reticulum Stress-Related Genes. *Cancer Res.* 2006; 66: 6748-6755.

Carter GT. Testimony for the American Medical Association, submitted in writing to the House of Delegates Meeting in Orlando, Florida, November 9, 2008.

Carter GT, Weydt P, Kyashna-Tocha M, Abrams DI. Medicinal Cannabis: Rational Guidelines for Dosing. *Drugs.* 2004; 7(5): 464-470.

Caspi A, Moffitt TE, Cannon M, McClay J, Murray R, Harrington H, Taylor A, Arseneault L, Williams B, Braithwaite A. Moderation of the effect of adolescent-onset cannabis use on adult psychosis by a functional polymorphism in the catechol-O-methyltransferase gene: Longitudinal evidence of a gene x environment interaction. *Biol Psychiatry.* 2005; 57: 1117-1127.

Caulkins JP, Pacula RL. Marijuana Markets: Inferences From Reports by the Household Population. *Journal of Drug Issues,* Winter, 2006: 173-199.

Cermak TL. Addiction Medicine Perspective on the Medicalization of Marijuana. *Journal of Psychoactive Drugs.* 1998; 30(2): 155-162.

Cermak TL. *Marijuana: What's a Parent to Believe?* Center City, Minnesota: Hazeldon, 2003.

Cermak TL. Cannabis: The Effect of THC on Our Endogenous Cannabinoid Neural System. CSAM Addiction Review Course, October 25, 2008. Available at: www.csam-asam.org/pdf/misc/Cermak-Cannaabis.pdf

Chapkis W, Webb R. *Dying to Get High: Marijuana as Medicine*. New York: New York University Press, 2008.

Chapman S. The folly of our drug policies. *Chicago Tribune*, December 4, 2004.

Chaturvedi K. Cannabis as a Psychotropic Medication. *Br J Psychiatry*. 2004; 185: 78.

Chesher GB, Bird KD, Jackson DM, Perrington A, Starmer GA. The effects of orally administered Delta(9)-Tetrahydrocananabinol in man on mood and performance measures: A dose-response study. *Pharmacology, Biochemistry & Behavior*. 1990; 35: 861-864.

Chesher GB, Longo M. Cannabis and Alcohol in Motor Vehicle Accidents. In Grotenhermen F, Russo E (Editors). *Cannabis and Cannabinoids: Pharmacology, Toxicology, and Therapeutic Potential*. New York: Haworth Integrative Healing Press, 2002: 313-323.

Chicago Tribune. Editorial: Truth and Medical Marijuana. February 24, 2007.

Cichewicz DL. Synergistic Interactions Between Cannabinoid and Opioid Analgesics. *Life Sci*. 2004; 74: 1317-1324.

Cichewicz DL, McCarthy EA. Antinociceptive Synergy Between Delta(9)-Tetrahydrocannabinol and Opioids After Oral Administration. *J Pharmacol Exp Ther*. 2003; 304: 1010-1015.

Colb SF. Why it was wrong to prosecute man for growing medicinal marijuana. FindLaw, CNN.com./Law Center, www.cnn.com/2003/LAW/02/12/findlaw.analysis.colb.marijuana/, February 12, 2003.

Bibliography

Cole J. End Prohibition Now. In Masters B (Editor). *The New Prohibition.* St. Louis: Accurate Press, 2004: 23-38.

Conrad C. Congressmembers, media ridicule FDA cannabis statement. *Oaksterdam News,* July 8, 2006.

Conrad C. *Hemp for Health: The Medicinal and Nutritional Uses of Cannabis Sativa.* Rochester, Vermont: Healing Arts Press, 1997.

Corey S. Recent Developments in the Therapeutic Potential of Cannabinoids. *P R Health Sci J.* 2005; 24(1): 19-26.

Corey-Bloom J, Wolfson T, Gamst A, Jin S, Marcotte T, Bentley H, Gouaux B. Short-term Effects of Medicinal Cannabis on Spasticity in Multiple Sclerosis. Poster presented at the 60th Annual Meeting of the American Academy of Neurology, Chicago, IL, 2008. Available at: http://www.cmcr.ucsd.edu/geninfo/jcb_aan_poster.pdf

Craker LE, Gardner ZE. Medicinal Plants and Tomorrow's Pharmacy. In Bogers RJ, Craker LE, Lange D (Editors). *Medicinal and Aromatic Plants.* The Netherlands: Springer, 2006: 29-41.

Cronkite W. Telling the Truth About the War on Drugs. *Huffington Post,* March 1, 2006.

Crouch S. Today's version of Prohibition is just as bad for America. *Chicago Sun-Times,* April 28, 2006.

Croxford JL, Yamamura T. Cannabinoids and the Immune System: Potential for the Treatment of Inflammatory Diseases? *J Neuroimmunol.* 2005; 166(1-2): 3-18.

Dalman C, Allebeck P, Gunnell D, Harrison G, Kristensson K, Lewis G, Lofving S, Rasmussen F, Wicks S, Karlsson H. Infections in the CNS During Childhood and the Risk of Subsequent Psychotic Illness: A Cohort Study of More Than One Million Swedish Subjects. *Am J Psychiatry.* 2008; 165: 59-65.

Dasgupta P, Rizwani W, Pillai S, Kinkade R, Kovacs M, Rastogi S, Banerjee S, Carless M, Kim E, Coppola D, Haura E, Chellappan S. Nicotine induces cell proliferation, invasion and epithelial-mesenchymal transition in a variety of human cancer cell lines. *International Journal of Cancer.* 2008; 124: 36-45.

Debusmann B. War on Drugs: Elusive Victory, Disputed Statistics. Reuters, March 7, 2006.

Degenhardt L, Hall WD, Lynskey M. Testing hypotheses about the relationship between cannabis use and psychosis. *Drug Alcohol Depend.* 2003; 71: 37-48.

De Jong FA, Engels FK, Mathijssen RHJ, van Zuylen L, Verweij J, Peters RPH, Sparreboom A. Medicinal Cannabis in Oncology Practice: Still a Bridge Too Far? *Journal of Clinical Oncology.* 2005; 23(13): 2886-2891.

DeLisi LE, Bertisch HC, Szulc KU, Majcher M, Brown K, Bappal A, Ardekani BA. A preliminary DTI study showing no brain structural change associated with adolescent cannabis use. *Harm Reduct J.* 2006; 3: 17.

De Meijer EPM, Bagatta M, Carboni A, Crucitti P, Moliterni VMC, Ranalli P, Mandolino G. The Inheritance of Chemical Phenotype in *Cannabis sativa* L. *Genetics.* 2003; 163: 335-346.

Denney PA. A Day in the Life of a Cannabis Consultant. *O'Shaughnessy's: The Journal of Cannabis in Clinical Practice.* Spring, 2006: 1,13.

Denson TF, Earleywine M. Decreased Depression in Marijuana Users. *Addictive Behaviors.* 2006; 31(4): 738-742.

Dervaux A, Goldberger C, Laqueille X, Krebs M-O. Cannabis and psychosis. *British Journal of Psychiatry.* 2004; 185: 352.

Dewey WL. Cannabinoid Pharmacology. *Pharmacological Reviews.* 1986; 38(2): 151-178.

Bibliography

Dietrich A, McDaniel WF. Endocannabinoids and exercise. *Br J Sports Med.* 2004; 38: 536-541.

Di Forti M, Morrison PD, Butt A, Murray RM. Cannabis Use and Psychiatric and Cognitive Disorders: The Chicken or the Egg? *Curr Opin Psychiatry.* 2007; 20: 228-234.

Drug Policy Alliance. Governor Rell Vetoes Medical Marijuana Bill. Available at: www.drugpolicy.org

Drug Policy Alliance. Marijuana: The Facts. Available at: www.drugpolicy.org/marijuana/ (2006).

Drug Policy Alliance. Proposition 36: Improving Lives, Delivering Results. A Review of the First Four Years of California's Substance Abuse and Crime Prevention Act of 2000. March, 2006. Available at: www.drugpolicy.org/library/Prop360306.cfm

Drug Policy Alliance. Raich Ruling Maintains Status Quo; Fight Moves to Congress. Drug Policy News, June 9, 2005. Available at: www.drugpolicy.org

Drug War Chronicle. Medical Marijuana: AFSCME Endorses Medical Marijuana. August 11, 2006. Available at: http://stopthedrugwar.org/chronicle/448/afscme_endorses_medical_marijuana.shtml

D'Souza DC, Perry E, MacDougall L, Ammerman Y, Cooper T, Wu Y, Braley G, Gueorguieva R, Krystal JH. The Psychotomimetic Effects of Intravenous Delta-9-Tetrahydrocannabinol in Healthy Individuals: Implications for Psychosis. *Neuropsychopharmacology.* 2004; 29: 1558-1572.

Dyck E. Flashback: Psychiatric Experimentation With LSD in Historical Perspective. *Canadian Journal of Psychiatry.* 2005; 50: 381-388.

Earleywine M. *Understanding Marijuana: A New Look at the Scientific Evidence.* Oxford: Oxford University Press, 2002.

Earleywine M (Editor). *Pot Politics: Marijuana and the Costs of Prohibition.* Oxford: Oxford University Press, 2007.

Editors. *The Economist.* How to Stop the Drug Wars. March 4, 2009.

Editors. *Foreign Policy,* September-October, 2007.

Editors. *Scientific American.* Marijuana Research: Current Restrictions on Marijuana Research Are Absurd. November 22, 2004.

Editors. *Scientific American.* Medical Marijuana's Catch-22. April 22, 2006.

Egan D, Miron JA. The Budgetary Implications of Marijuana Prohibition. In Earleywine M (Editor). *Pot Politics: Marijuana and the Costs of Prohibition.* Oxford: Oxford University Press, 2007.

Egelko B. Pot grower spared prison time, Medical marijuana advocates claim victory in pivotal Rosenthal sentencing. *San Francisco Chronicle,* June 4, 2003.

Ellis RJ, Toperoff W, Vaida F, van der Brande G, Gonzales J, Gouaux B, Bentley H, Atkinson JH. Smoked Medicinal Cannabis for Neuropathic Pain in HIV: A Randomized, Crossover Clinical Trial. *Neuropsychopharmacology.* 2008: 1-9; published online, 8/6/08.

ElSohly MA. Chemical Constituents of *Cannabis.* In Grotenhermen F, Russo E (Editors). *Cannabis and Cannabinoids: Pharmacology, Toxicology, and Therapeutic Potential.* New York: Haworth Integrative Healing Press, 2002: 27-36.

ElSohly MA, Slade D. Chemical Constituents of Marijuana: The Complex Mixture of Natural Cannabinoids. *Life Sci.* 2005; 78(5): 539-548.

Emrich HM, Leweke M, Schneider U. Towards a Cannabinoid Hypothesis of Schizophrenia: Cognitive Impairments Due to Dysregulation of the Endogenous Cannabinoid System. *Pharmacology, Biochemistry and Behavior.* 1997; 56(4): 803-807.

Estes C, Seymour RB, Yue MC. California Collaborative Center for Substance Abuse Policy Research: A History and Update. *Journal of Psychoactive Drugs.* 2001; 33(4): 339-342.

Evans E, Longshore D. Evaluation of the Substance Abuse and Crime Prevention Act: Treatment Clients and Program Types During the First Year of Implementation. *Journal of Psychoactive Drugs, SARC Supplement.* 2004; 2: 165-174.

Ewing P. Illinois legislature takes new look at medical marijuana. *St. Louis Post-Dispatch*, Springfield Bureau. St. Louis, Missouri, February 21, 2006.

Fadda P, Robinson L, Fratta W, Pertwee RG, Riedel G. Differential Effects of THC- or CBD-Rich Cannabis Extracts on Working Memory in Rats. *Neuropharmacology.* 2004; 47(8): 1170-1179.

Fattore L, Cossu G, Spano MS, Deiana S, Fadda P, Scherma M, Fratta W. Cannabinoids and Reward: Interactions with the Opioid System. *Crit Rev Neurobiol.* 2004; 16(1-2): 147-158.

Favrat B, Menetrey A, Augsburger M, Rothuizen LE, Appenzeller M, Buclin T, Pin M, Mangin P, Giroud C. Two Cases of "Cannabis Psychosis" Following the Administration of Oral Cannabis. *BMC Psychiatry.* 2005; 5(1):17.

Feldman HW, Mandel J. Providing Medical Marijuana: The Importance of Cannabis Clubs. *Journal of Psychoactive Drugs.* 1998; 30(2): 179-186.

Ferdinand R, et al.. Cannabis use predicts future psychotic symptoms, and vice versa. *Addiction.* 2005; 100: 612-618.

Fergusson D, et al. Cannabis and Psychosis. *British Medical Journal.* 2006; 332: 172-175.

Fergusson DM, Horwood JL, Swain-Campbell NR. Cannabis dependence and psychotic symptoms in young people. *Psychol Med.* 2003; 33:15-21.

Fichtner CG. Time to OK Use of Medical Marijuana in Illinois. *State Journal Register*, Op-Ed, p. 7, Springfield, Illinois, February 15, 2006.

Fichtner CG. Time for Legislature to Pass Medical Marijuana Bill. *Chicago Sun-Times*, Commentary, p. 14, Chicago, Illinois, February 26, 2006.

Fichtner CG, Cavanaugh Jr JL. Malignant Criminalization: From Hypothesis to Theory. *Psychiatric Services.* 2006; 57(10): 1511-1512.

Fichtner CG, Luchins DJ, Malan RD, Hanrahan P. Real-World Pharmacotherapy with Novel Antipsychotics. *Journal of Practical Psychiatry and Behavioral Health.* 1999; 5: 37-43.

Fichtner CG, Poddig BE, deVito RA. Post-Traumatic Stress Disorder: Pathophysiological Aspects and Pharmacological Approaches to Treatment. *CNS Drugs.* 1997; 8(4): 293-322.

Fligiel SEG, Roth MD, Kleerup EC, Barsky SH, Simmons MS, Tashkin DP. Tracheobronchial Histopathology in Habitual Smokers of Cocaine, Marijuana, and/or Tobacco. *Chest.* 1997; 112: 319-326.

Foley S. US interest in MS drug boosts GW. *The Independent*, April 25, 2006.

Forbes D. Winners in the War on Drugs: Congressional Family Drug Offenders Escape Mandatory Sentences, Get Favorable Treatment. Available at: www.intergate.com/~letterle/winners.html

Fosnight S. Medicinal marijuana: pot vs. pill. *Pioneer Press*, March 23, 2006, A11-A15.

Fox S, Armentano P, Tvert M. *Marijuana is Safer: So Why Are We Driving People to Drink?* White River Junction, Vermont: Chelsea Green Publishing Company, 2009.

Freking K. Anti-drug ads termed a big waste of money. Associated Press, from *The Salt Lake Tribune*, August 26, 2006.

Bibliography

French A. Up in Smoke: Office of National Drug Control Policy's Wasted Efforts in the War on Drugs. Washington, DC: Citizens Against Government Waste, May 11, 2005. Available at: www.cagw.org

Friedman M et al. An open letter to the President, Congress, Governors, and State Legislatures (2005). Available at: www.prohibitioncosts.org.

Galve-Roperh I, Sanchez C, Cortes ML, Gomez del Pulgar T, Izquierdo M, Guzman M. Anti-tumoral action of cannabinoids: Involvement of sustained ceramide accumulation and extracellular signal-regulated kinase activation. *Nature Medicine.* 2000; 3(6): 313-319.

Gaoni Y, Mechoulam R. Isolation, structure, and partial synthesis of an active constituent of hashish. *Journal of the American Chemical Society.* 1964; 86: 646-647.

Gardner F. Studies Confirm Beneficial Effects of CBD, Terpenes. *O'Shaughnessy's: The Journal of Cannabis in Clinical Practice,* Winter/Spring, 2008:1, 28-29.

Gardner F. Which Medical Conditions are Californians Actually Using Cannabis to Treat? *O'Shaughnessy's: Journal of the California Cannabis Research Medical Group,* Summer, 2003: 2-4.

Gerber RJ. *Legalizing Marijuana: Drug Policy Reform and Prohibition Politics.* Westport, CT: Praeger, 2004.

Gettman J. Marijuana Production in the United States (2006). *The Bulletin of Cannabis Reform,* December, 2006. Available at: http://www.drugscience.org/bcr/index.html

Gieringer D. Medical Use of Cannabis: Experience in California. In Grotenhermen F, Russo E (Editors). *Cannabis and Cannabinoids: Pharmacology, Toxicology, and Therapeutic Potential.* New York: Haworth Integrative Healing Press, 2002: 143-151.

Gieringer D, Rosenthal E, Carter GT. *Marijuana Medical Handbook:*

Practical Guide to the Therapeutic Uses of Marijuana. Oakland, CA: Quick American, 2008.

Gieringer D, St. Laurent J, Goodrich S. Cannabis Vaporizer Combines Efficient Delivery of THC with Effective Suppression of Pyrolytic Compounds. *J Cannabis Ther.* 2004; 4.

Gladwell M. *The Tipping Point.* New York: Little, Brown and Company, 2002.

Gonzalez S, Cebeira M, Fernandez-Ruiz J. Cannabinoid Tolerance and Dependence: A Review of Studies in Laboratory Animals. *Pharmacology, Biochemistry and Behavior.* 2005; 81(2): 300-318.

Gottfried RN. Medical Marijuana Overdue in New York. *Gay City News,* March 3, 2006.

Gottschalk M. *The Prison and the Gallows: The Politics of Mass Incarceration in America.* Cambridge: Cambridge University Press, 2006.

Graham AW, Schultz TK, Mayo-Smith MF, Ries RK, Wilford BB. *Principles of Addiction Medicine* (Third Edition). Chevy Chase, Maryland: American Society of Addiction Medicine, Inc., 2003.

Gray JP. *Why Our Drug Laws Have Failed and What We Can Do About It.* Philadelphia: Temple University Press, 2001.

Gray M. *Drug Crazy: How We Got Into this Mess and How We Can Get Out.* New York: Routledge, 2000. (Originally published by Random House, 1998.)

Gray M (Editor). *Busted: Stone Cowboys, Narco-Lords, and Washington's War on Drugs.* New York: Thunder's Mouth Press/Nation Books, 2002.

Greenberg G. An Interview With Lester Grinspoon, M.D. *Mother Jones,* October 17, 2005. Available at: www.motherjones.com/news/qa/2005/11/grinspoon.html.

Bibliography

Greenberg G. Respectable Reefer. *Mother Jones* November/December 2005, 4 pages. Available at: www.motherjones.com/news/feature/2005/11/Respectable_Reefer.html.

Greenwald MK, Stitzer ML. Antinociceptive, Subjective and Behavioral Effects of Smoked Marijuana in Humans. *Drug Alcohol Depend.* 2000; 59: 261-275.

Grinspoon L. Foreword. In Ratsch C. *Marijuana Medicine.* Rochester, Vermont: Healing Arts Press, English Translation, 2001: ix-xi.

Grinspoon L. The Marijuana Problem. *O'Shaughnessy's: Journal of the California Cannabis Research Medical Group,* Summer, 2003:14-17.

Grinspoon L. *Marijuana Reconsidered.* Cambridge: Harvard University Press, 1971

Grinspoon L. Opinion: Marijuana as Wonder Drug. *Boston Globe,* March 1, 2007.

Grinspoon L. Whither Medical Marijuana. In Gray (Ed.), *Busted: Stone Cowboys, Narco-Lords, and Washington's War on Drugs.* New York: Thunder's Mouth Press/Nation Books, 2002: 273-280.

Grinspoon L, Bakalar, JB. *Marihuana, the Forbidden Medicine.* New Haven: Yale University Press, 1997.

Grinspoon L, Bakalar JB. The Use of Cannabis as a Mood Stabilizer in Bipolar Disorder: Anecdotal Evidence and the Need for Clinical Research. *J Psychoactive Drugs.* 1998; 30(2): 171-177.

Grinspoon L, Bakalar JB, Doblin R. Marijuana, the AIDS Wasting Syndrome, and the U.S. Government. *New Eng J of Med.* 1995; 333: 670-671.

Grotenhermen F. Clinical Pharmacodynamics of Cannabinoids. In Russo EB, Grotenhermen F (Editors). *Handbook of Cannabis Therapeutics: From Bench to Bedside.* New York: Haworth Press, 2006: 117-170.

Grotenhermen F. Review of Therapeutic Effects. In Grotenhermen F, Russo E (Editors). *Cannabis and Cannabinoids: Pharmacology, Toxicology, and Therapeutic Potential.* New York: Haworth Integrative Healing Press, 2002: 123-142.

Grotenhermen F, Leson G, Berghaus G, Drummer OH, Krüger H-P, Longo M, Moskowitz H, Perrine B, Ramaekers J, Smiley A, Tunbridge R. Developing Science-Based Per Se Limits for Driving under the Influence of Cannabis: Findings and Recommendations by an Expert Panel. International Association for Cannabis Medicine, September, 2005. Available at: www.canorml.org/healthfacts/DUICreport.2005.pdf

Grotenhermen F, Russo E (Editors). *Cannabis and Cannabinoids: Pharmacology, Toxicology, and Therapeutic Potential.* New York: Haworth Integrative Healing Press, 2002.

Gruber AJ, Pope Jr. HG, Brown ME. Do Patients Use Marijuana as an Antidepressant? *Depression.* 1996; 4(2): 77-80.

Guither P. Why is Marijuana Illegal? Drug War Rant. Available at: www.marijuana.drugwarrant.com, updated August 1, 2009.

Gurley RJ, Aranow R, Katz M. Medicinal Marijuana: A Comprehensive Review. *Journal of Psychoactive Drugs.* 1998; 30(2): 137-147.

Hall W. The mental health risks of adolescent cannabis use. PLOS Medicine 3, 2006.

Hall W. Is cannabis use psychotogenic? *Lancet.* 2006; 367: 193-195.

Hall W, Degenhardt L. Medical Marijuana Initiatives: Are They Justified? How Successful Are They Likely to Be? *CNS Drugs.* 2003; 17(10): 689-697.

Hall W, Solowij N. Adverse Effects of Cannabis. *Lancet.* 1998; 352: 1611-1616.

Hampson AJ, Grimaldi M, Axelrod J, Wink D. Cannabidiol and (-) Delta(9)-tetrahydrocannabinol are neuroprotective antioxidants. *Proc Natl Acad Sci.* 1998; 95: 8268-8273.

Haney M, Gunderson EW, Rabkin J, Hart CL, Vosburg SK, Comer SD, Foltin RW. Dronabinol and marijuana in HIV-positive marijuana smokers. Caloric intake, mood, and sleep. *J Acquir Defic Syndr.* 2007; 45(5): 545-554.

Haney M, Rabkin J, Gunderson E, Foltin RW. Dronabinol and marijuana in HIV(+) smokers: acute effects on caloric intake and mood. *Psychopharmacology.* 2005; 181: 170-178.

Harder S, Rietbrock S. Concentration-Effect Relationship of Delta-9-Tetrahydrocannabinol and Prediction of Psychotropic Effects After Smoking Marijuana. *Int J Clin Pharmacol Ther.* 1997; 35: 155-159.

Harris G. F.D.A. Dismisses Medical Benefit from Marijuana. *New York Times,* April 20, 2006.

Harrison PM, Beck AJ: Prison and jail inmates at midyear 2005. Washington, DC: U.S. Department of Justice, Office of Justice Programs, Bureau of Justice Statistics Bulletin, May, 2006. Available at: www.ojp.usdoj.gov/bjs/

Harrop F. Drug Warriors Make Millions off Marijuana. *The Providence Journal,* December 19, 2004.

Hart CL, van Gorp W, Haney M, Foltin RW, Fischman MW. Effects of Acute Smoked Marijuana on Complex Cognitive Performance. *Neuropsychopharmacology.* 2001; 25: 757-765.

Hartney C. U.S. Rates of Incarceration: A Global Perspective. Fact Sheet, Research from the National Council on Crime and Delinquency, November 2006.

Harvey J. *The Abilene Paradox and Other Meditations on Management.* San Francisco: Jossey-Bass, 1988.

Hasin DS, Keyes KM, Alderson D, Wang S, Aharonovich E, Grant BF. Cannabis Withdrawal in the United States: results from NESARC. *J Clin Psychiatry.* 2008; 69: 1354-1363.

Hazekamp A, Ruhaak R, Zuurman L, van Gerven J, Verpoorte R. Evaluation of a Vaporizing Device (Volcano®) for the Pulmonary Administration of Tetrahydrocannabinol. *Journal of Pharmaceutical Sciences.* 2006; 95: 1308-1317.

Henican E. War on Drugs – Is It Really 'Right'? *Newsday,* February 12, 2006.

Henquet C, Krabbendam L, Spauwen J, Kaplan C, Lieb R, Wittchen H-U, van Os J. Prospective Cohort Study of Cannabis Use, Predisposition for Psychosis, and Psychotic Symptoms in Young People. *British Medical Journal (BMJ),* doi:10.1136/bmj.38267.664086.63 (published 1 December 2004).

Henquet C, Murray R, Linszen D, van Os J. The environment and schizophrenia: the role of cannabis use. *Schizophr Bull.* 2005; 31: 608-612.

Hensen B. Cannabinoid therapeutics: high hopes for the future. *Drug Discovery Today.* 2005; 10(7): 459-462.

Herer J. *The Emperor Wears No Clothes (*11th Edition*).* Van Nuys, California: AH HA Publishing, 2000.

Hill MN, Ho W-S V, Sinopoli KJ, Viau V, Hillard CJ, Gorzalka BB. Involvement of the Endocannabinoid System in the Ability of Long-Term Tricyclic Antidepressant Treatment to Suppress Stress-Induced Activation of the Hypothalamic-Pituitary-Adrenal Axis. *Neuropsychopharmacology,* April 3, 2006: Available at http://www.acnp.org/citations/Npp040306060001/default.pdf

Hirschler B. GW wins okay for pivotal cannabis drug study. Reuters, January 4, 2006.

Hoffman A. Judge rejects counties' challenge to California marijuana law. Associated Press, San Diego, California, December 6, 2006.

Available at: www.sfgate.com/cgi-bin/article.cgi?file=/news/archive/2006/12/06/state/n171545S10.DTL

Hollister LE. Health Aspects of Cannabis. *Pharmacological Reviews.* 1986; 38(1): 1-20.

House of Commons, Science and Technology Committee. Drug Classification: Making a Hash of It? Fifth Report of Session 2005-06. London: The Stationery Office Limited, July 31, 2006.

Huh J. Medical cannabis bill gains momentum: Legislation makes third appearance in General Assembly. *State Journal Register*, State Capitol Bureau, Springfield, Illinois, February 20, 2006.

Ilan AB, Gevins A, Coleman M, ElSohly M, de Wit H. Neurophysiological and Subjective Profile of Marijuana with Varying Concentrations of Cannabinoids. *Behavioral Pharmacology.* 2005; 16: 487-496.

Illinois Criminal Justice Information Authority, 2003.

Indian Hemp Drugs Commission. *Report of the Indian Hemp Drugs Commission.* Simla, India: Government Central Printing Office, 1894.

Iversen LL. Long-term effects of exposure to cannabis. *Current Opinion in Pharmacology.* 2005; 5: 69-72.

Iversen LL. *The Science of Marijuana.* Oxford: Oxford University Press, 2000.

Jacobson M. *Downsizing Prisons: How to Reduce Crime and End Mass Incarceration.* New York: New York University Press, 2005.

Jeffries D, Jeffries L. *Jeffrey's Journey.* Oakland, California: Quick American, 2005.

Jiang W, Zhang Y, Xiao L, Van Cleemput J, Ji S-P, Bai G, Zhang X. Cannabinoids Promote Embryonic and Adult Hippocampus Neurogenesis and Produce Anxiolytic- and Antidepressant-Like Effects. *Journal of Clinical Investigation.* 2005; 115(11): 3104-3116.

Joffe A. Response to the American Academy of Pediatrics Report on Legalization of Marijuana: In Reply. *Pediatrics.* 2005; 116(5): 1257 (doi:10.1542/peds.2005-1893).

Joffe A, Yancy WS, Committee on Substance Abuse and Committee on Adolescence. Legalization of Marijuana: Potential Impact on Youth. *Pediatrics.* 2004; 113(6): e632-e638.

Johnson ML. Rhode Island Legalizes Medical Marijuana. Providence, Rhode Island. *Associated Press,* January 3, 2006. Available at: http://news.yahoo.com/s/ap/20060103/ap_on_he_me/medical_marijuana

Joy JE, Watson Jr SJ, Benson JA (Editors). *Marijuana and Medicine: Assessing the Science Base.* Institute of Medicine. Washington, DC: National Academy Press, 1999.

Junginger J, Claypoole K, Laygo R, Crisanti A. Effects of serious mental illness and substance abuse on criminal offenses. *Psychiatric Services.* 2006; 57: 879-882.

Justinova Z, Goldberg SR, Heishman SJ, Tanda G. Self-Administration of Cannabinoids by Experimental Animals and Human Marijuana Smokers. *Pharmacology, Biochemistry and Behavior.* 2005; 81(2): 285-299.

Kandel DB, Davies M. High school students who use crack and other drugs. *Arch Gen Psychiatry.* 1996; 53: 71-80.

Kane JL. Policy is not a synonym for justice. In Masters B (Editor). *The New Prohibition: Voices of Dissent Challenge the Drug War.* St Louis, MO: Accurate Press, 2004: 41-49.

Kane-Willis K, Janichek J, Clark D. *Intersecting Voices: Impacts of Illinois' Drug Policies.* Chicago: Illinois Consortium on Drug Policy, Institute for Metropolitan Affairs, Roosevelt University, 2006.

Kassirer JP. Federal Foolishness and Marijuana. *New Engl J Med.* 1997; 336: 366-367.

Bibliography

Katona S, Kaminski E, Sanders H, Zajicek J. Cannabinoid Influence on Cytokine Profile in Multiple Sclerosis. *Clin Exp Immunol.* 2005; 140(3): 580-585.

Kaufman M. Prescription Errors Kill, Injure Americans, Report Says. *Washington Post*, July 20, 2006.

Killestein J, Hoogervorst EL, Reif M, Blauw B, Smits M, Uitdehaag BM, Nagelkerken L, Polman CH. Immunomodulatory Effects of Orally Administered Cannabinoids in Multiple Sclerosis. *J Neuroimmunol.* 2003; 137(1-2): 140-143.

Kinzie JD, Leung P. Clonidine in Cambodian patients with posttraumatic stress disorder. *J Nerv Ment Dis.* 1989; 177: 546-550.

Klausner MS. Feds should stop harassing sick patients who have the legal right to use cannabis. *Los Angeles Times*, January 26, 2007.

Knapp W. Dethrone the Drug Czar. *New York Times* (Op-Ed), May 9, 1993.

Koenig JI, Carpenter WT. Cannabis and psychosis. *Br J Psychiatry.* 2004; 185: 352.

Komp E. Counties Challenge Law Creating I.D. Card Program; California Changes Record-Keeping Requirements. *O'Shaughnessy's: The Journal of Cannabis in Clinical Practice*, Spring, 2006: 20-21.

Krebs M-O, Leroy S, Duaux E, et al. Vulnerability to cannabis, schizophrenia and the (ATT) N polymorphism of the cannabinoid receptor type I (CMR) gene. *Schizophrenia Research.* 2002; 53(Suppl 3): 72.

Kuhn TS. *The Structure of Scientific Revolutions.* Chicago: The University of Chicago Press, 1962.

Kuipers D. The Strange, Seedy Case of Marc Emery. AlterNet Mobile Edition. September 26, 2005.

Lafferty L. Marijuana Use Prevention: The In-DEPTH Model Program. *Journal of Psychoactive Drugs.* 1998; 30(2): 205-208.

Lancet (Editorial). Alcohol misuse needs a global response. *Lancet.* 2009; 373: 433.

Lancet (Editorial). Rehashing the evidence on psychosis and cannabis. *Lancet.* 2007; 370: 292.

Largen C. On Post Traumatic Stress. *O'Shaughnessy's: The Journal of Cannabis in Clinical Practice*, Spring, 2006: 8.

Laumon B, Gadegbeku B, Martin J-L, Biecheler M-B. Cannabis Intoxication and fatal road crashes in France: population-based case-control study. *British Medical Journal* doi:10.1136/bmj.38648.617986.1F, December 2, 2005.

Lawson G. The Making of a Narco State. *Rolling Stone*, March 4, 2009.

Lawson G. The War Next Door. *Rolling Stone*, November 13, 2008.

Leite JR, Carlini EA, Lander N, Mechoulam R. Anticonvulsant Effects of the (-) and (+) Isomers of Cannabidiol and Their Dimethylheptyl Homologs. *Pharmacology.* 1982; 24(3):141-146.

Leweke M, Kampmann C, Radwan M, Dietrich DE, Johannes S, Emrich HM, Munte TF. The Effects of Tetrahydrocannabinol on the Recognition of Emotionally Charged Words: An Analysis Using Event-Related Brain Potentials. *Neuropsychobiology.* 1998; 37: 104-111.

Liang C, McClean MD, Marsit C, Christensen B, Peters E, Nelson HH, Kelsey KT. A Population-Based Case-Control Study of Marijuana Use and Head and Neck Squamous Cell Carcinoma. *Cancer Prev Res*, July 28, 2009. Epub ahead of print, available at: www.ncbi.nlm.nih.gov/pubmed/19638490

Ligresti A, Moriello AS, Starowicz K, Matias I, Pisanti S, De Petrocellis L, Laezza C, Portella G, Bifulco M, Di Marzo V. Anti-Tumor Activity of Plant Cannabinoids with Emphasis on the Effect of Cannabidiol on Human Breast Carcinoma. *J Pharmacol Exp Ther.* 2006; 318(3): 1375-1387.

Bibliography

Little D. Drug war enforcement hits minorities hardest. *Chicago Tribune*, Headline Article, July 22, 2007.

Lorenz R. On the Application of Cannabis in Paediatrics and Epileptology. *Neuro Endocrinol Lett.* 2004; 25(1-2): 40-44.

Los Angeles Daily News (Editorial). See No Evil. April 24, 2006. Americans for Safe Access, www.safeaccessnow.org

Los Angeles Times (Editorial). Ending the Marijuana Monopoly: Federal officials should allow competition in growing the drug for needed studies on its medical use. *Los Angeles Times*, May 31, 2007.

Lowenstein SR, Koziol-McLain J. Drugs and traffic crash responsibility: a study of injured motorists in Colorado. *J Trauma.* 2001; 50(2): 313-330.

Lupien JC. Unraveling an American Dilemma: The Demonization of Marihuana. Masters Thesis, Pepperdine University, Division of Humanities, April, 1995. Available at: www.druglibrary.org/schaffer/hemp/history/conspiracy_toc.htm

Lurie P, Almeida C, Stine N, Stine AR, Wolfe S. Financial Conflict of Interest Disclosure and Voting Patterns at Food and Drug Administration Drug Advisory Committee Meetings. *JAMA.* 2006; 295: 1921-1929.

Lyketsos CG, Garrett E, Liang K-Y, Anthony JC. Cannabis Use and Cognitive Decline in Persons Under 65 Years of Age. *American Journal of Epidemiology.* 1999; 149(9): 794-800.

Maccarrone M. Involvement of the Endocannabinoid System in Cancer. In Onaivi ES, Sugiura T, Di Marzo V (Editors). *Endocannabinoids: The Brain and Body's Marijuana and Beyond.* Boca Raton, FL: Taylor & Francis, 2006: 451-466.

Mack A, Joy J. *Marijuana as Medicine? The Science Beyond the Controversy.* Washington, DC: National Academy Press, 2000.

Macleod J, Oakes R, Copello A, Crome I, Egger M, Hickman M, Oppenkowski T, Stokes-Lampard H, Smith GD. Psychological and social sequelae of cannabis and other illicit drug use by young people: a systematic review of longitudinal, general population studies. *Lancet.* 2004; 363: 1579-1588.

Macleod J, Smith GD, Hickman M. Does cannabis use cause schizophrenia? *Lancet.* 2006; 367: 1055.

Main F. Cop wants to fine—not jail—potheads. *Chicago Sun-Times,* September 20, 2004.

Malik AR, D'Souza DC. Gone to Pot: The Association Between Cannabis and Psychosis. *Psychiatric Times,* April 1, 2006.

Mangini M. Treatment of Alcoholism Using Psychedelic Drugs: A Review of the Program of Research. *Journal of Psychoactive Drugs.* 1998; 30(4): 381-418.

MAPS. DEA Judge Recommends End to Government Obstruction of Medical Marijuana Research. MAPS, PR Newswire, February 13, 2007. Available at: www.prnewswire.com

Marchalant Y, Brothers HM, Wenk GL. Inflammation and aging: can endocannabinoids help? *Biomed Pharmacother.* 2008; 62(4): 212-217.

Marchalant Y, Rosi S, Wenk GL. Anti-inflammatory property of the cannabinoid agonist WIN-55212-2 in a rodent model of chronic brain inflammation. *Neuroscience.* 2007; 144(4): 1516-1522.

Margolin BM. *The Margolin Guide: State of California and United States Federal Marijuana Laws.* West Hollywood, CA: Law Offices of Bruce M. Margolin, 2008.

Marijuana Policy Project. New Reports All Agree: Marijuana Prohibition is an Expensive Failure. 2005, Available at: www.mpp.org

Marijuana Policy Project, 2004 data. Available at: www.mpp.org/site/c.glKZLeMQIsG/b.1146183/k.AE54/FAQ.htm

Bibliography

Marsicano G, Wotjak CT, Azad SC, Bisogno T, Rammes G, Cascio MG, Hermann H, Tang J, Hofmann C, Zieglgansberger W, et al. The endogenous cannabinoid system controls extinction of aversive memories. *Nature.* 2002; 418: 530-534.

Martin BR. Cellular Effects of Cannabinoids. *Pharmacological Reviews.* 1986; 38(1): 45-74.

Masters B (Editor). *The New Prohibition: Voices of Dissent Challenge the Drug War.* St. Louis: Accurate Press, 2004.

Masters B. Shoveling hay in Mayberry. In Masters B (Editor). *The New Prohibition: Voices of Dissent Challenge the Drug War.* St Louis: Accurate Press, 2004: 3-9.

Mathre ML. Cannabis and Harm Reduction: A Nursing Perspective. In Russo E, Grotenhermen F (Editors). *Handbook of Cannabis Therapeutics: From Bench to Bedside.* New York: Haworth Press, 2006: 383-398.

Matthias P, Tashkin DP, Marques-Magallanes JA, Wilkins JN, Simmons MS. Effects of Varying Marijuana Potency on Deposition of Tar and Delta(9)-THC in the Lung During Smoking. *Pharmacol Biochem Behav.* 1997; 58: 1145-1150.

Mauer M. *Race to Incarcerate* (Revised and Updated). The Sentencing Project. New York: The New Press, 2006.

Mayerowitz S, Gregg K, Gudrais E. Medical marijuana approved: Legislators override veto, then begin new session. *The Providence Journal,* January 4, 2006.

Mayo Clinic Staff. Multiple Sclerosis. Mayo Clinic website at: http://www.mayoclinic.com/health/multiple-sclerosis/DS00188, updated February 3, 2009.

Mayor's Committee on Marihuana. *The Marihuana Problem in the City of New York: Sociological, Medical, Psychological, and Pharmacological Studies.* Lancaster, PA: Jacques Cattel Press, 1944.

Mbvundula EC, Rainsford KD, Bunning RA. Cannabinoids in Pain and Inflammation. *Inflammopharmacology.* 2004; 12(2): 99-114.

McDonald J, Schleifer L, Richards JB, de Wit H. Effects of THC on Behavioral Measures of Impulsivity in Humans. *Neuropsychopharmacology.* 2003; 28: 1356-1365.

McKeon L. Lies cloud medical marijuana debate. *Chicago Sun-Times,* February 13, 2005.

McKinley Jr JC. Two Sides of a Border: One Violent, One Peaceful. *New York Times,* January 23, 2009.

McPartland JM. Contaminants and Adulterants in Herbal Cannabis. In Grotenhermen F, Russo E (Editors). *Cannabis and Cannabinoids: Pharmacology, Toxicology, and Therapeutic Potential.* New York: Haworth Integrative Healing Press, 2002: 337-343.

McPartland JM, Pruitt PL. Medical Marijuana and its Use by the Immunocompromised. *Altern Ther Health Med.* 1997; 3: 39-45.

McPartland JM, Russo EB. Cannabis and Cannabis Extracts: Greater Than the Sum of Their Parts? In Russo EB, Grotenhermen F (Editors). *Handbook of Cannabis Therapeutics: From Bench to Bedside.* New York: Haworth Press, 2006: 171-204.

McVay DA (Editor). *Drug War Facts* (Sixth Edition). Common Sense for Drug Policy. Printed in Canada, 2007.

Mechoulam R, Fride E, Di Marzo V. Endocannabinoids. *European Journal of Pharmacology.* 1998; 359: 1-18.

Mechoulam R, Hanus L. Cannabidiol: An Overview of Some Chemical and Pharmacological Aspects. Part I: Chemical Aspects. *Chem Phys Lipids.* 2002; 121(1-2): 35-43.

Mechoulam R, Parker LA, Gallily R. Cannabidiol: An Overview of Some Pharmacological Aspects. *J Clin Pharmacol.* 2002; 42(11 Suppl): 11S-19S.

Bibliography

Mechoulam R (Editor). *Cannabinoids as Therapeutics.* Basel: Birkhauser Verlag, 2005.

Melamede R. Cannabis and tobacco smoke are not equally carcinogenic. *Harm Reduction Journal.* 2005; 2: 21.

Melamede R. Endocannabinoids: Multi-scaled, Global Homeostatic Regulators of Cells and Society. Abstract. Paper #70. Proceedings of the Sixth International Conference on Complex Systems, 2006.

Melamede R. Harm reduction: the cannabis paradox: Is appropriate use of cannabis better than no use? *O'Shaughnessy's: The Journal of Cannabis in Clinical Practice*, Spring, 2006: 14-19.

Melck D, Bisogno T, De Petrocellis L, Beaulieu P, Rice AS, Di Marzo V. Cannabimimetic eicosanoids in cancer and inflammation: an update. *Advances in Experimental Medicine and Biology.* 2002; 507: 381-386.

Melloan G. Musings About the War on Drugs. *The Wall Street Journal*, February 21, 2006.

Menetrey A, Augsburger M, Favrat B, Pin MA, Rothuizen LE, Appenzeller M, Buclin T, Mangin P, Giroud C. Assessment of Driving Capability Through the Use of Clinical and Psychomotor Tests in Relation to Blood Cannabinoids Levels Following Oral Administration of 20 mg Dronabinol or of a Cannabis Decoction Made with 20 mg or 60 mg Delta9-THC. *J Anal Toxicol.* 2005; 29(5): 327-338.

Messinis L, Kyprianidou A, Malefaki S, Papathanasopoulos P. Neuropsychological Deficits in Long-term Frequent Cannabis Users. *Neurology.* 2006; 66: 737-739.

Mikuriya T. Cannabis Eases Post-Traumatic Stress. *O'Shaughnessy's: The Journal of Cannabis in Clinical Practice*, Spring, 2006: 11-12.

Mikuriya T. Cannabis as a Substitute for Alcohol. *O'Shaughnessy's: Journal of the California Cannabis Research Medical Group*, Summer, 2003:5-8.

Mikuriya T. Dependency and Cannabis. In Grotenhermen F, Russo E (Eds). *Cannabis and Cannabinoids: Pharmacology, Toxicology, and Therapeutic Potential.* New York: Haworth Integrative Healing Press, 2002: 225-230.

Miller GE, Hill MN, Ho WSV, Gorzalka BB, Hillard CJ. Bidirectional alterations in serum endocannabnoids in minor and major depression. *Soc Neurosci Abstr.* 2005;107: 3.

Miller LL, McFarland D, Cornett TL, Brightwell D. Marijuana and Memory Impairment: Effect on Free Recall and Recognition Memory. *Pharmacol Biochem Behav.* 1977; 7: 99-103.

Ministry of Health, Welfare, and Sport. Drug Policy in the Netherlands: Continuity and Change. The Netherlands, 1995.

Minna JD. Nicotine exposure and bronchial epithelial cell nicotinic acetylcholine receptor expression in the pathogenesis of lung cancer. *J Clin Invest.* 2003; 111: 31-33.

Miron JA. The budgetary implications of marijuana prohibition. Report to the Marijuana Policy Project. Available at: www.prohibitioncosts.org, June, 2005.

Miron JA. Liberal Versus Libertarian Views on Drug Legalization. In Masters B (Editor), *The New Prohibition: Voices of Dissent Challenge the Drug War.* St. Louis: Accurate Press, 2004: 173-82.

Mitchell SW. The Case of George Dedlow. *Atlantic Monthly,* 1866.

Mitchell SW. *The Injuries of Nerves.* New York: Dover, 1872/1965.

Moffat AC. The Legalization of Cannabis for Medical Use. *Sci Justice.* 2002; 42(1): 55-57.

Moore THM, Zammit S, Lingford-Hughes A, Barnes TRE, Jones PB, Burke M, Lewis G. Cannabis use and risk of psychotic or affective mental health outcomes: a systematic review. *Lancet.* 2007; 370: 319-328.

Morgan G. *Images of Organization* (Second Edition). Thousand Oaks, CA: Sage Publications, 1997.

Movig KLL, et al. Psychoactive substance use and the risk of motor vehicle accidents [in the Netherlands]. *Accident Analysis and Prevention.* 2004; 36: 631-636.

Muller-Vahl KR. Cannabinoids Reduce Symptoms of Tourette's Syndrome. *Expert Opin Pharmacother.* 2003; 4(10): 1717-1725.

Multidisciplinary Association for Psychedelic Studies (MAPS). The UMass Amherst MMJ Production Facility Project. Available at: www.maps.org/mmj/mmjfacility.html, 2006.

Munzar P. Mechanisms of drug addiction. *N Engl J Med.* 2003; 349(24): 2365.

Nadelman EA. An End to Marijuana Prohibition. *National Review,* July 12, 2004.

Nadelman EA. The Future of an Illusion: On the drug war, believe your own eyes. *National Review,* September 27, 2004: 42-43.

Nadelman EA. Drugs. *Foreign Policy.* 2007; 162 (September/October): 24-30.

Nahas G, Harvey DJ, Sutin K, Turndorf H, Cancro R. A Molecular Basis of the Therapeutic and Psychoactive Properties of Cannabis (Delta9-Tetrahydrocannabinol). *Prog Neuropsychopharmacol Biol Psychiatry,* 2002; 26(4): 721-730.

National Commission on Marihuana and Drug Abuse. *Marihuana: A Signal of Misunderstanding.* Washington, DC: U.S. Government Printing Office, 1972.

National Institute on Alcohol Abuse and Alcoholism. Parents—Spring Break Is Another Important Time to Discuss College Drinking. NIAAA Spring Break Fact Sheet 2007, NIH Publication No. 05-5642. Rockville, MD: National Institutes of Health, March, 2007.

National Multiple Sclerosis Society, at www.nationalmssociety.org/index.aspx

National Organization for the Reform of Marijuana Laws (NORML). Medical Use. Favorable Medical Marijuana Polls. Available at: www.norml.org.

National Organization for the Reform of Marijuana Laws (NORML). Valerie Corral. Available at: www.norml.org

National Research Council. *An Analysis of Marijuana Policy.* Washington, DC: National Academy Press, 1982.

Nelson RA. The History of Hemp. The Online Reefer Madness Teaching Museum. Available at: www.reefermadnessteachingmuseum.org/hemphistory.htm

New Mexico Department of Health. Medical Cannabis Program Update. Available at: www.health.state.nm.us/marijuana.html

New Scientist (UK). FDA Ignores Cannabis Potential. April 28, 2006.

Nicholson AN, Turner C, Stone BM, Robson PJ. Effect of Delta-9-Tetrahydrocannabinol and Cannabidiol on Nocturnal Sleep and Early-Morning Behavior in Young Adults. *Journal of Clinical Psychopharmacology.* 2004; 24(3): 305-313.

Nicholson T, White J, Duncan DF. A Survey of Adult Recreational Drug Use Via the World Wide Web: The DRUGNET Study. *Journal of Psychoactive Drugs.* 1999; 31(4): 415-422.

Nicoll RA, Alger BE. The Brain's Own Marijuana. *Scientific American,* December, 2004: 69-76.

Nordentoft M, Hjorthoj C. Cannabis use and risk of psychosis in later life. *Lancet.* 2007; 370: 293-294.

Notcutt W, Price M, Miller R, Newport S, Phillips C, Simmons S, Sansom C. Initial experiences with medicinal extracts of cannabis for chronic pain: Results from 34 'N of 1' studies. *Anaesthesia.* 2004; 59: 440-452.

Nurnberger Jr JI. New Hope for Pharmacogenetic Testing. *Am J Psychiatry.* 2009; 166: 635-638.

Nutt D, King LA, Saulsbury W, Blakemore C. Development of a rational scale to assess the harm of drugs of potential misuse. *Lancet.* 2007; 369: 1047-1053.

Ogborne AC, Smart RG, Weber T, Birchmore-Timney C. Who is Using Cannabis as a Medicine and Why: An Exploratory Study. *Journal of Psychoactive Drugs.* 2000; 32(4): 435-443.

O'Keefe K, Earleywine M, Mirken B. Marijuana Use by Young People: The Impact of State Medical Marijuana Laws. Available at: www.mpp.org/research/teen-use-report.html. Released September 7, 2005. Updated September, 2008.

Onaivi ES, Ishiguro H, Zhang PW, Lin Z, Akinshola BE, Leonard CM, Chirwa SS, Gong J, Uhl GR. Endocannabinoid Receptor Genetics and Marijuana Use. In Onaivi ES, Sugiura T, Di Marzo V (Editors). *Endocannabinoids: The Brain and Body's Marijuana and Beyond.* Boca Raton, FL: Taylor & Francis, 2006: 57-118.

Onaivi ES, Sugiura T, Di Marzo V (Editors). *Endocannabinoids: The Brain and Body's Marijuana and Beyond.* Boca Raton, FL: Taylor & Francis, 2006.

O'Reilly B. If marijuana can help the sick, let doctors prescribe it. *Chicago Sun-Times*, March 24, 2007.

O'Shaughnessy's: The Journal of Cannabis in Clinical Practice. Spring 2006.

Ostrow D. Research, not rhetoric: Marijuana can save lives. *Chicago Sun-Times*, March 5, 2007.

Ostrow DG, Medical Marijuana Policy Advocacy Project. White Paper: The Medical Use of Marijuana and Cannabinoids. Syllabus,

Symposium in Exile, Chicago, Illinois, June 23, 2007.

Parker RN. Alcohol and Violence: Connections, Evidence and Possibilities for Prevention. *Journal of Psychoactive Drugs, SARC Supplement.* 2004; 2:157-163.

Parolaro D, Massi P, Rubino T, Monti E. Endocannabinoids in the immune system and cancer. *Prostaglandins, Leukotrienes and Essential Fatty Acids.* 2002; 66: 319-332.

Patton GC, Coffey C, Carlin JB, Degenhardt L, Lynskey M, Hall W. Cannabis Use and Mental Health in Young People: Cohort Study. *British Medical Journal.* 2002; 325: 1195-1198.

Pearson H. Joint Suits Aim to Weed Out Agencies' Red Tape. *Nature.* 2004; 430(6999): 492.

Peralta V, Cuesta MJ. Influence of Cannabis Abuse on Schizophrenic Psychopathology. *Acta Psychiatrica Scandinavica.* 1992; 85: 127-130.

Perlis RH, Smoller JW, Ferreira MAR, McQuillin A, Bass N, Lawrence J, Sachs GS, Nimgaonkar V, Scolnick EM, Gurling H, Sklar P, Purcell S. A Genomewide Association Study of Response to Lithium for Prevention of Recurrence in Bipolar Disorder. *Am J Psychiatry.* 2009; 166: 718-725.

Perras C. Sativex for the Management of Multiple Sclerosis Symptoms. *Issues Emerg Health Technol.* 2005; 72: 1-4.

Perry BD, Giller EL, Southwick SM. Altered platelet alpha-2-adrenergic receptor affinity states in post-traumatic stress disorder. *Am J Psychiatry.* 1987; 144: 1511-1512.

Pitts L. Let's at least begin talking about legalizing drugs. *McClatchy Newspapers.* In *Camera,* Commentary. Boulder, CO: Boulder Publishing, April 6, 2009.

Plasse T. Antiemetic Effects of Cannabinoids. In Grotenhermen F, Russo E (Editors). *Cannabis and Cannabinoids: Pharmacology,*

Toxicology, and Therapeutic Potential. New York: Haworth Integrative Healing Press, 2002: 165-180.

Plasse T, Gorter RW, Krasnow SH, Lane M, Shepard KV, Wadleigh RG. Recent clinical experience with dronabinol. *Pharmacol Biochem Behav.* 1991; 40: 695-700.

Pollan M. *The Botany of Desire*. New York: Random House, 2001.

Pope Jr HG, Gruber AJ, Hudson JI, Huestas MA, Yurgelun-Todd D. Neuropsychological Performance in Long-term Cannabis Users. *Arch Gen Psychiatry.* 2001; 58: 909-915.

Pope Jr HG, Gruber AG, Yurgelun-Todd D. Residual Neuropsychologic Effects of Cannabis. *Curr Psychiatry Rep.* 2001; 3: 507-512.

Pope Jr HG, Ionescu-Pioggia M, Aizley HG, Varma DK. Drug use and lifestyle among college undergraduates in 1989: A comparison with 1969 and 1978. *Am J Psychiatry.* 1990; 147: 998-1001.

Pope Jr HG, Yurgelun-Todd D. The Residual Cognitive Effects of Heavy Marijuana Use in College Students. *JAMA.* 1996; 275(7): 521-527.

Pranis K. Progress and Challenges: An analysis of drug treatment and imprisonment in Maryland from 2000 to 2005. A Justice Policy Institute Report. Justice Policy Institute, September 19, 2006.

President's Commission on Care for America's Returning Wounded Warriors. Final Report—July 2007 (Draft, July 24 Edit).

Pryce G, Baker D. Emerging Properties of Cannabinoid Medicines in Management of Multiple Sclerosis. *Trends in Neuroscience.* 2006; 28(5): 272-276.

Quinones S. 23 seconds of the Mexican drug war. *Los Angeles Times*, December 7, 2008.

Quinones S. Phoenix, kidnap-for-ransom capitol. *Los Angeles Times*, February 12, 2009.

Quinones S. Senators take their concerns to the border. *Los Angeles Times*, March 31, 2009.

Quinones S. State of War. *Foreign Policy*, March/April, 2009.

Ramos JA, Gonzalez S, Sagredo O, Gomez-Ruiz M, Fernandez-Ruiz J. Therapeutic Potential of the Endocannabinoid System in the Brain. *Mini Rev Med Chem.* 2005; 5(7): 609-617.

Ratsch C. *Marijuana Medicine: A World Tour of the Healing and Visionary Powers of Cannabis* (Baker J, translator). Rochester, Vermont: Healing Arts Press, 2001 (Engl. Trans.; original, 1998).

Razdan RJ. Structure-Activity Relationships in Cannabinoids. *Pharmacol Rev.* 1986; 38: 75-149.

Rebellon CJ, Van Gundy K. Can Social Psychological Delinquency Theory Explain the Link Between Marijuana and Other Illicit Drug Use? A Longitudinal Analysis of the Gateway Hypothesis. *Journal of Drug Issues.* 2006; 36(3): 387-411.

Rey JM, Tennant CC. Cannabis and Mental Health. *British Medical Journal.* 2002; 325: 1183-1184.

Ritsher JB, Lucksted A, Otilingam PG, Grajales M. Hearing voices: Explanations and implications. *Psychiatric Rehabilitation Journal.* 2004; 27: 219-227.

Riverside County District Attorney's Office—White Paper. Medical Marijuana: History and Current Complications, September, 2006. Available at: www.rivcoda.org/News/press_releases.html

Robinson FP, Fratta W, Pertwee RG, Riedel G. Differential effects of THC- or CBD-rich cannabis extracts on working memory in rats. *Neuropharmacology.* 2004; 47(8): 1170-1179.

Robinson R. Focus on Violence, Not Pot. *Ithaca Journal*, February 20, 2006.

Roehr B. FDA: Marijuana not a medicine. *Bay Area Reporter*, April 27, 2006.

Roffman RA, Stephens RS (Editors). *Cannabis Dependence: Its Nature, Consequences and Treatment.* Cambridge, UK: Cambridge University Press, 2006.

Rog DJ, Nurmikko TJ, Friede T, Young CA. Randomized, Controlled Trial of Cannabis-Based Medicine in Central Pain in Multiple Sclerosis. *Neurology.* 2005; 65: 812-819.

Room R. Trends and Issues in the International Drug Control System—Vienna 2003. *Journal of Psychoactive Drugs.* 2005; 37(4): 373-383.

Ropper AH, Samuels MA. *Adams & Victor's Principles of Neurology,* Ninth Edition. New York: McGraw-Hill, 2009.

Rorty R. *Contingency, Irony, and Solidarity.* Cambridge: Cambridge University Press, 1989.

Rosenbaum M. "Just Say Know" to Teenagers and Marijuana. *Journal of Psychoactive Drugs.* 1998; 30(2): 197-203.

Rosenblatt KA, Daling JR, Chen C, Sherman KJ, Schwartz SM. Marijuana Use and Risk of Oral Squamous Cell Carcinoma. *Cancer Research.* 2004; 64: 4049-4054.

Rosenthal E, Kubby S. *Why Marijuana Should Be Legal.* New York: Thunder's Mouth Press, 2003.

Ross RA. Book Review: Cannabinoids as Therapeutics (Mechoulam R, Editor). *British Journal of Clinical Pharmacology.* 2005; 61(2): 242.

Roth MD, Arora A, Barsky SH, Kleerup EC, Simmons M, Tashkin DP. Airway Inflammation in Young Marijuana and Tobacco Smokers. *Am J Respir Crit Care Med.* 1998; 157: 928-937.

Rowe TC. *Federal Narcotics Laws and the War on Drugs: Money Down a Rat Hole.* New York: Haworth Press, 2006.

Russo E. Cannabis and Cannabis Based Medicine Extracts: Additional Results. *Journal of Cannabis Therapeutics.* 2003; 3(4): 153-161.

Russo E. Clinical Endocannabinoid Deficiency (CECD): Can this Concept Explain Therapeutic Benefits of Cannabis in Migraine, Fibromyalgia, Irritable Bowel Syndrome and other Treatment-Resistant Conditions? *Neuroendocrinology Letters.* 2004; 25(1/2): 31-39.

Russo E. Introduction: Cannabis: From Pariah to Prescription. *Journal of Cannabis Therapeutics.* 2003; 3(3): 1-29.

Russo E. Migraine. In Grotenhermen F, Russo E (Editors). *Cannabis and Cannabinoids: Pharmacology, Toxicology, and Therapeutic Potential.* New York: Haworth Integrative Healing Press, 2002: 187-193.

Russo E, Grotenhermen F (Editors). *Handbook of Cannabis Therapeutics: From Bench to Bedside.* New York: The Haworth Press, 2006.

Russo E, Guy GW. A Tale of Two Cannabinoids: The Therapeutic Rationale for Combining Tetrahydrocannabinol and Cannabidiol. *Medical Hypotheses.* 2006; 66(2): 234-246.

Russo E, Mathre ML, Byrne A, Velin R, Bach PJ, Sanchez-Ramos J, Kirlin KA. Chronic Cannabis Use in the Compassionate Investigational New Drug Program: An Examination of Benefits and Adverse Effects of Legal Clinical Cannabis. In Russo EB, Grotenhermen F (Editors). *Handbook of Cannabis Therapeutics: From Bench to Bedside.* New York: The Haworth Press, 2006: 399-447.

Russo E, McPartland JM. Cannabis is More than Simply Delta(9)-Tetrahydrocannabinol. *Psychopharmacology* (Berl). 2003; 165(4): 431-432.

Sacks O. *Musicophilia: Tales of Music and the Brain.* New York: Alfred A. Knopf, Inc., 2007.

SAFER Colorado. Op-ed: No logical reason to punish adults for using marijuana over alcohol. *Rocky Mountain News*, October 21, 2006. Available at: www.safercolorado.org

Salerian AJ. Successful Treatment of Sexual Dysfunction with Dronabinol: A Case Report. *J Clin Psychiatry.* 2004; 65(8): 1146-1147.

Sandyk R, Snider SR, Consroe P, Elias SM. Cannabidiol in Dystonic Movement Disorders. *Psychiatry Research.* 1986; 18: 291.

Scheck J, Woo S. With 'Med Pot' Raids Halted, Selling Grass Grows Greener. *Wall Street Journal,* July 23, 2009.

Schiffman J, Nakamura B, Earleywine M, LaBrie, J. Symptoms of Schizotypy precede cannabis use. *Psychiatric Research.* 2005; 134: 37-42.

Schlosser E. *Reefer Madness: Sex, Drugs, and Cheap Labor in the American Black Market.* Boston: Houghton Mifflin, Mariner Books Edition, 2004.

Schmoke K. Forging a new consensus in the war on drugs. In Masters B (Editor). *The New Prohibition: Voices of Dissent Challenge the Drug War.* St Louis: Accurate Press, 2004: 59-66.

Schneier FR, Siris SG. A Review of Psychoactive Substance Use and Abuse in Schizophrenia: Patterns of Drug Choice. *Journal of Nervous and Mental Disease.* 1987; 175(11): 641-652.

Schor E. New lobbying group presses for medical marijuana use. *The Hill,* June 21, 2006.

Schuckit MA. Alcohol-use disorders. *Lancet.* 2009; 373: 492-501.

Scientific American. Large Study Finds No Link between Marijuana and Lung Cancer. *Scientific American.com,* May 24, 2006.

Semple DM, McIntosh AM, Lawrie SM. Cannabis as a risk factor for psychosis: systemic review. *Journal of Psychopharmacology.* 2005; 19: 187-194.

Senate Standing Committee on Social Welfare. Drug Problems in Australia—An Intoxicated Society? Canberra: Australian Commonwealth Government Printing Office, 1977.

Serrano RA, Quinones S. Mexico drug wars spill across the border. *Los Angeles Times*, November 16, 2008.

Sharp D. Highs and Lows of Cannabis. *Lancet*. 2004; 363(9406): 344.

Shedler J, Block J. Adolescent Drug Use and Psychological Health. *American Psychologist*. 1990; 45(5): 612-630.

Sidney S, Beck JE, Tekawa IS, Quesenberry CP, Friedman GD. Marijuana use and mortality. *American Journal of Public Health*. 1997; 87(4): 585-590.

Sidney S, Quesenberry Jr CP, Friedman GD, Tekawa IS. Marijuana use and cancer incidence. *Cancer Causes Control*. 1997; 8: 722-728.

Silja JA. Smoked Out. AlterNet Mobile Edition. September 12, 2005.

Singer JA. Medicalization as an Alternative to the Drug War. In Masters B (Editor). *The New Prohibition: Voices of Dissent Challenge the Drug War*. St. Louis: Accurate Press, 2004: 183-197.

Smiley A. Marijuana: On-Road and Driving Simulator Studies. *Alcohol, Drugs, and Driving*. 1986; 2: 121-134.

Smith DE. Review of the American Medical Association Council on Scientific Affairs Report on Medical Marijuana. *Journal of Psychoactive Drugs*. 1998; 30(2): 127-136.

Smith DE, Heilig S, Seymour RB. Marijuana at the Millenium: Medical and Social Implications. *Journal of Psychoactive Drugs*. 1998; 30(2): 123-125.

Smith FA. A neglected revenue source for California—marijuana. *San Francisco Chronicle*, January 13, 2009.

Smothers R. Freshman's Drinking Death Stuns New Jersey University. *New York Times*, March 31, 2007.

Soderpalm A, Schuster A, de Wit H. Antiemetic Efficacy of Smoked Marijuana: Subjective and Behavioral Effects on Nausea Induced by Syrup of Ipecac. *Pharmacol Biochem Behav.* 2001; 69: 343-350.

Soderstrom C, et al. Crash Culpability Relative to Age and Sex for Injured Drivers Using Alcohol, Marijuana or Cocaine. *49th Annual Proceedings of the Association for the Advancement of Automotive Medicine*, September 13-14, 2005.

Solowij N, Michie PT. Cannabis and cognitive dysfunction: parallels with endophenotypes of schizophrenia? *J Psychiatry Neurosci.* 2007; 32: 30-52.

Solowij N, Stephens RS, Roffman RA, Babor T, Kadden R, Miller M, Christiansen K, McRee B, Vendetti J for the Marijuana Treatment Project Research Group. Cognitive Functioning of Long-term Heavy Cannabis Users Seeking Treatment. *JAMA.* 2002; 287: 1123-1131.

Stahl S. Editor's Note: Speak Your Mind and Skirt Abilene. *Information Week*, October 4, 2004.

Stamper N. *Breaking Rank: A Top Cop's Expose of the Dark Side of American Policing.* New York: Nation Books, 2005.

Stamper N. Foreword. In Fox S, Armentano P, Tvert M. *Marijuana is Safer: So Why Are We Driving People to Drink?* White River Junction, Vermont: Chelsea Green Publishing Company, 2009.

Stamper N. In Law Enforcement Against Prohibition (LEAP), 12-Minute Video. Produced by Common Sense for Drug Policy. Camera: Mike Gray; Sound: Jim Dennett, 2006.

Stamper N. Leave the Dopers Alone. *AlterNet.* October 20, 2005.

Stateman A. Can Marijuana Help Rescue California's Economy? *Time.com*, March 13, 2009.

Sterling EE. A Businessperson's Guide to the Drug Problem. In Masters B (Editor). *The New Prohibition: Voices of Dissent Challenge the Drug War.* St. Louis: Accurate Press, 2004: 69-84.

Sterling EE. Drug Policy: A Challenge of Values. *Journal of Religion & Spirituality in Social Work.* 2004; 23 (1/2):51-81.

Sterling EE. *Maryland Medical Marijuana Criminal Defense Manual,* (Revised). Silver Spring, Maryland: The Criminal Justice Policy Foundation, 2004.

Stolberg SG. Obama's twist on town hall; top Internet query was about marijuana. *New York Times,* March 27, 2009.

Stoll AL. *The Omega-3 Connection.* New York: Simon & Schuster (Fireside Edition), 2002.

Stoll AL, Severus WE, Freeman MP, Rueter S, Zboyan HA, Diamond E, Cress KK, Marangell LB. Omega -3 fatty acids in bipolar disorder: A preliminary double-blind, placebo-controlled trial. *Arch Gen Psychiatry.* 1999; 56: 407-412.

Strakowski SM, DelBello MP, Fleck DE, Adler CM, Anthenelli RM, Keck Jr PE, Arnold LM, Amicone J. Effects of co-occurring alcohol abuse on the course of bipolar disorder following a first hospitalization for mania. *Arch Gen Psychiatry.* 2005; 62(8): 851-858.

Sullum J. Jury Rigging: Ed Rosenthal never had a chance. Creator's Syndicate, *Reason Magazine,* February 7, 2003. Available at: www.reason.com/news/show/35620.html

Sullum J. Potheads, puritans and pragmatists: Two marijuana initiatives put drug warriors on the defensive. *Townhall.com,* October 18, 2006.

Sullum J. *Saying Yes.* New York: Jeremy P. Tarcher/Putnam, 2003.

Sylvestre DL, Clements BJ, Malibu Y. Cannabis use improves retention and virological outcomes in patients treated for hepatitis C. *European Journal of Gastroenterology & Hepatology.* 2006; 18: 1057-1063.

Szalavitz M. The New Reefer Madness. *Chicago Sun-Times,* Sunday, October 2, 2005.

Bibliography

Talvi SJA. Smoked Out. *AlterNet*, September 12, 2005.

Tashkin DP. Respiratory Risks from Marijuana Smoking. In Grotenhermen F, Russo E (Editors). *Cannabis and Cannabinoids: Pharmacology, Toxicology, and Therapeutic Potential.* New York: Haworth Integrative Healing Press, 2002: 325-335.

Tashkin DP, Simmons MS, Sherrill DL, Coulson AH. Heavy Habitual Marijuana Smoking Does Not Cause an Accelerated Decline in FEV1 With Age. *Am J Respir Crit Care Med.* 1997; 155: 141-148.

Tennessean (Editorial). FDA fails to ease the pain. April 25, 2006. Americans for Safe Access, www.safeaccessnow.org

Thakur GA, Duclos Jr RI, Makriyannis A. Natural Cannabinoids: Templates for Drug Discovery. *Life Sci.* 2005; 78(5): 454-466.

Thornicroft G. Cannabis and psychosis. Is there epidemiological evidence for an association? *Br J Psychiatry.* 1990; 157: 25-33.

Tomida I, Pertwee RG, Azuara-Blanco A. Cannabinoids and Glaucoma. *Br J Ophthalmol.* 2004; 88(5): 708-713.

Toussaint C. With Chronic Pain, Discrimination Hurts. *Los Angeles Times*, January 31, 2004.

Tracy Press (CA), Editorial. Blowing smoke at the White House, April 28, 2006. Americans for Safe Access, www.safeaccessnow.org

Transform Drug Policy Foundation. A Comparison of the Cost-Effectiveness of the Prohibition and Regulation of Drugs. April, 2009. Available at: www.tdpf.org.uk

Treffert DA. Marijuana Use in Schizophrenia: A Clear Hazard. *Am J Psychiatry.* 1978; 135(10): 1213-1215.

Trippet P. *Urziceanu* Ruling Protects Sales, Distribution. *O'Shaughnessy's: The Journal of Cannabis in Clinical Practice*, Spring, 2006: 22.

Tuller D. Britain Poised to Approve Medicine Derived From Marijuana. *New York Times,* January 27, 2004.

Turkanis SA, Smiley KA, Borys HK, Olsen DM, Karler R. An Electrophysiological Analysis of the Anticonvulsant Action of Cannabidiol on Limbic Seizures in Conscious Rats. *Epilepsia.* 1979; 20(4): 351-363.

United States Department of Health and Human Services, National Institute on Alcohol Abuse and Alcoholism. Parents—Spring Break is Another Important Time to Discuss College Drinking. Information for Parents, 2006.

United States Department of Justice, Drug Enforcement Administration. In the Matter of Lyle E. Cracker, Ph.D. (Docket No. 05-16). Opinion and Recommended Ruling, Findings of Fact, Conclusions of Law, and Decision of the Administrative Law Judge. Mary Ellen Bittner, Administrative Law Judge, February 12, 2007.

United States Department of Justice, Drug Enforcement Administration. Lyle E. Cracker, Ph.D., Denial of Application (Docket No. 05-16). Michele M. Leonhart, Deputy Administrator, January 7, 2009.

United States Government, Office of Management and Budget, Department of Health and Human Services. Available at: www.whitehouse.gov/omb/budget/fy2006/hhs.html

van Os J, Bak M, Hanssen M, Bijl RV, de Graaf R, Verdoux H. Cannabis Use and Psychosis: A Longitudinal Population-Based Study. *Am J Epidemiology.* 2002; 156(4): 319-327.

Varma P. Public Health Issue Brief: Medical Marijuana: Year End Report-2004. *Issue Brief Health Policy Track Serv.* 2004; 31: 1-9.

Vaughan CW, Christie MJ. An Analgesic Role for Cannabinoids. *Med J Aust.* 2000; 173: 270-272.

Veen ND, Selten JP, van der Tweel I, Feller WG, Hoek HW, Kahn

RS. Cannabis use and age at onset of schizophrenia. *Am J Psychiatry.* 2004; 161: 501-506.

Vickers SP, Kennett GA. Cannabinoids and the Regulation of Ingestive Behaviour. *Curr Drug Targets.* 2005; 6(2): 215-223.

Wachtel SR, ElSohly MA, Ross SA, Ambre J, de Wit H. Comparison of the Subjective Effects of Delta-9-Tetrahydrocannabinol and Marijuana in Humans. *Psychopharmacology.* 2002; 161: 331-339.

Wade DT, Makela P, Robson P, House H, Bateman C. Do Cannabis-Based Medicinal Extracts Have General or Specific Effects on Symptoms in Multiple Sclerosis? A Double-Blind, Randomized, Placebo-Controlled Study on 160 Patients. *Multiple Sclerosis.* 2004; 10: 434-441.

Wade DT, Robson P, House H, Makela P, Aram J. A Preliminary Controlled Study to Determine Whether Whole-Plant Cannabis Extracts Can Improve Intractable Neurogenic Symptoms. *Clinical Rehabilitation.* 2003; 17: 18-26.

Walker JM, Hohmann AG. Cannabinoid Mechanisms of Pain Suppression. *Handb Exp Pharmacol.* 2005; 509-554.

Wallace M, Schulteis G, Atkinson JH, Wolfson T, Lazzaretto D, Bentley H, Gouaux B, Abramson I. Dose-dependent Effects of Smoked Cannabis on Capsaicin-induced Pain and Hyperalgesia in Healthy Volunteers. *Anesthesiology.* 2007; 107(5): 785-796.

Wallace-Wells B. How America lost the war on drugs. *Rolling Stone,* December 13, 2007.

Walters JP. No Surrender: The drug war saves lives. *National Review,* September 27, 2004: 41-42.

Walther S, Mahlberg R, Eichmann U, Kunz D. Delta-9-tetrahydrocannabinol for nighttime agitation in severe dementia. *Psychopharmacology.* 2006; 185: 524-528.

Ware MA, Adams H, Guy GW. The medicinal use of cannabis in the UK: Results of a nationwide survey. *Int J Clin Pract.* 2005; 59: 291–295.

Ware MA, Doyle CR, Woods R, Lynch ME, Clark AJ. Cannabis Use for Chronic Non-Cancer Pain: Results of a Prospective Survey. *Pain.* 2003; 102: 211-216.

Ware MA, Ducruet T, Robinson AR. Evaluation of herbal cannabis characteristics by medical users: a randomized trial. *Harm Reduction Journal.* 2006; 3: 32. Available at: http://www.harmreductionjournal.com/content/3/1/32

Ware MA, Gamsa A, Persson J, Fitzcharles MA. Cannabis for chronic pain: Case series and implications for clinicians. *Pain Res Manage.* 2002; 7: 95-99.

Warf C. Response to the American Academy of Pediatrics Report on Legalization of Marijuana. *Pediatrics.* November 2005; 116(5): 1256-1257 (doi:10.1542/peds.2005-0128)

Washburn JJ, Romero EG, Welty LJ, Abram KM, Teplin LA, McClelland GM, Paskar LD. Development of Antisocial Personality Disorder in Detained Youths: The Predictive Value of Mental Disorders. *Journal of Consulting and Clinical Psychology.* 2007; 75(2): 221-231.

Weil AT. Adverse Reactions to Marijuana: Classification and Suggested Treatment. *New England Journal of Medicine.* 1970; 282(18): 997-1000.

Weil AT, Rosen W. *From Chocolate to Morphine* (Revised Edition). Boston: Houghton Mifflin, Mariner Books Edition, 2004.

Weil AT, Zinberg NE, Nelsen JM. Clinical and Psychological Effects of Marihuana in Man. *Science.* 1968; 162: 1234-1242.

Werkgroep Verdovende Middelen. *Background and Risks of Drug Use.* The Hague: Staatsuitgeverij, 1972.

Bibliography

Werner E. Medical Marijuana Advocates Implore Congress for Reform. *Associated Press*, May 4, 2005.

Whalen J. Medical Marijuana Gets Backing. *Wall Street Journal*, February 8, 2005.

Wheatley MJ. *Leadership and the New Science: Discovering Order in a Chaotic World*. San Francisco: Berrett-Koehler Publishers, 1999.

Whybrow PC. *American Mania: When More Is Not Enough*. New York: WW Norton & Company, 2005.

Wilber K. *A Theory of Everything: An Integral Vision for Business, Politics, Science, and Spirituality*. Boston: Shambhala Publications, Inc., 2001.

Wilber K. *No Boundary: Eastern and Western Approaches to Personal Growth*. Boston: Shambhala Publications, Inc., 2001.

Wilkinson JD, Whalley BJ, Baker D, Pryce G, Constanti A, Gibbons S, Williamson EM. Medicinal Cannabis: Is Delta9-Tetrahydrocannabinol Necessary for All its Effects? *J Pharm Pharmacol*. 2003; 55(12): 1687-1694.

Williams M. Fighting for your life shouldn't be a crime. *Chicago Tribune*, Commentary, February 14, 2005.

Williamson EM, Evans FJ. Cannabinoids in Clinical Practice. *Drugs*. 2000; 60: 1303-1314.

Wilner LS, Arnold RM. Canabinoids in the Treatment of Symptoms in Cancer and AIDS #93. *J Palliat Med*. 2006; 9(3): 802-804.

Wilsey B, Marcotte T, Tsodikov A, Millman J, Bentley H, Gouaux B, Fishman S. A Randomized, Placebo-Controlled, Crossover Trial of Cannabis Cigarettes in Neuropathic Pain. *Journal of Pain*. 2008; 9(6): 506-521.

Wilson C. Miracle Weed: Cannabis Can Be a Lifeline, and a Fortunate Few Will Soon Get It on Prescription. *New Sci*. 2005; 185(2485): 38-41.

Winter J. Weed Control. *Boston Sunday Globe*, May 28, 2006.

Woodson C. First Federal Medical Marijuana Trial in 3 Years Starts Tomorrow. Americans for Safe Access, November 6, 2006. Available at: www.safeaccessnow.org

Yamamura K. Schwarzenegger says 'time for debate' on legal marijuana. *Sacramento Bee*, May 5, 2009.

Zajicek JP, Sanders HP, Wright DE, Vickery PJ, Ingram WM, Reilly SM, Nunn AJ, Teare LJ, Fox PJ, Thompson AJ. Cannabinoids in Multiple Sclerosis (CAMS) Study: Safety and Efficacy Data for 12 Months Follow Up. *J Neurol Neurosurg Psychiatry*. 2005; 76(12): 1664-1669.

Zammit S, Allebeck P, Andreasson S, Lundberg I, Lewis G. Self reported cannabis use as a risk factor for schizophrenia in Swedish conscripts of 1969: A historical cohort study. *British Medical Journal*. 2002; 325: 1199-1201.

Zhang Z-F, Morgenstern H, Spitz MR, Tashkin DP, Yu G-P, Marshall JR, Hsu TC, Schantz SP. Marijuana Use and Increased Risk of Squamous Cell Carcinoma of the Head and Neck. *Cancer Epidemiology Biomarkers & Prevention*. 1999; 8: 1071-1078.

Zimmer L, Morgan JP. *Marijuana Myths, Marijuana Facts: A Review of the Scientific Evidence*. New York: The Lindesmith Center, 1997.

Zuardi AW, Crippa JAS, Hallak JEC, Moreira FA, Guimaraes FS. Cannabidiol, a *Cannabis sativa* constituent, as an Antipsychotic Drug. *Brazilian Journal of Medical and Biological Research*. 2006; 39(4): 421-429.

Zuardi AW, Guimaraes FS, Guimares VMC, Del Bel EA. Cannabidiol: Possible Therapeutic Application. In Grotenhermen F, Russo E (Editors). *Cannabis and Cannabinoids: Pharmacology, Toxicology, and Therapeutic Potential*. New York: Haworth Integrative Healing Press, 2002: 359-369.

Bibliography

Zuardi AW, Morais SL, Guimaraes FS, Mechoulam R. Antipsychotic Effect of Cannabidiol. *J Clin Psychiatry.* 1995; 56(10): 485-486.

Zuardi AW, Shirakawa I, Finkelfarb E, Karniol IG. Action of cannabidiol on the anxiety and other effects produced by delta 9-THC in normal subjects. *Psychopharmacology.* 1982; 76(3): 245-250.

Zurier RB. Prospects for Cannabinoids as Anti-Inflammatory Agents. *J Cell Biochem.* 2003; 88(3): 462-466.

INDEX

A

Abilene Paradox, 7, 8–10, 176
  definition, 9
  as group behavior dynamic,
    241n15
  illustration of social management,
    15, 16
Abilify®, 168
Abrams, Donald, 72, 75–76, 87, 231
acamprosate
  medication to support abstinence
    from alcohol, 155, 171
ACP, 43, 175, 276n71
Acquired Immune Deficiency Syndrome. *See* AIDS
ADHD, 97, 98, 167, 168
adherence to treatment
  definition, 107
adolescents
  cannabis use and psychosis, 160,
    62, 163–164, 165
  drug use, 138–139, 140, 141, 143
  See also schizophrenia
Afghanistan drug trafficking, xxiii, 13
AFSCME, 267n30
Aggarwal, Sunil, 232
AIDS, 38, 41, 53, 54, 66, 72, 75, 76,
  88, 113
Aigner, Frederick, 231
Akerlof, George, 181

alcohol
  abstinence, 155
  abuse and cannabis use, 22, 71
  cannabis as alternative to alcohol
    use, 114, 118,138, 153, 154,
    156–157, 166–167, 169,
    171–172, 182, 195, 196, 209,
    213–214, 221, 239
  compared to cannabis use,
    134–144, 153
  damaging effects of, 135–136, 137,
    139, 140, 141, 142, 143
  dependence, 152
  Health Fact, 145
  poisoning and student deaths, 139,
    140, 141
  prohibition, 36, 278n16, 279n18
alcohol-marijuana equalization campaign, 134
Alcohol-Marijuana Equalization
  Initiative 2005, 195
Alsup, William, 55
Alzheimer's Disease, 113
AMA, 43, 56, 64, 77, 105, 175
American College of Physicians. *See*
  ACP
American Federation of State, County,
  and Municipal Employees. *See*
  AFSCME